High Performance Machining

by Miles Arnone

Hanser Gardner Publications
Cincinnati

Arnone, Miles, 1969-
High performance machining / by Miles Arnone
        p.   cm.
        Includes index.
        ISBN 1-56990-246-1 (hardcover)
        1. Machining   2. Manufacturing processes.
I. Title.
TJ1185.A685 1998   98-28907
671.3'5--dc21   CIP

A *Modern Machine Shop* book published by
Gardner Publications, Metalworking's Premier Publisher
www.mmsonline.com

Hanser Gardner Publications
6915 Valley Avenue
Cincinnati, OH 45244-3029
www.hansergardner.com

2 3 4 5 6   01 00

Acknowledgments

This book would not have been possible without the assistance, encouragement, critical thought, and grammar checking supplied by those listed below. Thank you!

Toni and Quinn Arnone
Boston Digital Corporation

Aesop, Inc.
Deanna and Cyrus Arnone III
Ara Aykanian
Marinus B. Bosma,
   and Bosma Machine and Tool Corporation
Ryan Brath
Campbell Grinder Company
Norm Campbell
Terry Capuano, and Precision Polymer Casting, Ltd.
Norman Chapdelaine
Woodrow Chapman,
   and Hanser Gardner Publishing
Robert Ciocca
John Crean
Henry Demers
Richard DiMartino
Laurent Duchesne
Walter Durandetto
Jim Flinch, and Weldon Machine Tool, Inc.
John Floresta, and Kollmorgen Motion Technologies Group
Dick Fruit, and Service Tool & Die
Dick Garski
Don Golini, and QED, LLC.
Bruce Hammond
Carsten Hochmuth
George Jaffe, and Schneeberger, Inc.
Hiro Kashiwakura,
   and Heartech Precision Inc.
Bruce Keibach
Ralf Kraemer, and EROWA
Tom Linn
Modern Machine Shop
Greg Matulonis,
   and Lovejoy Tool Company, Inc.

Gordon McLean
Tim Meador
Wolfried Mielert, and Millstar, LLC.
David Montgomery,
   and Dayton Machine Tool Co.
Mike Napolitano
John R. Norris, and Norris & Company
Marian Noronha, and Turbocam Inc.
Mary Pascal
Ben Pascucci, and Heidenhein Corporation
Jon Peirce
John R. Pfeiffer, and Institute of Advanced Manufacturing Sciences, Inc.
Jeffrey Pfeiffer, and Pope Corporation
The Precise Corporation
Ayn Rand
Tim Ripka, and Renishaw Inc.
Allen Roberts, and Komo Machine, Inc
Chuck Sanders
Kevin Saylor, and Schunk Inc.
Roger Schroeder
Jack Sebzda, and System 3R
Jim Silver, and Charterhouse Group International, Inc.
Professor Alex Slocum, M.I.T
Gerry Stilwell
Arkady Teslyar
Dave Thomas
Bob Thomas, and A.S. Thomas
Jane Watts
Mike Webber
Jared Wheelock
Dick White, and Mark Tech, Inc.
Dr. James Womack,
   and Lean Enterprise Institute
Gary Zurick

Table of Contents

Introduction

This book explores the subject of *high performance machining* — the combination of high precision and high speed machining. Today, high performance machining is not widely practiced, but it is rapidly emerging as a prerequisite for the success and profitability of machining operations. Our goal is to provide a road map starting from current practice, as embodied in most machine shops, and arriving at a higher level, as dictated by customer requirements and the increasing pressures of a world economy.

Our discussion will provide in-depth information on high performance machining in the context of 3-axis vertical machining centers. Special considerations for 4- and 5-axis machining are also discussed. The principles presented apply to a wide array of machining disciplines beyond milling, including turning and grinding. So, while examples specific to milling processes are employed throughout, the general principles can be applied to a wider range of machining arts.

High Performance Machining was written for machining practitioners, namely machine shop owners, shop managers, CNC programmers, and machinists. As such, it focuses on the practical implications and implementation of high performance machining principles in a manufacturing environment. The book also takes aim at "accuracy inflation," which is the widespread problem of overstating the capabilities of machining processes. It is not uncommon for machine tool builders to claim that their machines are accurate to 80-millionths of an inch, even when they have never cut a test part to a tolerance even twice this amount. Likewise, it is routine for machine shops to claim that they are capable of machining complex 3D surfaces to 0.0002" TIR, even when a measuring device better than a micrometer is nowhere to be found in the shop.

Accuracy inflation is dangerous because it creates unrealistic expectations among design engineers, and reduces their appreciation for the true cost of achieving precision in machined components. This leads to the design of components with out-of-this-world tolerances, which are unnecessary for part functionality and lead to higher production costs. The response of machine shops to these tolerance requests is to inflate their capabilities, charge more for the work, or to (rarely) "no quote." To ascertain which came first — inflation on the machining side or unrealistic tolerancing on the engineering side — is a "chicken or the egg" dilemma which will not be debated here. Nonetheless, in discussing the true requirements for high performance machining, we seek to create more reasonable expectations for machining processes among engineers and machine tool users, while promoting the adoption of techniques that can help machine shops to produce components faster and more accurately — in other words, more profitably — than they do now.

This book is not intended for those seeking to design machine tools (although it may be a useful "practical guide" for machine designers), nor does it focus on the achievement of ultra-precision in the context of complex surfaces, i.e., tolerances of better than ±0.0002". While there are technologies for producing such tolerances, they are out of reach for all but a minuscule fraction of the manufacturing community. As such, we focus on the next logical step for the majority of machining practitioners, getting tolerances down to between ±0.0005" and ±0.0002" on complex contoured parts while simultaneously increasing throughput. For those interested in ultra-precision and machine design, two excellent books are Alexander Slocum's Precision Machine Design (Prentice-Hall), and Fundamentals of Mechanical Accuracy by Wayne R. Moore (available through the Moore Special Tool Company, Bridgeport, CT).

Finally, throughout this text we refer to "machine shops." This is not to say that the information presented here is relevant only to the build-to-order machining subcontractor. We use the term machine shop as a convenient catchall for any and all businesses which perform machining operations, whether they are production lines, prototype shops, mold builders, captive aerospace parts producers, or the garage-based machine shop.

Going Forward

The remainder of this book discusses the range of disciplines which must be mastered to become a practitioner of high performance machining. Some of these disciplines are the province of machine tool builders, others concern machine tool users. Nonetheless, it is helpful for all machining related businesses to have a good grasp of the relevant issues in each area. The six disciplines discussed, each covered in its own chapter, are as follows.

- Machine Geometry and Construction
- Motion Control (CNC) and Drive Train
- Spindle Technology
- Thermal Growth and Control
- Part Processing
- Real-time Performance Monitoring

Prior to these chapters, a survey on high performance machining is provided. The survey, which is an aid to getting the most out of the book, helps shops establish a benchmark against which they can measure future progress towards the adoption of high performance machining principles.

Following the aforementioned chapters, a test suite is presented. It can be used to monitor and qualify machine tools as they relate to high performance machining. The test suite is slanted towards vertical machining centers, and includes supplemental tests for 4- and 5-axis machines. Resourceful readers will modify the survey to reflect the specifics of lathes and other machine tools.

Chapter 1

What is High Performance Machining, and Why is It Important?

High performance machining is the fusion of high precision and high speed machining. We will define these two disciplines, and then discuss the importance of adopting *both*, in order for a machine shop to remain competitive into the 21st century.

High Precision Machining Defined

High precision machining is the production of complex components to tolerances of between ±0.0005" and ±0.0002" with high quality surface finishes (a relative term). Below this tolerance band (better than ±0.0002") lies the realm of ultra-precision, for which an entirely different set of processing technologies are required. In addition to the ±0.0005" to ±0.0002" tolerance band itself, the environment in which these results must be achieved is an integral part of the high precision machining definition.

Machined components are becoming significantly more complex as CAD and CAM tools become more sophisticated. Parametric and three-dimensional CAD packages make it easier for engineers to create parts which are optimized for a wide array of properties, including mass, inertia, internal stress fields, stiffness, damping, thermal properties, and, of course, aesthetics. Anyone not convinced of this evolution need only compare an automobile made today with one made ten (or even five) years ago. The level of sophistication, and the complexity of the surfaces used on the vast array of body panels, switches, knobs, engine components, etc., is astounding. Armed with advanced CAD packages, engineers are creating parts which perform better, but which are also more difficult to manufacture. This evolution is occurring in all industries, including consumer electronics, packaging, leisure goods, transportation, and heavy machinery.

Naturally, the boundaries of high precision are not so rigid that anything outside the ±0.0005" to ±0.0002" window is automatically excluded. Generally speaking, we are seeking to identify capabilities beyond, but immediately adjacent to, those achievable using conventional methods with commodity CNC machining centers. These machines typically have a base price of less than $100,000, and make up the vast majority of VMCs purchased today.

The definition of high precision machining also changes as a function of the type of component being machined. Again, when we speak of high precision machining, we are referring to tolerances that are beyond those readily achieved with conventional CNC equipment and process technology. For example, on small rotary dies less than 250 lb, tolerances between ±0.0005" and ±0.0002" are considered high precision (Figure 1-1). But on rotary dies weighing over 1,500 lb, tolerances of between ±0.001" and ±0.0005" would be classified as high precision. Tolerances worse than these figures are achievable with conventional machine tools and processes.

When 5-axis machining is considered, the boundaries of high precision machining change considerably. When machining blade forms, impellers, or other turbo-machinery components, tolerances of ±0.001" to ±0.002" on the airfoil are classified as high precision. Tolerances better than ±0.001" on a turbo-machinery airfoil constitute ultra-precision. This shift in what is considered high precision is caused by the addition of two more degrees of freedom (two more axes) in the machine tool, which is a problem that will arise throughout the book.

Figure 1-1:
This rotary cutting die is used to manufacture the heavy paper backing for switch plates and electrical outlets. The cutting lands on small- to mid-sized rotary dies will be sharpened to tolerances between ±0.0005" and ±0.0002".

High Speed Machining Defined

High speed machining is loosely defined as the use of higher spindle speeds and axis feed rates to achieve high material removal rates *without a degradation of part accuracy or quality*. An exact definition encompassing speeds and feeds is elusive because it is heavily dependent upon the type of component being machined. We can only define high speed machining in relative terms; by comparing it to the performance regularly achieved via conventional methods and standard machining centers. Typically we would expect feed rates and speeds at least 50% higher than those conventionally used.

High speed machining appeals to most manufacturers for three reasons. First, time is money. If the same part can be manufactured more rapidly, it can be sold for less, and/or additional profits can be earned by increasing the effective capacity of the machine tool. Second, manufacturers are anxious to adopt high speed machining techniques to respond to customers' demands for shorter lead times. In the mold industry, for example, molds that used to be delivered with a lead time of over 24 weeks can now be expected in 8 to 12 weeks depending upon the cavitation, engineering requirements, and lead times for mold components such as manifolds. Finally, intense competition with low labor cost regions or nations means that economies with expensive labor must produce components in less time to compete.

For example, the local mold building industry in Leominster, MA, and surrounding areas was once the dominant producer of molds for toy manufacturers located in New England. But, because so many new toys are flops, toy manufacturers sought to minimize their up-front investment in production tooling. As a result, Portugal now manufactures many of the molds destined for Rhode Island based toy manufacturers and others, even though lead times for their molds are significantly longer than for those sourced locally. Portugal's principal advantage is not one of better technology or better quality, but simply lower labor costs in comparison to high-cost Massachusetts. By adopting high speed machining techniques, and further compressing lead times, local mold builders hope to reclaim some of this business by enabling toy manufacturers to bring new products to market faster.

The Future of Machining

The importance of adopting high precision and high speed machining techniques is based upon changes in the market for machined parts.

Standard Machining as a Commodity Service

Standard machining is becoming a commodity business. The production of simple, non-contoured parts with tolerances from ±0.001" to ±0.005" is satisfied by a wide range of commodity machine tools, affordable to almost any operation. There has also been an explosion in the number of CAM solutions for dealing with non-contoured and 2D or 2.5D work. Because there are so many inexpensive machine tool and CAM solutions for dealing with these parts, it has become relatively easy to manufacture them. With such low barriers to entry, this work goes to the shops, regions, and nations willing to work the longest hours for the lowest pay. As a result, the amount of money one can earn making such parts will decrease, and competition in this field will increase both locally and internationally.

At the time of this writing, the North American economies are growing. As a result, many U.S. shops involved in the production of standard machined components see business increasing, not shrinking as asserted above. As long as economic growth continues, there will continue to be an abundance of standard machining work on the market. In fact, it is true that there will always be more standard machined parts to produce than high precision parts. But, even within our growing economy, the pressure to reduce manufacturing costs is intense. This pressure is undoubtedly felt most by those engaged in the production of what must now be considered commodity parts. As a result, profit margins will decrease, and many shops will find growth bittersweet. If they don't expand, shops can't get the high volume jobs they need to prosper. But, even with sales growth, the profits to be made on these jobs are less than in years past.

Once the economy slows, and enters an inevitable downturn, there will be a shakeout among those shops making non-contoured, open tolerance parts. Many will go out of business as excess machining capacity leads to rampant price cutting. Because machining "standard" components is a commodity business, buyers will be driven exclusively by price and delivery once their own businesses come under financial pressure. Under these conditions, production of open tolerance, non-contoured parts will move to the lowest cost supplier. This supplier is probably a shop where employees work off the books on ten-year-old machines. And, as a downturn takes greater hold over the economy, the competition will become a shop in Mexico, or possibly China, where the monthly wage for a skilled machinist is approximately $50.

High Performance Machining —
A Differentiated Industry

Whereas the production of open tolerance non-contoured components is fast becoming a commodity business, high performance machining promises to emerge as a highly profitable growth industry.

High performance machining requires a higher skill base than the production of commodity parts. Process related knowledge is more critical to producing components in this market because the margin for error is low. The parts are more expensive, more complex, and, therefore, much more difficult to manufacture. As a result, the ability of a firm to identify and cultivate talented employees is more important than in the commodity machining industry. High performance machine shops can differentiate themselves on the basis of their skill set, rather than simply based upon how low they can drive their costs. High performance shops develop a specialty within machining (e.g., mold cavities, racing heads, roll dies, forging dies, or a specific material) and are sought by customers because of the skills they bring to bear upon a difficult job. Rarely do high performance machine shops accept any and all work that will fit on their machine tools, as do commodity manufacturers. Customers of high performance machine shops are seeking partners rather than "at arm's length" suppliers. These elements can lead to higher profit margins because expertise is a scarce and valued resource.

The selection of appropriate machinery, tooling, CAM, and process is more important in this segment as well. The high performance machining industry is much more capital intensive than the standard machining segment. Because high performance machine shops are likely to specialize, making the right decision with respect to the tools for the job is critical. By purchasing top-end machine tools and CAM systems, high performance machine shops can further differentiate themselves from the competition, whether they are commodity oriented shops or other high end machine shops. By virtue of having the optimal machine for the job and a well educated work force, high performance machine shops can again gain higher margins because their production processes are significantly more accurate, faster, and there is less risk that they will machine scrap.

The ultimate differentiator between the high performance machine shop and the commodity machine shop is the depth of their process knowledge. The presence of top-shelf personnel and highly capable capital equipment provides these shops with the opportunity to build up a unique body of valuable process knowledge. By refining this knowledge, integrating it into their production processes, and defending it against competitors, the high performance machine shop can offer more than simply "machine hours," which is really all that the commodity shop is selling. In addition to posting higher profits, the high performance machine shop is better positioned to defend itself against low-cost suppliers, both domestically and internationally, and is more likely to weather economic downturns because the competitive advantage it provides its customers remains critical to their business regardless of the economic climate.

The Relative Importance of Accuracy and Speed

In discussing the merits of high performance machining from a business standpoint, it is important to understand the relative importance of "high precision" as compared to "high speed." While the adoption of both is important to running a successful machining operation, a tradeoff between the two is often required. For example, when selecting a piece of capital equipment, one machine will invariably be more accurate, while another will be faster.

Generally speaking, precision, and the ability to manufacture a better part in terms of tolerances and surface finish, is more important to the high performance machine shop than the ability to just produce a part quickly. This is because a high speed process is no more cost effective than many slow, inexpensive processes taking place in parallel.

Consider a hypothetical example. A commodity oriented machine shop in the United States decides to upgrade its capabilities by seeking higher metal removal rates. It purchases a state of the art machining center capable of feed rates up to 1,200 IPM and accelerations of 1 g for $220,000, replacing a machine that cost $85,000. The tolerances achievable in practice with the new machine at these rates are equivalent to the equipment it replaced, i.e., ±0.001". Now the shop can produce the same open tolerance components that used to take 1 hour to machine in only 20 minutes. A good move? Not necessarily, because somewhere in Slovakia (for example), a company has just lined up 10 workers on knee mills with digital readouts to manufacture the same parts, and while it will take each worker there 2 hours to make the part, the cost per part will only be 40% of what it costs the U.S. manufacturer to produce it. Further, in the two hours that it takes the U.S. shop to make six parts, the shop in Slovakia has made 10 pieces. By pursuing a "high speed only" solution, this shop did not, and almost definitely can not, gain back enough time to remain competitive against low wage producers.

If, on the other hand, the shop had adopted technology that provided not only an increase in speed, but a meaningful increase in product quality as measured by the customer, it would be much more difficult for shops with low wage structures (domestically or abroad) to compete. High precision, and increased product quality, is much harder to achieve than is speed, because speed can simply be combated through the use of cheaper resources. This is true even if it takes longer to do the same job because less expensive resources can be utilized in parallel, creating more effective output. Precision, on the other hand, cannot easily be replicated using lesser equipment over a longer period of time. This is increasingly true as part tolerances are constricted into the ±0.0005" to ±0.0002" band, and contoured surfaces become more prevalent.

This is not to say that speed is unimportant, but rather that speed should always be sought in the context of the highest level of precision applicable to the task at hand. Neither can be neglected, but when a trade-off must be made, quality and precision should be chosen over speed when formulating a strategy to convert a commodity oriented business into a high performance machining operation.

The Inevitable Evolution

The argument has been made that adopting high performance machining techniques increases the profitability and competitiveness of a machine shop. A further argument can be made that the adoption of high performance machining is inevitable within the machining industry as a whole, and that embracing these technologies is not an option, but rather a prerequisite for survival.

Since the pioneering work of Henry Maudsley and others in the 1800's, the capabilities of metal cutting machine tools have continually improved. This evolutionary process continually defines new levels of performance as the "standard." Businesses that refuse to adopt the new standard typically stagnate or go out of business. Those operating within the standard operate principally as producers of commodity goods in a highly competitive marketplace. Those operating above the standard operate, as a whole, at above-average profit margins. At any given time, the vast majority of shops fit within the "standard" performance band.

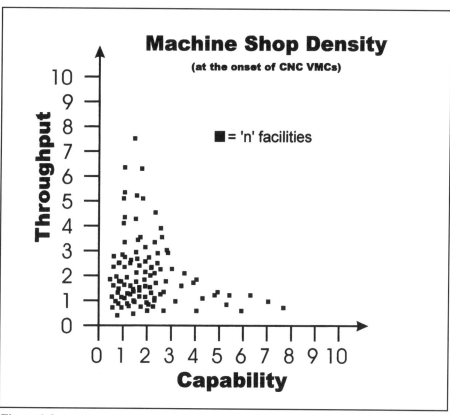

Figure 1-2:
Population density of U.S. machine shops in terms of process capability and throughput as CNC machining centers were beginning to be adopted across the industry. Note that the center of the market is near the point (2,2), and that the available technology made shops choose between throughput and capability. It was very difficult to cost-effectively achieve both in a given machining center.

Figures 1-2, 1-3, and 1-4 illustrate this concept for milling in the context of two dimensions of machining performance — throughput (speed of part processing) and capability (accuracy, surface finish, etc.). Each metric is represented on a scale of 1 - 10, with 10 representing the highest level of performance. The charts plot the relative population of machine shops at different performance levels with respect to milling. Figure 1-2 illustrates the population density of machine shops before the widespread adoption of CNC driven vertical machining centers with automatic tool changers. Most shops were filled with manual machine tools, and this was in fact the dominant technology. A small proportion of jobs were produced using CNC machines, which were more advanced than the manual equipment, but little was available in the realm of what we would today call "high performance" machinery. Only minimal 3D contouring occurred. Finally, there was a strong tradeoff between accuracy and speed. One tended to come very much at the expense of the other, such that

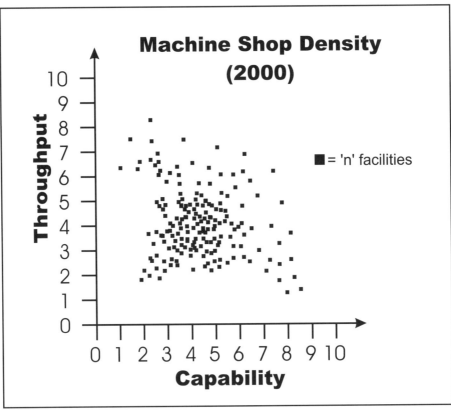

Figure 1-3:
Population density of U.S. machine shops today, when CNC vertical machining centers dominate the milling market. The center of the marketplace now resides near the point (4,4), and today's technology makes it more practical to achieve both high throughput and high capability in the same machine tool. Market leaders reside on the "frontier" which arcs from (8,3) to (7,6) to (3,8).

machines tended to be highly biased toward high throughput or high capability, but not both.

Figure 1-3 approximates the population distribution of shops at the present time, when CNC VMCs costing $80,000 to $100,000 dominate the marketplace. The market has shifted toward both higher capability and higher throughput. The widespread adoption of CNC, automatic tool changers, and other technologies has facilitated this change. Note that while sub-$100,000 VMC technology is utilized by the majority of shops, there are still some shops utilizing principally 1980's technology, and an increased number of shops using more sophisticated, high performance technology. The reasons for this evolution are clear. Shops adopted the new technology or lost business to those that did. New shops emerged that were more willing to adopt the CNC machinery, displacing established shops that were not comfortable with the new methods. Interestingly, the most profitable machine tool builders supplying the market today are for the most part a different set of companies than in the 1970's or 1980's.

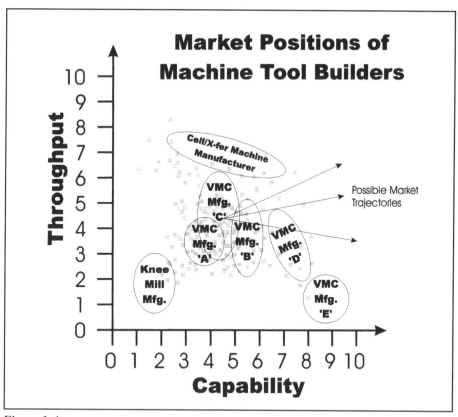

Figure 1-4:
Product offerings of typical machine tool builders overlaid on the shop population. The knee mill manufacturer is serving a smaller marketplace with less demanding performance requirements, while the products of VMC manufacturers A, B, and C target the heart of the market. Manufacturers D and E, and the Cell/X-fer Machine Manufacturer target smaller, more specialized segments of the marketplace. In the years ahead, the marketplace will progress along one of the illustrated trajectories. Machine tool builders will upgrade their products accordingly or serve smaller, less profitable market segments.

This evolution continues with respect to CNC machining technologies, and over the next several years (exactly how many is difficult to gauge), a greater proportion of new machine tool sales will reside at a higher level of performance. Figure 1-4 plots possible trajectories for this evolution, while indicating the market positions of prototypical machine tool builders. While it is clear that higher throughput and higher capability will be required going forward, it is not entirely clear which mix of the two is "the right combination." In the author's opinion, the balance will lean toward capability (e.g. accuracy), for the reasons previously cited.

It would be incorrect to conclude that today's standard CNC machinery will be relegated to the junk heap in high performance machine shops, but commodity CNC machinery will take on the same role that knee mills fill today: every shop has them and needs them, but they are not the principle means by which the shop makes money. In fact, today, there are more knee mills in existence than CNC VMC's, and many new knee mills are sold. But, the knee mill has become a commodity, and price and delivery are the principle dimensions of competition in the knee mill market. The market is extremely competitive, global in nature, and profit margins are low. Most knee mills are imported from lower wage countries. Sound familiar?

High Performance Machining Survey

To aid readers in getting the most out of the information presented in this book, the following survey is presented. Spending a few minutes answering these questions before reading further makes it easier to relate the book's contents to a given shop's conditions and requirements. When used over time, the survey audits a shop's high performance machining capabilities. Appendix B contains a discussion of each survey question with reference to relevant passages in the text. As a last note, each question should be answered in terms of how the shop in question currently operates, not in terms of how it operates in theory! (This survey may be photocopied.)

1. What is the maximum temperature swing in your machining area over the course of one day?
   A. 2°F   B. 5°F   C. 10°F   D. 20°F

2. What is the typical machining tolerance handled in your shop on a routine basis?
   A. ±0.005"   B. ±0.001"   C. ±0.0005" D. ±0.0002"   E. ±0.0001"

3. What is the tightest tolerance and machined surface finish (R_A) your shop would guarantee on a steel cavity the size of a cell phone with a 3D contoured surface?
   A. ±0.005"   B. ±0.001"   C. ±0.0005" D. ±0.0002"   E. ±0.0001"
   A. 64 μin   B. 32 μin   C. 16 μin   D. 10 μin   E. 8 μin

4. With what would you measure the part produced in question 3 to verify its accuracy?
   <u>Dimensional Tolerances</u>   <u>Surface Finish</u>
   A. Manual measuring tools   A. Visual inspection against samples
   B. Machine mounted touch probe   B. Profilometer
   C. Specialized gauging
   D. CMM (manual or CNC ?)
   E. Nothing

5. Ball end mills are procured through . . .
   A. Standard, supplied off-the-shelf
   B. Special order from tool manufacturers to your specification
   C. In-house cutter grind shop

6. *What feed rates are programmed for the milling of complex graphite electrodes when using small (less than 0.125" ⌀) cutters ?*
   A. 10 - 20 IPM
   B. 21 - 50 IPM
   C. 51 - 100 IPM
   D. 101 - 150 IPM
   E. 151 - 200 IPM

7. *What feed rates do the machining centers actually achieve when programmed as in question 6 ?*
   A. As programmed
   B. 90% of the programmed value
   C. 80% of the programmed value
   D. Less than 70% of the programmed value
   E. 0% of the programmed value

8. *What is the maximum temperature swing in the inspection area over the course of one day?*
   A. 2°F   B. 5°F   C. 10°F   D. Same as answer to question 1. All inspection is done at or near the machine.

9. *What acceleration is your best machining center capable of (1 g = 32 ft/s²) ?*
   A. 0.1g   B. 0.25g   C. 0.5g   D. 1g   E. 1.5g+   F. No idea

10. *When programming a surface to achieve the tightest tolerances your shop can guarantee, what chordal deviation value is programmed into your CAM system?*

A. 0.001"	B. 0.0005"	C. 0.0002"
D. 0.0001"	E. 0.00005"	F. 0.00001"

11.   *The proportion of components your shop produces which require 3D contour machining has, over the past three years, . . .*
   A. Increased   B. Remained the same   C. Decreased

12. *The typical spindle used in your shop for conventional milling of small- to mid-sized steel components is . . .*

A. <8,000 RPM	A. 5HP	A. #25 taper
B. 10,000 RPM	B. 10 HP	B. #40 taper
C. 12,000 RPM	C. 20 HP	C. #50 taper
D. 15,000 RPM	D. 30 HP+	D. HSK tapers

13. *The typical spindle used in your shop for high speed machining of small-to mid-sized steel components is . . .*

A. 10,000 RPM	A. <5 HP	A. #25 taper
B. 15,000 RPM	B. 5 HP	B. #40 taper
C. 25,000 RPM	C. 10 HP	C. #50 taper
D. 30,000 RPM	D. 15 HP	D. HSK63
E. 40,000+ RPM	E. 20+ HP	E. HSK 25 or 32

14. *How would the answers to questions 12 and 13 change for graphite? hard (50 Rc+) steel? aluminum?*

15. *Does your shop own a CMM? If so, what is its accuracy?* _____

16. *Circularity of your best machining center as measured by the ball bar test is _____ on a 12" diameter at 20 IPM.*

17. *How often are your machining centers recalibrated with a laser interferometer to adjust for lead error and backlash?*
    A. Every three months
    B. Every six months
    C. Every year
    D. Every five years
    E. When an accuracy problem appears
    F. It hasn't been done since the machine was purchased

18. *What is the axial and radial run-out of your best machining center's spindle at the spindle nose ? _____ How was this measured?*

19. *The market price for a given 2D component (e.g., a plate with pockets and holes) over the past three years has . . .*
    A. Increased   B. Remained the same   C. Decreased

20. *Annual turnover of machinists at your shop runs about . . .*
    A. 5%   B. 10%   C. 15%   D. 20%   E. 20%+

21. *Over the past three years, wages for qualified machinists (not operators) have . . .*
    A. Increased by over 50%
    B. Increased by over 25%
    C. Increased by less than 25%
    D. Remained stable
    E. Decreased

22. *Your most accurate machining center holds positioning tolerances of_____ inches (eg., ± 0.0005") per axis, according to the _____ [ISO, JIS] standard.*

23. *When contouring, your most accurate machining center holds tolerances, which are _____ those of question 22.*
    A. Better than
    B. Equal to
    C. Slightly worse than
    D. Significantly worse than

24. *The block processing rate of your CNC is _____ blocks per second.*

25. *The block processing rate of your CNC is affected by which of the following factors ?*
    A. Use of tool length compensation
    B. Use of variables
    C. Length of the lines in the program
    D. Use of more than 3 axes
    E. All of the above

26. *To run a large (several MB) program on your CNC, you would*
    A. Drip feed it over DNC as it runs
    B. Load the entire program into RAM via DNC and then run it
    C. Ethernet the program to the CNC's hard disk and then run it
    D. Ethernet the program to a PC next to (or inside) the CNC, and then drip feed it from this PC to another computer inside the CNC as it runs

27. *How is length and diameter set for the tools used on your VMC's ?*
    A. Off-line with a micrometer and height stand
    B. Off-line with an optoelectronic presetter
    C. On the machine using gauge blocks, dial indicators, and machine jog functions
    D. Using a touch probe on the machine tool for length and diameter
    E. Using a laser probe on the machine to measure length and diameter as the tool rotates

Chapter 2

Machine Construction and Geometry

Overview

High precision machining changes the requirements for machine tool design and construction. To achieve tighter tolerances, machine structures must be more geometrically accurate over the entire work volume than conventional machine structures, and must possess a high degree of thermal stability.

High speed machining techniques significantly alter the nature of machine tools as well. Cutting forces are the same or lower than in conventional machining processes because higher spindle speeds are used, and the amount of torque applied is less. On the other hand, axis feed rates and accelerations/decelerations are significantly higher than conventional machining processes. As a result, the dynamic loads placed upon the machine can be very high. While the forces exerted by cutting loads must still be considered, dynamic loads play an ever larger role in the design of high performance machining centers.

Consider a conventional c-frame VMC with a 1,500 lb table, capable of accelerations of 0.4 g. When this machine is brought to a full stop as quickly as possible, a load of 600 lb•f is placed upon the ball screw, support bearings, and machine structure. If the table was moving at 150 IPM prior to the onset of deceleration, this load would be present for 0.016 seconds. A high speed machining center, on the other hand, might possess a 1,000 lb table, and be capable of accelerations of 0.8 g. When this machine is brought to a full stop, a load of 800 lb•f is generated for 0.008 seconds, despite the lighter table. This example contradicts the popular perception that a high speed machining center needs to be lightweight to enable higher feed rates. While it is true that a lighter structure facilitates high speed motion, a robust structure is still required to handle high dynamic loads.

Beyond the magnitude of cutting forces and dynamic loads, their frequency must also be considered. A conventional machining center might utilize a 6,000 RPM spindle with a 4-flute cutter; the excitation frequency generated by cutting in this manner is 400 Hz. A high speed machining center might utilize a 25,000 RPM spindle with a 4-flute cutter; the frequency generated by cutting action on this machine would be 1,666 Hz.

Cutting action can easily become a source of unwanted vibration during machining. Machine construction and geometry play an important role in preventing the energy released by cutting processes from adversely affecting accuracy, surface finish, and machine life. As the above example shows, the range of frequencies which must be accommodated can vary greatly from conventional to high performance machining processes, affecting both machine and process design.

Additional sources of vibration within the machine tool range from the cogging action of servo motors, to the meshing of gears in a spindle head, to the motion of steel balls through the tracks and return tubes of ball screws. Each of these repetitive motions generates a disturbance of different magnitude over a range of frequencies. These disturbances can impact the machining process by degrading surface finish, or by preventing the use of high feed rates or accelerations due to the excessive vibration they may generate. Designers strive to create a machine that is resistant to vibration at the frequencies expected during operation. When they are unsuccessful, the operating range of the machine is limited in terms of accelerations/decelerations, spindle speed, and feed rates.

Construction

The role of the machine structure is to provide stiffness, accuracy, thermal stability, good damping, an adequate work volume, and ease of operator access. For high performance machining, these characteristics must be provided in the context of rapid feed rates, high spindle speeds, and quick accelerations. This environment varies greatly from that of conventional machining processes.

Static and Dynamic Stiffness

Static stiffness, measured in units of [lb•f/inch] or [N/mm], measures the resistance of a body to deflection under load. A straightforward example of the embodiment of static stiffness is a linear spring (Figure 2-1). Behavior of the linear spring is represented by the equation $F=KX$, where F is the force applied [lb•f], K is the stiffness constant [lb•f/in], and X [in] is the deflection of the spring.

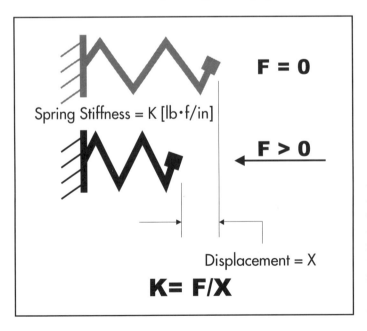

Spring Stiffness = K [lb•f/in]

F = 0

F > 0

Displacement = X

K= F/X

Figure 2-1: A linear spring deflects by an amount X in response to a force, F. The resulting stiffness of the spring is K, equal to F/X.

The stiffness of machine tool structures is of interest because it is closely related to machine tool capability. Stiffness directly affects machine accuracy, and the extent to which the machine can support high feed rates and accelerations. Unfortunately, determining the stiffness of a machine tool is more complex than for the linear spring. Machine tool stiffness varies for each axis (X, Y, Z), and can be strongly influenced by the position of the spindle within the work area.

The results from static stiffness tests on a number of machining centers from different manufacturers, and built with different construction methodologies, are presented in Table 2-1. The static stiffness values were measured using the setup similar to that in Figure 2-2. To measure the Z-axis static loop stiffness, for example, the spindle was brought into contact with the load cell. A Z-axis move of 0.004" was then commanded. Since the spindle is blocked up against the load cell, the 0.004" is lost as deflection within the machine structure. The load cell measures the force required to hold position, and the stiffness is inferred by dividing the force by the displacement.

This setup measures the "closed loop stiffness" of the system, rather than the individual stiffness of each axis. The loop stiffness accounts for deflections throughout the system, including each axis and the spindle. When testing Z-axis loop stiffness on a VMC, for example, the following are some of the effects that come into play:

- Z-axis ball screw compression,
- column deflection,
- bending of the bolster casting,

Machine Description	X-axis Stiffness (lb·f/in)	Y-axis Stiffness (lb·f/in)	Z-axis Stiffness (lb·f/in)
CNC Knee Mill	71,000	74,000	52,000
Small 3-axis bridge VMC	24,500	Not measured	66,300
Small 5-axis bridge VMC	24,500	Not Measured	24,700
Mid-size 3-axis c-frame VMC #1	178,000	199,000	355,000
Mid-size 3-axis c-frame VMC #2	74,000	84,000	132,000
Large 3-axis c-frame VMC	141,000	200,000	355,000
Large Horizontal MC	620,000	1,727,500	737,400

Table 2-1:
Closed loop stiffness for a range of machining centers. The stiffness values vary as a function of machine construction, spindle type, and wear state of the machine.

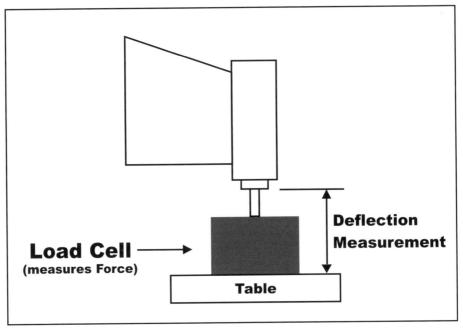

Figure 2-2:
Closed loop static stiffness for the Z-axis is determined using a load cell to measure the force applied when a specified axis move is commanded. The distance between the spindle nose and table top is measured to determine overall deflection of the machine. The distance between the table and other parts of the machine can also be measured to determine subsystem stiffness values.

- compression of the table and saddle assemblies (castings, bearings),
- axial deflection of the spindle and spindle housing, and
- compression of the 1"∅ bar (simulated tool) and tool holder in the spindle.

Note that the stiffness of a machine is not solely a function of machine size. The components used, the overall design, the number of axes, and the wear condition of the machine strongly impact stiffness. For example, the loop stiffness of a machine can be reduced dramatically depending upon the spindle used. If a 12,000 RPM 20 HP belted spindle with axial stiffness of 750,000 lb•f/in were replaced on a large VMC with a 30 HP 30,000 RPM spindle with axial stiffness of only380,000 lb•f/in, the Z-axis static loop stiffness of the machine would decrease significantly.

An alternate method for measuring static machine stiffness is to test each axis in isolation. To test the Z-axis, for example, a measured load would be applied to the slide, and the deflection of the slide would be measured as in Figure 2-3. This "open loop" test method is inadequate because it does not measure deflection in the entire system. Compliance in the spindle and table-saddle assemblies have been ignored. Open loop tests provide much higher stiffness values than loop stiffness measurements, and are not a good measure of overall system stiffness because they look at only one component of the system. The open loop Z-axis stiffness of the large VMC above, for example, was measured as approaching 500,000 lb•f/in compared to a loop stiffness value of only 355,000 lb•f/in.

Because the loads applied to machine tools occur at various frequencies, the dynamic stiffness of a machine tool is also an important measure of machine performance (see Table 2-2 for an example). By measuring the deflection in each axis under the presence of vibratory loading, the structural loop stiffness as a function of load frequency can be established for machine tools. Further, machine tools do not typically experience constant forces and the stiffness of the machine is rarely linear. Because of the nature of the cutting process, machine tools experience variable, or dynamic, forces. The aforementioned 25,000 RPM spindle with a four-flute cutter, for example, generates varying cutting forces at a frequency of 1,666 Hz. Loads also vary because machine motion is not constant. The machine constantly changes direction and feed rate, giving rise to various accelerations and decelerations, and thereby forces.

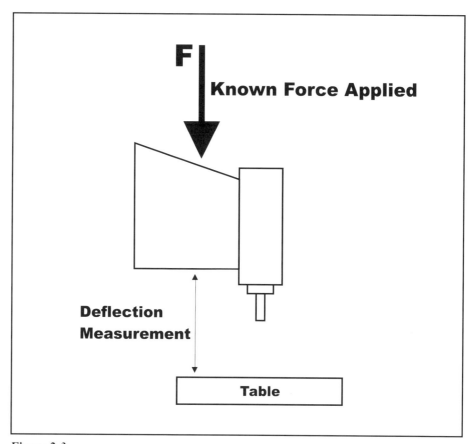

Figure 2-3:
Open loop static stiffness of the Z-axis is measured by applying a known force to the Z-axis slide, and measuring its deflection. Because a "closed loop" is not formed, only the stiffness of the drive train, slide, and column is measured.

The dynamic stiffness of a machine tool is lower than the static stiffness, and varies with frequency. The dynamic stiffness at the machine's lowest resonant frequency is of greatest interest. The resonant frequency is a frequency at which vibration is not adequately damped, thereby affecting controllability of the system, surface finish and accuracy.

Mid-size c-frame VMC	X-axis (lb·f/in)	Y-axis (lb·f/in)	Z-axis (lb·f/in)
Static Stiffness	178,000	199,000	355,000
Dynamic Stiffness	63,100 @ 800 Hz	56,200 @ 760 Hz	89,100 @ 92 Hz

Table 2-2:
The static closed loop stiffness and the dynamic stiffness at its limiting mode (first resonant frequency) are compared for a mid-sized VMC.

It is difficult to give explicit recommendations for machine stiffness when selecting a high performance machining center, as the stiffness measurements can vary with machine size and other factors, and the actual stiffness required is a strong function of the types of parts being machined. As a point of comparison, high efficiency deep grinding machines (HEDG), also known as superabrasive grinding machines, using CBN wheels are expected to possess stiffness values of at least 400,000 lb•f/in per axis (Figure 2-4).

When evaluating machine tools for purchase, consumers should request information from builders as to the stiffness of their machines. This information can be used, with care, to make comparisons between the products of different firms. It is easier to make comparisons between different machine brands based upon the static stiffness rather than the dynamic stiffness. This is because when testing for dynamic stiffness, the testing method can significantly impact results, while static stiffness values are determined in a more straightforward, and therefore easily compared, manner. Nonetheless, when evaluating static machine stiffness values, it is important to compare only machines intended for similar purposes, and to ensure that closed loop stiffness values, rather than open loop values, are being provided.

Damping

Damping, like stiffness, is a critical element of high performance machine tools. Damping is the quality of a machine which dissipates vibration. Machine tools with increased damping will absorb more of the vibration induced by cutting action or other sources, such as an out-of-balance tool or tool holder. Well damped machine tools provide better surface finishes, and support higher accelerations and feed rates because more aggressive control algorithms can be used. These algorithms employ powerful high frequency torque signals, which can cause unstable behavior, in the form of oscillation, in the absence of adequate damping.

Figure 2-4:
Superabrasive grinders such as this, used to manufacture a range of difficult-to-machine materials using vitrified or plated CBN wheels, are designed to provide axial static stiffnesses of 500,000 lb·f/in. (Courtesy of Campbell Grinder Co.)

While it is difficult to measure and quantify damping, most machinists have experienced it, or rather the lack of it. When a machine tool enters a cut, and begins to vibrate violently, the cutting action has excited a natural frequency of the machine, and a lack of damping allows the vibration to be amplified to the point where it interferes with proper operation of the machine tool. Additional damping would absorb the vibratory energy, reducing its negative effects. Figure 2-5 illustrates the effects of increased damping upon the magnitude of vibration in a second-order dynamic system. The effects illustrated are similar to, but less complex than, what happens when a milling cutter first enters a workpiece or, more catastrophically, when a spindle is crashed into a machine table.

Most damping in a machine tool comes not from the structural materials themselves, but from the joints between components, and from the more compliant (less stiff) parts of the machine structure, which provide damping by deflecting or deforming, thereby absorbing energy. Because deflections and deformations absorb energy, damping is often at odds with stiffness. To obtain a stiff machine tool structure requires that the amount of damping provided by the structure decrease, and vice versa. This tradeoff between stiffness and damping has not been well addressed in many machine tool designs. But with the proper application of highly damped materials like polymer concrete, and the application of specific damping elements like tuned mass dampers to machine tool

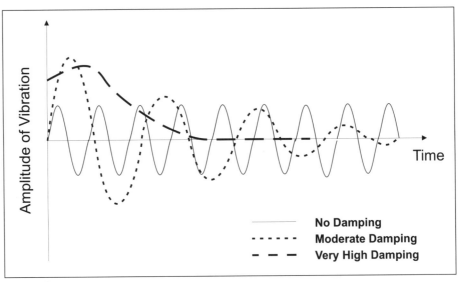

Figure 2-5:
The decrease in amplitude over time is illustrated for varying amounts of damping. With no damping, the vibration continues indefinitely. As the damping increases the amplitude of vibration is reduced more quickly. The very highly damped system is "critically damped" such that no oscillation occurs.

structures, the ability to apply damping to a machine structure without reducing stiffness is improving.

One novel approach for providing enhanced damping in machine structures is called a shear-tube damper. Figure 2-6 illustrates the base of a Weldon 1632 Gold grinder, in which this technology has been employed. By fitting a series of steel tubes within the machine base, and surrounding them with a viscoelastic polymer, a structure was created which carries high bending and torsional loads through the outer skin, and which dissipates vibration through shearing action in the embedded polymer. The benefits of this construction are illustrated in Figure 2-7, which contrasts the attenuation of vibration in the Weldon base with damping in a concrete-filled weldment.

Structural Materials

A variety of structural materials are used today in the production of machine tools. The suitability of these materials for high performance machine tools must be considered in terms of cost, stiffness, damping, thermal expansion, long-term stability, and thermal conductivity. Additional considerations, such as moisture absorption, must also be considered for specific materials such as polymer concrete.

Structural materials for high performance machine tools can be reduced down to three basic choices: gray cast iron, polymer concretes, and weldments (filled or hollow). While other materials have been employed, particularly in ultra-precision machine tools, they remain cost prohibitive for all but a select few customers.

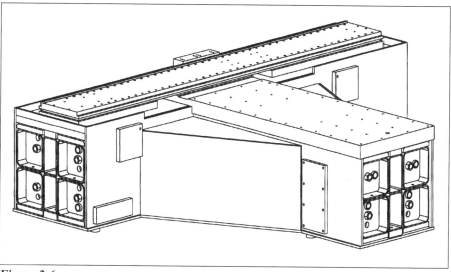

Figure 2-6:
CAD drawing of a Weldon 1632 Gold grinder base. Four shear tubes in each section of the base are visible. (Courtesy of Weldon Machine Tool, Inc.)

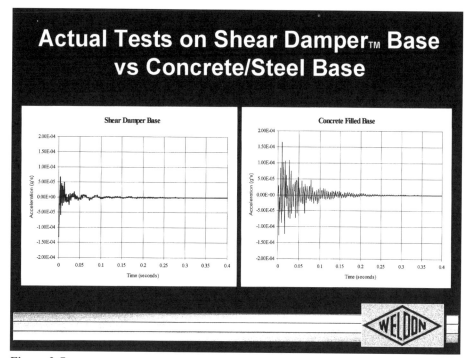

Figure 2-7:
Shear damper bases provide superior damping properties compared to concrete filled weldments as evidenced by the larger amplitude of vibration and greater settling time for the concrete/steel base. (Courtesy of Weldon Machine Tool, Inc.)

Gray Cast Iron

Gray cast iron has long been a popular material for machine tool structures. It provides good stiffness, and moderate damping. It is readily available and possesses good machinability. But, it is inadequate for a machine tool builder to note in their brochure that they are using cast iron. Gray cast iron, which is used for most machine tool castings, is available in a wide array of grades, from class 20 to class 60. The class represents the minimum tensile strength of the material in pounds per square inch (psi). Gray irons in class 20 through 35 are characterized by excellent machinability, high damping, low modulus of elasticity (akin to stiffness), and are easier to form into castings. Class 40 through 60 gray irons, on the other hand, have less damping, higher stiffnesses, and are more difficult to pour into castings and machine.

Because most of the damping provided by a machine tool is not directly a function of the damping properties of the structural materials themselves, it is highly recommended that consumers seek at least class 40 (and preferably class 50) cast iron, depending upon the size of the machine, and the structural role of the casting in question. While class 50 iron castings are more expensive to manufacture and machine, the benefits in stiffness are well worth the additional cost.

The importance of utilizing a high strength cast iron is demonstrated by considering a 2" square beam, 24" in length. In tension, the deflection of this beam is

$$\delta_{axial} = FL/AE$$

where F is the tensile load applied (lb•f), L is the length of the beam, A is the cross-sectional area, and E is the elastic modulus. For class 25 iron, $E_{class\ 25}$ = 12,000,000 psi. For class 50 iron, $E_{class\ 50}$ = 18,000,000 psi. Plugging these values into the above equation, with a load of 500 lb•f, yields

$$\delta_{class\ 25} = 0.0005" \qquad\qquad \delta_{class\ 50} = 0.00033"$$

such that the deflection of the class 50 beam is 33% less than that of the class 25 beam. Deflection of a machine tool structure, in either tension, compression, or bending, is inversely proportional to the elastic modulus (stiffness) of the material. Similar relationships hold for torsion as well, although the shear modulus G applies rather than E, the elastic modulus.

Beyond the class of iron employed, the dimensional characteristics of the casting are also important. The wall thickness, the number and pattern of ribs in the casting, and the overall cross section greatly affect overall stiffness. Consider two simplified class 50 iron machine tables less ribs, each overhanging the saddle by 40", and with the cross sections and structural overhang shown in Figure 2-8. If each table overhangs the saddle casting as shown, the deflection due to gravity is as follows. The presence of ribs within the casting would significantly reduce overall deflection in either case.

$$\delta_{box\ section} = 0.00093" \qquad\qquad \delta_{open\ section} = 0.0012"$$

The difference in deflection is a result of differences in the moment of inertia and weight of each table type. To obtain maximum stiffness and minimize deflection, mass should be provided as far from the centerline of bending (e.g., neutral axis) as possible. The same principle applies to other structural elements, such as saddle castings in machines where a fully supported table sits atop an overhung saddle. Deflections such as these can be avoided through designs with fully supported table and saddle castings. But, other drawbacks often accompany such designs, such as increased friction due to the use of four (or more) way systems, or reduced accuracy due to overconstrained way systems.

Polymer Concretes

Polymer concrete is being employed with increasing frequency in the machine tool industry. Its popularity stems from the fact that it provides superior damp-

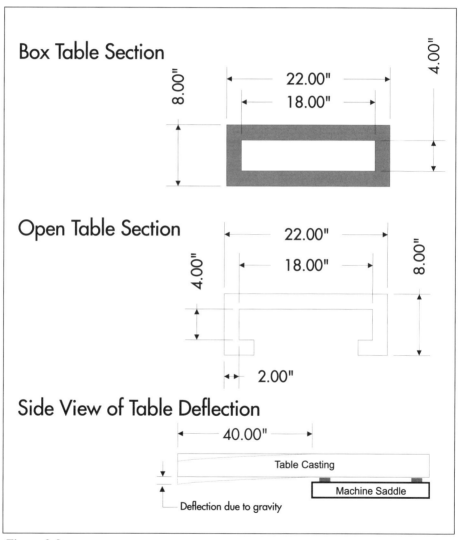

Figure 2-8:
Varying cross sections impact overall stiffness of machine structural elements such as tables.

ing properties, about ten times that of cast iron. Table 2-3 compares some of the key characteristics of polymer concrete with class 50 gray cast iron. Like cast iron, many grades of polymer concrete are available, with a range of properties. The information in Table 2-3 is typical.

Material Property	Class 50 Cast Gray Iron	Precision Polymer's Polymer Concrete
Modulus of Elasticity, E (psi)	18,000,000	6,000,000 (33%)
Ultimate Tensile Strength (psi)	50,000	3,500 (7%)
Ultimate Compressive Strength (psi)	150,000	18,000 (12%)
Coefficient of Thermal Expansion (in/°F•in)	6.7×10^{-6}	6.8×10^{-6} (101%)
Thermal Conductivity (BTU/°F•ft•hr)	1,300	91 (7%)
Density (lb/in^3)	0.260	0.085 (33%)
Damping	Fair	Excellent
Machinability	Moderate	Low

Table 2-3:
Selected material properties of class 50 gray iron, and Zaniteä polymer concrete as supplied by Precision Polymer Castings, Ltd. of Chardon, OH. Values for polymer concrete are also represented as percentages of the values for class 50 gray iron.

From Table 2-3 it is clear that in terms of strength, polymer concrete is inferior to cast iron. But because their coefficients of thermal expansion are within 1%, polymer concrete can be used in conjunction with cast iron to provide very highly damped components for machine structures. If the coefficient was not similar, temperature changes would cause the iron and polymer elements to expand or contract differently relative to one another, negatively impacting geometric accuracy of the machine.

Polymer concrete has been used for many years in lathe beds and machine and instrument bases to provide a well-damped foundation. It has not been significantly employed in machine columns, tables, or other structural elements that are subject to high bending loads, particularly in machines providing high material removal rates in metals. On the other hand, polymer concrete has been used quite successfully in smaller machines where cutting forces are low, but where very fast axis motions and accelerations are required. The gantry style machine pictured in Figure 2-9, which is used to grind optics, utilizes a base and column of polymer concrete. Only the X and Z slides are made of cast iron. The base and column assembly prior to painting for this machine is depicted in Figure 2-10.

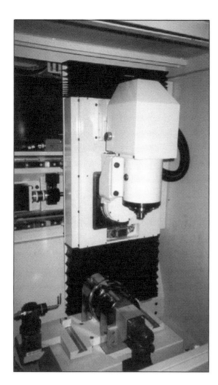

Figure 2-9:
MRF lens polishing machine (shown with some covers removed) requires a highly damped machine structure. Polymer concrete was an ideal choice. (Courtesy of QED.)

One of the drawbacks of polymer concrete is that its thermal conductivity is very low. As a result, hot spots can develop in the material, and it is very important that heat generating elements, such as servo motors and ball screws, be properly ventilated or cooled. Otherwise, heat transfer into the polymer concrete can cause local heating, which in turn can cause the structure to warp, degrading geometric accuracies. By the same token, the low thermal conductivity of polymer concrete serves to partially insulate it against external temperature changes, such as those caused when factory doors are opened in the winter, etc.

The fact that polymer concrete is not easily machined requires that threaded inserts and metal plates be cast into the polymer to facilitate the attachment of way structures and other devices during machine construction. This adds to the cost of manufacturing polymer concrete castings, but also has benefits, including the ability to cast in wire ways and other conduits. While some manufacturers have reported success in grinding polymer concrete to create surfaces for mounting linear rails in lieu of using inserts, this process has not been met with universal acceptance.

To conclude, polymer concrete is not a replacement for cast iron, but rather a material that can be employed successfully in specific machine elements to provide additional damping. In smaller machines, and those where machining forces are low (e.g., graphite machining, engraving, die sharpening, EDM machines), it can be used with confidence in a broad range of structural components.

Figure 2-10:
Assembled base and column for the QED MRF lens polishing machine ready for painting. The ability to cast inserts into the polymer concrete simplified assembly of the linear rails, and allowed fluid handling conduits to be integrated into the base. (Courtesy of QED.)

Weldments

Weldments, consisting of steel plate welded together, and often filled with sand, shot, or sometimes polymer concrete, have been used in machine tool structures for many years. Because tooling costs associated with weldments are low compared to the cost for cast iron patterns or polymer concrete molds, they are more economical for very low volume machine production.

Weldments, particularly when unfilled, possess several drawbacks relative to cast iron. First, the structure is nonuniform in its properties, and very hard to model and optimize, due to the presence of weld seams. Because it is fabricated from steel plate, damping is exceptionally low in unfilled weldments. The cost to fabricate weldments is also very high, and machinability is lower than that of cast iron. The change in shape of a weldment when subject to varying thermal conditions is difficult to predict, and typically less uniform than homogeneous structures made of cast iron or polymer concrete. This can lead to bending and twisting under thermal loads, greatly distorting machine geometry.

The strength of welded structures under constant loads approximates the strength of the plate and weld materials. In the case of butt welds, the weld material, if not ground off, provides static reinforcement, but under dynamic loading, the weld serves as a stress concentrator, reducing overall fatigue strength. Similarly, fillet welds act as stress concentrators, reducing the effective load bearing capacity of a welded structure under dynamic loads. The fact that welds can act as stress concentrators detracts from their suitability for high performance machine tools. [1]

---

[1]Fundamentals of Machine Component Design, 2e, by Robert Juvinall and Kurt Marshek, New York, John Wiley and Sons, 1991, New York.

When weldments are filled, their properties improve markedly, particularly with respect to damping. But to recognize these benefits it is necessary to ensure that the fill, particularly if it is polymer concrete, adheres to the walls of the structure. If the two materials separate, much of the damping potential of the fill is wasted because shear forces are not effectively transferred to the polymer concrete, thereby limiting energy dissipation.

When comparing high performance machine tools, structures of cast iron and/or polymer concrete are generally preferred over weldments. The exception to this rule is highly specialized machinery, where the cost of patterns or molds to produce one or a handful of machines is prohibitive. In such cases, ensure that adequate damping has been provided in the structure through other means, and that the welds are of the highest quality.

Structural Design

A wide range of machine tool designs have been employed, with varying degrees of success, to the task of high performance machining. In evaluating the fitness of a specific machine geometry for high performance machining, a number of guidelines should be followed. Following a discussion of these guidelines, a number of the more popular VMC geometries are compared.

Smaller is Better

Often when shops purchase a new machine, the tendency is to purchase a machine sized to handle 95%+ of the part sizes that may come through the door. If 90% of the shop's milling work fits within a 6" cube, and the remaining 10% requires a 20" cube, a 32"×22"×22" machine is more likely to be purchased than a machine with a 12"×12"×12" work volume. By purchasing the larger machine, the flexibility to take on any job that comes through the door improves, and scheduling work through the shop is made simpler.

Unfortunately, when it comes to high performance machining, this strategy backfires. The larger the machine, the less stiff it is likely to be due to larger overhung loads. The ability to accelerate and decelerate rapidly is also compromised because larger masses, such as tables and slides, need to be moved. Thermal effects are also magnified because of the greater size of the machine elements. For the same change in temperature, thermal expansion is directly proportional to the size of the element. If the column is twice as high, it will grow twice as much as the smaller column given the same change in temperature.

Larger machines cost more to manufacture, and as high performance machine tools are expensive to begin with, the additional cost to move up in size can be substantial. The cost of additional structural materials (e.g., cast iron) alone can add $10,000 to the builder's expenses, not to mention the additional expense for longer and higher capacity rails and screws.

Shops seeking to adopt high performance machining techniques should limit themselves to the smallest machine possible given the work they expect to perform. Unlike general purpose machining, where open tolerances and simple geometries allow a wide range of part sizes and materials to be produced with a single machine configuration, the level of optimization needed for high performance machining mandates specialization.

Seek Wide Way Spacing, Minimum Overhangs

When evaluating machine tool designs for high performance machining, large overhung loads should be avoided. Consider the machine column, bolster, and spindle configuration of a c-frame VMC in Figure 2-11. In terms of the bolster, the deflection δ at the spindle nose under cutting loads applied in the X-, Y-, and Z-axes is proportional to the machine geometry as follows.

$$\delta_x \sim D^3, 1/W^3$$
$$\delta_y \sim D, 1/H, 1/W$$
$$\delta_z \sim D^3, 1/H^3, 1/W$$
$$\text{Stiffness } (K) \sim 1/\delta$$

If the Y-axis travel (and the distance between the spindle and the column) of a VMC increased from 22" to 30" (an increase of 36%), without other significant changes in the machine structure, the stiffness of the machine in the X-axis would drop by 252%!

Many machine tool builders seek to extend their product lines by "stretching" the axes to provide for large part machining. As this example illustrates, doing so can have a significant negative impact upon machine stiffness, accuracy, and the machine's ability to rapidly remove material.

While Figure 2-11 illustrates a c-frame VMC, the same effect applies to a bridge-type machining center. There, the effect can be worse, as the bridge is usually significantly above the work area, and the Z-axis must extend through most of its travel to machine a part located on the table below. Thus, under cutting and dynamic loads, the Z-slide will deflect similarly to the bolster of the c-frame VMC.

This example illustrates the importance of a wide way stance in machine tools. Spacing the ways and bearing cartridges further apart greatly increases machine stiffness, just as an automobile becomes more stable as the tires are pushed out toward the corners of the vehicle. Increased spacing of the ways and cartridges adds to the manufacturing expense for the machine builder, as it is harder to ensure the straightness and parallelism of the ways. Shops adopting high performance machining should seek machine tool designs that have widely spaced way systems, and avoid excessively overhung machine elements.

Ram type vertical machining centers (Figure 2-12) present a unique set of problems for high performance machining because machine stiffness changes when the ram extends, creating a variable overhung load. As the ram is extended, stiffness with respect to bending drops as

$$K \sim 1/Y^3.$$

Further, because the ram is essentially an unsupported beam, it droops a bit, and so the angle between the spindle center line and the machine table is no longer 90°, resulting in a slight out-of-square condition. Because the amount of

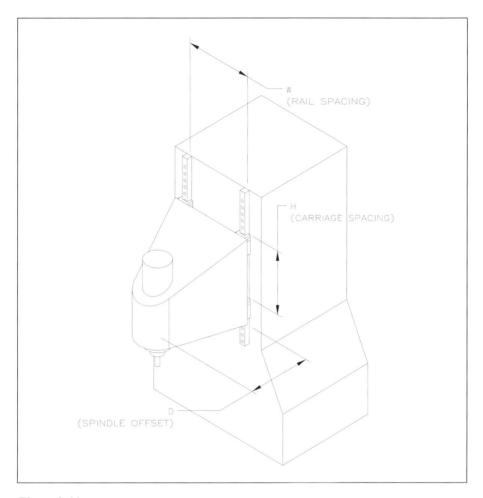

W
(RAIL SPACING)

H
(CARRIAGE SPACING)

D
(SPINDLE OFFSET)

Figure 2-11:
The spindle-slide-column assembly of a vertical machining center must be constructed so as to provide adequate way spacing relative to Y-axis throat (*D*). Stiffness drops rapidly with increasing *D* and decreasing *H* and *W*.

droop is variable, the spindle alignment cannot be corrected by "scraping in" the spindle. In this regard, droop in a ram is similar to that of the unsupported table or saddle previously discussed.

Avoid Large Axis Stackups

Angular errors are the scourge of precision machining. Unlike linear errors, which simply add to one another, the effects of angular errors are *multiplied* with increasing distance from the source of the error. As a result, it is of critical importance to avoid large axis stackups in a high performance machine tool.

For example, consider the X-Y stage in Figure 2-13. The Y-axis way system has a convex pitch error of only 0.0001" over 12" inches. The saddle, X-axis ways, machine table, and part form a stack 8" tall. Because of the multi-

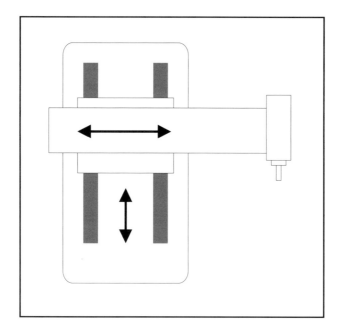

Figure 2-12:
In ram machining centers (a schematic of which is illustrated), the Y-axis ram overhangs the column by a variable amount, dependent upon axis position. This leads to changes in stiffness, spindle alignment, and dynamic performance with different spindle positions.

plicative effect of angular errors, the positioning error at the top of the part is 0.0053". If the axis stack were only 4" tall, the displacement error at the workpiece would have dropped by 50% as well.

To minimize the accumulation of angular errors, the distance between axes drive trains and the tool – work interface must be minimized. In a 3-axis machine, this means splitting up the axes into a 2-axis pair, and a single axis, as is done on c-frame VMCs. Traveling column machines are examples of machines that do not separate the axes. Because all three axes are stacked on top of one another, the tool tip is located very far from the X-axis ball screw and ways, decreasing geometric accuracy and stiffness.

A high performance machine tool should be designed to minimize the distance between stacked axes. In a c-frame VMC, the saddle, which mounts between the Y and X axes, and the work table should be as thin as possible while providing adequate stiffness. This can be achieved through innovative design, and the use of stiff structural materials and way systems.

Avoid Outboard Drives and Measurement Devices

The multiplication of angular errors with distance strongly influences the ideal positioning of ball screws and measuring devices such as linear encoders.

Whenever possible, ball screws should be located midway between the way systems so that they are driving the slide at its center of mass. When ball screws are located off-center, a moment is created around the center of mass of the slide. This will cause the slide to skew and bind as it moves along. This skewing action can in turn cause errors in machined features and premature wear of the screw. Sometimes, particularly in horizontal machining centers, or 5-axis machines, it is very difficult to mount the ball screw on-center.

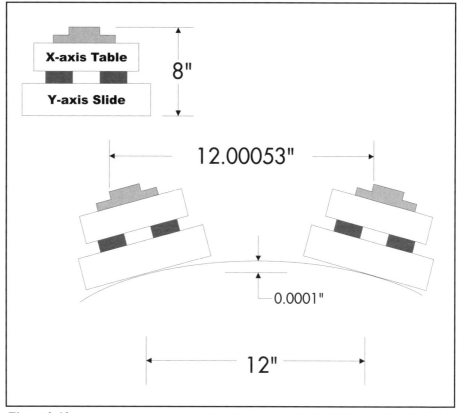

Figure 2-13:
The impact of angular errors is magnified with distance. As a result it is important to minimize the distance between the axes of motion in a machine tool and the tool – part interface.

Many machines that use linear encoders for feedback mount them outboard of the way system. This is not ideal. Instead, linear feedback devices should be mounted as close to the ball screw and the midpoint of the ways as possible. An inboard position ensures a more accurate measure of slide position because error is not introduced due to any skewing of the slide which may occur under machining loads. When the scale is outboard of the ways, displacement due to skewing is interpreted as linear motion by the scale, causing erroneous readings. Another disadvantage of mounting the linear scale outboard is that it is less well protected against chips and other contaminants.

Comparison of Popular VMC Designs

Among general purpose 3-axis vertical machining centers, a number of platforms have become popular, including fixed column c-frame, traveling column c-frame, gantry bridge, fixed rail bridge, fixed column ram, and traveling column ram. Other designs are often combinations of the above, and their characteristics can be derived from this list. Table 2-4 compares these designs in accordance with high performance machining requirements. In comparing each design, it should be noted that the choice of structural materials, drive train components, CNCs, etc., will affect overall machine performance. Table 2-4 compares the strengths and weaknesses of machine geometries, independent of these other factors. Each design can be manufactured into a high performance machine tool. But the overall suitability of a given design to the task will dictate the cost to create a viable high performance machine. Those designs with higher overall ranking can be brought to a higher level of performance more cost-effectively for a given part size.

Characteristic	c-Frame –Fixed Column	c-Frame –Traveling Column	Gantry Bridge	Fixed Rail Bridge	Ram – Fixed Column	Ram – Traveling Column
Stiffness	★★★★	★★	★★	★★★	★★	★½
Geometric Accuracy	★★★★	★★	★★	★★★	★★	★½
Thermal Stability	★★½	★★	★★★	★★★★	★★	★★
Dynamic Behavior	★★★★	★	★★★	★★★½	★★	★
Cost	★★★★	★★	★★	★★★★	★★★★	★★
Suitability for small parts	★★★★	★½	★★	★★★	★★★	★★
Suitability for medium parts	★★★½	★★	★★★	★★★½	★★★	★★½
Suitability for large parts	★	★★★	★★★★	★★★	★★	★★
Operator Access	★★★	★★★★	★★★★	★★★	★★★★	★★★★
Workpiece Changing	★★	★★★★	★★★★	★★★	★★★	★★★★
Auto. Tool Changing	★★★	★★★	★★	★★	★★	★★
Ranking: small, or medium parts	★★★★	★★	★★★	★★★★	★★★	★★½
Ranking: large parts	★★½	★★★	★★★½	★★★½	★★½	★★★

Table 2-4:
Suitability of 3-axis VMC designs for high performance machining. '★★★★' represents the highest ranking, '★' the lowest. Rankings for large parts are lower on average because of the difficulty in achieving tight tolerances on large complex components relative to small or medium parts.

Fixed Column c-Frame

In terms of stiffness, the fixed column c-frame (Figure 2-14) is ideal for parts such as mold cavities, plate work, electrodes, and other parts where the X-Y dimensions typically exceed the height of the part. Because the stiffness of the c-frame decreases with increased Z-height, the "sweet spot" is close to the table. Other features of the design that promote a high degree of stiffness include a minimum of overhung axes, and the location of the X- and Y-axes directly below the part. This minimizes torsional loads on the X- and Y-axes during cutting.

Figure 2-14: BostoMatic™ 32 High Performance Machining Center provides accuracies to ±0.0001" ISO at feed rates to 450 IPM. The machine is intended for the production of high precision molds, dies, and tooling.

Geometric accuracy is also excellent with this design because the distances between the way systems and the tool – work interface are relatively small. The X-axis ball screw is usually within 6 to 8" of the workpiece, and the Y-axis is also relatively close. Only the Z-axis ball screw and way system is located far (an amount approximately equal to Y-axis travel) from the workpiece.

Thermal stability of the c-frame is only average, because of the asymmetric construction of the Z-axis assembly (Figure 2-11). Heat is likely to be generated at the front of the column in the work area, which is where the ball screw and ways are mounted. As a result, there is a tendency for the column to bend backwards slightly because the front of the column will be warmer than the rear of the column. Further, the fact that the machine's axes, and most of its structure, are located within the work area makes it hard to isolate them from heat (or contaminants) thrown off from the cutting process in chips or coolant.

Dynamic behavior of the c-frame VMC is excellent because of high overall machine stiffness, and the compact nature of the machine for small- to mid-sized parts. Manufacturing costs are low, and a high degree of accuracy can be established cost-effectively. Operator access is good, although it is limited relative to other designs by the presence of the Y-axis ways and way covers, which extend beyond the table towards the front of the machine. This prevents the operator from getting as close to the spindle and work area as with other designs.

In terms of automatic tool changing, because only one machine axis (Z) must move to bring the spindle into tool change position, this design has potentially fast tool change times. But, unlike traveling column and bridge designs, tool changers for fixed column c-frames are typically more expensive because axis motions cannot be used to bring the spindle to the tools. More importantly, the fact that only one axis needs to move to facilitate tool changes means that the machine will return to the workpiece with a high degree of repeatability after tool changes.

In terms of automatic workpiece changing, the fixed column c-frame design requires that all three axes move to facilitate coordination with a pallet shuttle. After the Z-axis moves up, the X- and Y-axes must position the pallet in-line with the pallet receiver. As a result, machine repeatability comes into greater play when trying to change pallets in this fashion.

Once parts begin to require large Y-axis travels (above 22 to 25"), the benefits of the c-frame geometry become weaknesses. The spindle must be pushed away from the Z-axis way system, magnifying angular errors, and reducing stiffness. Likewise, for very tall parts, additional angular errors are created because the tool – work interface is now far from the X- and Y-axes. As parts become excessively large, the weight of the parts upon the X- and Y-axes negatively impacts dynamic performance, and increases machine wear. As a rule of thumb, if parts weigh over 2,500 lb, other machine designs should be considered.

Traveling Column c-Frame Machines

Traveling column c-frame machines are best suited to applications where high production volumes are required, or where very large, heavy parts must be accommodated. They provide the user with excellent access to the work area, and can be setup with several independent work zones through the use of software or hardware fences (Figure 2-15) allowing work to be setup in one zone, while machining continues in the other. They are also well suited to automatic work changing systems, as only the Z-axis needs to move to clear the work and facilitate the pallet change.

Stiffness and geometric accuracy are decreased in a traveling column machine because the axes are typically located very far from the tool – work interface. Because the entire column assembly must be carried by the X- and Y-axes, dynamic performance is reduced, and accelerations are limited relative to a comparably sized fixed column c-frame. The column's center of mass is also located far from the X- and Y-axis drive trains. This creates an inverted pendulum effect as the column moves back and forth, imposing large moment loads upon the axes, and making the system more susceptible to vibration when high acceleration movements are employed.

Traveling column machines are best for large squat parts, such as mold bases and certain automotive body panel dies, where tolerances are more open than ±0.0005". Long, slender parts requiring 3-axis or 4-axis machining are also handled well by this machine geometry. Dynamic performance is independent of the part weight in this design, unlike the fixed column c-frame, and operator access to the work area is excellent. For large parts, traveling column machines represent a cost-effective alternative to the more expensive bridge type machining centers. For small- to mid-sized parts, the manufacturing cost for such machines is high because the X- and Y-axes must carry much higher loads than in a fixed column c-frame design.

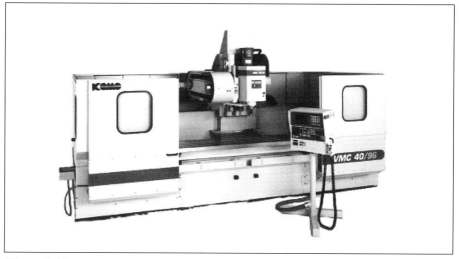

Figure 2-15:
Komo 40/96 traveling column machining center provides excellent user access, while enabling a number of independent work zones to be setup. Part weight is effectively unlimited, and the machine carries its automatic tool changer on the column.
(Courtesy of Komo Machine Inc.)

Tool changing on a traveling column c-frame tend to be accurate if the tools are carried with the column. If the tool carousel is mounted at the end of the X-axis, off the column, all three axes must be actuated to perform a tool change. In this case, tool-to-tool repeatability on the workpiece can be adversely affected.

Gantry Bridge

The gantry bridge design (Figure 2-16) stacks all three axes onto an overhead frame, much like a gantry crane. To accommodate Z-axis motion, the three axes are typically located a significant distance from the work area, particularly with respect to smaller, relatively squat parts. For example, a small bridge machine may have 12" of Z travel. When machining a 3" high steel cavity, the X- and Y-axes are at least 10" – 12" away from the tool – work interface, magnifying the effects of angular errors in these axes. As parts get taller, this effect decreases. Generally speaking, because all three axes are stacked on top of one another, stiffness and geometric accuracy are reduced when working near the table.

Figure 2-16:
Dayton Machine Tool Company manufactures large 5-axis gantry machine tools. The machine illustrated provides positioning accuracies of ±0.0004". Maximum axis feed rates of 1,200 IPM are achieved. (Courtesy of DMT.)

Thermal stability of this design is good because the axes are removed from the work area, and the structure is highly symmetrical, as compared to a c-frame column assembly. Dynamic performance is also good, although the large extensions required of the Z-axis away from the axes drive trains create problems similar to the traveling column c-frame. But, because the mass of the Z-slide assembly is often less than that of the traveling column, the dynamic performance can exceed that of the traveling column c-frame.

Because the motions of the axes are independent of the part size and weight, the value of this design grows with increased part size. Also, the profile of the Z-axis slide and spindle allows bridge designs to work within deeper cavities with shorter tools than any of the c-frame or ram designs, improving part access and reducing cutter deflection. As a result of these benefits, the largest dies and molds are often machined on gantry machines. But, as with the large traveling column c-frame design, tolerances of ±0.0002" to ±0.0005" are extremely difficult to hold when machining extra-large components with complex surfaces.

The fact that all three axes of motion are in the spindle also makes automatic tool changing very cost effective. Tools can be stored inside the machine travels, and no additional mechanisms are necessary to present the tools to the spindle. The drawback of this approach is that all machine axes are used to go to, and return from, the tool change position. As a result, machine repeatability comes into greater play than with the fixed rail bridge or fixed column c-frame when trying to accurately match successive tool paths on a given part.

Fixed Rail Bridge

The fixed rail bridge design utilizes an X-Z assembly mounted to an overhead bridge, with an independent Y-axis carrying the workpiece (Figure 2-17). Like the fixed column c-frame, this design splits up the axes so as to reduce the multiplication of angular errors over extended stackups. But, because the Z-axis must be extended down from the fixed rail, it is susceptible to magnified positional errors due to sag or twist in the rail, or angular errors in the Z-axis way system. As a result, this design is slightly less geometrically accurate than the fixed column c-frame in relation to small parts.

Thermal stability of this design is excellent. The machine is highly symmetrical, and most of the axes are removed from the work area. One element that does require close attention in this regard is the Z-axis way system. As the Z-axis extends down into the work area with the spindle, it is important that the ways be well protected against chips, coolant, graphite dust, etc. This concern also applies to the gantry bridge design.

Dynamic behavior of this design is excellent, and represents an improvement over the gantry design because only two, rather than three, of the axes are far removed from the work area. Cost to manufacture this design is similar to that of the fixed column c-frame, as it is, in effect, a c-frame machine laid on its back with the table and spindle swapping positions.

As parts become larger, the fixed rail design is strongly preferred over the fixed column c-frame; although for the largest parts, its performance is still limited by the fact that the Y-axis carries the full weight of the part.

Fixed Column and Traveling Column Rams

Fixed column ram machines utilize a Z-Y assembly on the column with an independent X-axis table. These machines are stiffer and have the potential to be more geometrically accurate than traveling column c-frame machines. But they are typically less accurate and stiff than comparably sized fixed column c-frames because the Y- and Z-axes are located far from the work zone, exposing them to high moment loads and increased deflection. The fact that machine stiffness is strongly a function of Z- and Y-axis position also detracts from the dynamic performance of this design.

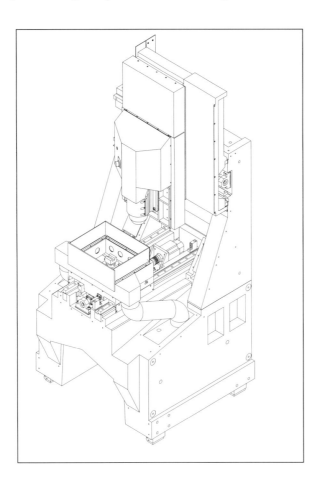

Figure 2-17:
View of a small 3-axis fixed bridge VMC. This machine is intended for hard die milling and the production of copper and graphite electrodes. Its working volume is 12"×12"×12". (Courtesy of Boston Digital Corporation.)

Thermal stability is also an issue with ram machines, particularly when the ram is mounted to the side of the column, rather than center mounted within an H-type column design. When mounted side-saddle, the column is likely to twist front to back as with a c-frame design, and also from side to side.

Operator access for both ram styles is excellent, as the machine table does not move forward and back relative to the operator. The action of the ram also brings the spindle out to the operator for easy access. Automatic work changing is easily supported on both models, with the edge going to the traveling column ram because fewer axes need to move to facilitate workpiece changing. With respect to automatic tool changing, at least two axes motions (Z, Y) are required to perform a tool change, making it somewhat less suitable for high performance machining than the fixed column c-frame design.

The Trouble with Hexapods

One machine design conspicuously absent from the above comparison is the hexapod. These machines utilize six driven legs to move a platform containing a spindle. Some models include additional degrees of freedom in the spindle head to provide an improved range of motion. A number of manufacturers have successfully built hexapods, including Giddings & Lewis, and Ingersoll Milling Machine Co. A number of smaller firms are similarly attempting to commercialize the technology for machining. While some of the benefits of hexapods are extremely appealing, namely stiffness values significantly higher than conventional machine designs, it is the author's opinion that the hexapod will remain a highly specialized machine tool configuration used primarily in R&D, and is unlikely to be adopted broadly.

The reasons for this pessimism stem from the practical difficulties surrounding hexapods. First, the kinematics of motion are much more complex than conventional designs, making efficient motion control more difficult and costly. Second, the thermal properties of the design are also very complex and difficult to model. Third, the work volume (a truncated hexa-cone) is not a good match for most parts, namely because the orientation of the spindle is a function of machine position. This high degree of coupling between spindle orientation and position (something avoided in most other designs), means that hexapods become large relative to the part size they can machine in order to maintain the necessary spindle orientation (usually orthogonal) relative to the part. The Geodetic G500 hexapod, for example, is said to have a machining envelope of 55"×55"×19.6", but the largest prismatic part that can be machined is significantly smaller due to machine kinematics. The Giddings & Lewis® Variax™ machine requires a space measuring 264"×258"×170" high to house the machine, while supporting a 25" work cube. Tool changing and work changing are also difficult with these designs because of their unique kinematics.

As a result of their singular characteristics, hexapods are expensive, and are likely to remain so compared to more conventional designs. With the advent of new machine component technologies such as linear motors, hydrostatic way systems, and improved structural materials, "conventional" machine geometries, based around the use of orthogonal, decoupled axes, will continue to provide improved performance at a reasonable cost, thereby dominating the machining field.

As with numerous other innovations which were technically superior from a performance standpoint, the hexapod will not be adopted on a large scale because the compromises required to achieve that performance make them commercially unattractive. It is more likely that the hexapod concept will be successfully applied to a specialized range of activities, including mobile machining, where the machine is brought to the workpiece rather than vice versa, and tasks typically associated with robotics, such as painting, riveting, and assembling. In these areas, the high stiffness of the platform provides significant performance and economic benefits over conventional serial-link robot technology.

Way Systems

Each of the machine geometries described above can be manufactured using a range of structural materials and way systems. The way system, also known as the linear bearing system, is one of the more critical aspects of a high performance machine tool. Linear bearings are generally the least stiff element in the machine. As a result, they play a strong role in dictating overall machine stiffness and natural frequency. Linear bearing designs also differ greatly in terms of the damping they provide, and in their ability to provide a long, accurate service life. Three fundamental way system types, and their suitability for high performance machining, are discussed: hydrodynamic bearings, rolling element bearings, and hydrostatic bearings.

Hydrodynamic Ways

Hydrodynamic ways (or hydrodynamic bearings) consist of ground flat ways or V-ways, on which a slide or carraige rides atop a film of oil. The oil is pumped into the gap between the slide and ways intermittently in a fixed dosage. Low friction pads, made of Diamant® Moglice™ or other material, are used to line the slide surfaces and to provide oil flow passages. Tapered gibs provide a manual adjustment for wear in the bearing system. Hydrodynamic ways, commonly referred to as "hardened ground ways," are used on a large percentage of machine tools today, and as recently as five years ago were the dominant way system on a wide range of machinery.

The oil film in hydrodynamic way systems is only stable when the slide is in motion. When the slide stops moving, the thickness of the oil film decreases, causing a loss in accuracy. The thickness of the oil film is also affected by temperature, so tight temperature control of the way system is required to ensure accuracy. Because the thickness of the oil film diminishes when the machine tool is not moving, static friction is higher in hydrodynamic way systems than other bearing types. As a result, contouring accuracy is reduced, particularly during axis reversals. The high stick – slip friction present in this linear bearing type can be seen when machining a circle. During each axis reversal (X-axis at 0° and 180°, Y-axis at 90° and 270°), a significant positioning error is generated as the reversing axis tries to break free from the high static friction. Dynamic friction is also greater in hydrodynamic ways than in rolling element bearings.

Additional inaccuracies are introduced when the oil dispensing system is actuated (an intermittent process). When oil is forced into the gap between the way surface and slide, the slide will float slightly. This effect can be monitored by placing an indicator on the top of a VMC table and tracking its position through a lubrication cycle. This error can amount to 0.0001", depending upon the amount of wear in the gibs and low friction pads and the regularity with which maintenance is performed.

Hydrodynamic way systems are expensive to manufacture due to the amount of precision grinding, and the large number of support components required. They also create waste oil which can get into coolant, fouling it, and they require periodic maintenance in the field to ensure that a constant oil gap is maintained. This generally requires tightening of the gibs; but over longer periods of time requires that the gibs be replaced.

The primary drawback of hydrodynamic ways, namely high friction due to shearing of the fluid film, also leads to its greatest strength, a high degree of damping. This high friction means that hydrodynamic way systems are best suited to machines that do not frequently change direction, or which do so off the part. Reciprocating grinders operating at low to moderate feeds represent a machine type to which hydrodynamic bearings are successfully applied while providing a high degree of accuracy. The use of hydrodynamic way systems on high performance machining centers, where frequent axes reversals and low friction are required, is problematic.

Rolling Element Bearings

Rolling element bearings (Figure 2-18) possess low static and dynamic friction, about 70% to 85% less than that of hydrodynamic ways. These way systems are modular, facilitating machine assembly, and, if necessary, replacement of the ways in the field.

Rolling element bearings are constructed with either rollers or balls. Roller bearings are stiffer and have higher load capacities than balls, but are more susceptible to bearing misalignment, contamination, and scuffing in the presence of structural deflection.

Both types of bearings can be lubricated using grease or oil. When grease is used, it can be applied at infrequent intervals, such as every 1,000 hours, for example. The use of grease minimizes cost and reduces contamination of coolants and the environment. Because the use of grease does not flush out the bearings as effectively as oil-based lubrication, it is important to shield grease lubricated roller element bearings from contamination. This is achieved through shields on the bearing cartridges, and well designed way covers.

A properly selected roller bearing can provide higher effective stiffness than comparably sized hardened and ground way (hydrodynamic) systems. This finding is counterintuitive to most machine tool users. Because machine tools traditionally employed hydrodynamic way systems, and because roller element bearings are more compact, it is assumed that roller bearings are less stiff. The effective stiffness in hydrodynamic way systems can be lower because there is

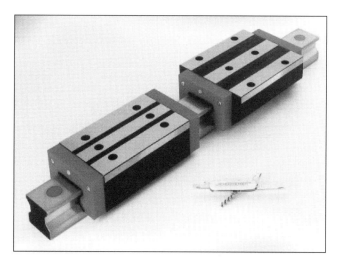

Figure 2-18:
Linear roller way system, shown with two different carriage configurations. These "65 monorail" roller ways combine very low friction with high stiffness and long life. (Courtesy of Schneeberger, Inc.)

inherent play between the bearing surfaces. While the stiffness of a hydrodynamic system is quite high once the play has been taken out under load, there can be sizable deflections at the onset of loading, as when entering a cut, or when motion first takes place.

Naturally, there is a wide range of performance characteristics across rolling element bearings from different manufacturers, with lower quality linear bearings providing less stiffness and accuracy. Roller bearings, for example, can be built with either convex (barrel) or straight rollers. Barrel rollers are preferred because they provide higher dynamic load capacity, smoother motion, and longer operating lives than straight rollers.

The importance of stiffness in a way system is illustrated by considering the Z-axis assembly of a small bridge machining center as shown in Figure 2-19. Y-axis deflection of the tool under a 40 lb•f load in the Y direction (as might be experienced when taking cuts in graphite or light cuts in aluminum), due to deflections of the Z-axis bearing carriages is calculated for roller and ball ways. In each case, the carriages are the same package size with similar preloads. In this scenario, the carriages nearest the spindle experience compressive loads, while those furthest from the spindle are loaded in tension.

$$F = \text{cutting force in Y-axis} = 40 \text{ lb•f}$$
$$L_1 = Z \text{ distance from tool tip to carriage \#1} = 6 \text{ in}$$
$$L_2 = Z \text{ distance between carriages \#1 and \#3} = 6 \text{ in}$$
$$K^C = \text{stiffness of one carriage in compression}$$
$$K^T = \text{stiffness of one carriage in tension}$$
$$\delta_1 = \text{deflection of carriage \#1}$$

$$\delta_1 = \delta_2, \, \delta_3 = \delta_4$$
$$\Sigma F_Y = 0: F + 2K^C \cdot \delta_1 + 2K^T \cdot \delta_3 = 0$$
$$\Sigma M_X = 0: F \cdot (L_1 + L_2) - 2K^C \cdot \delta_1 \cdot L_2 = 0$$

Solving:

$$\delta_1 = F \cdot (L_1 + L_2) \, , (2K^C \cdot L_2)$$
$$\delta_3 = - (F + 2K^C \cdot d_1) \, , 2K^T$$

For rollers:

$K^T_{roller} = 480,000 \text{ lb/in}$
$K^C_{roller} = 695,000 \text{ lb/in}$
$\delta_1 = 0.000056"$
$\delta_3 = -0.00012"$

For balls:

$K^T_{ball} = 390,000 \text{ lb/in}$
$K^C_{ball} = 555,000 \text{ lb/in}$
$\delta_1 = 0.00007"$
$\delta_3 = -0.00015"$

When these deflections are extrapolated linearly to the location of the spindle (and assuming that the Z-slide is rigid and does not deflect), we determine that the spindle would be displaced by about 0.00030" from its original position in the case of roller ways, and 0.00037" in the case of ball ways. One must keep in mind that this example only approximates deflection due to the Z-axis way system. Deflection in the X-axis way system and structural elements would also contribute to overall error in the Y-axis.

To fully realize the benefits of roller bearings, it is important that the ma-

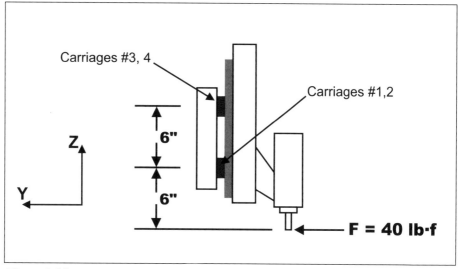

Figure 2-19:
Side view of Z-axis assembly of a small bridge machining center. The slide runs on two rails, each supported by two carriages. The lower carriages (1,2) and the upper carriages (3,4) deflect due to a Y-axis cutting force.

chine tool structure to which they are mounted be very stiff. Otherwise, structural deflection will cause the rollers to skew and scuff, reducing the stiffness and accuracy of the bearing, and shortening its service life. When evaluating a high performance machining center outfitted with linear bearings, ensure that there is plenty of mass surrounding the bearing mounting surfaces, and that they are not mounted on narrow "pillars," extended significantly beyond main body of the machine structure (Figure 2-20).

While roller element bearings (REB's) can be stiffer than hydrodynamic bearings, neither type of REB provides more damping than the oil film based way system. When using roller element bearings in high performance machining centers, it is important to ensure that additional measures are taken to damp the machine structure.

A final, important, consideration when evaluating machines with rolling element bearings is that the life of the bearing is finite. The rolling elements (rollers or balls) and rails will wear over time, and play will develop in the bearing. Over time, accuracy will degrade along with stiffness. The life of a rolling element bearing decreases with the dynamic load as follows, where L is the bearing life in distance traveled, C is the basic dynamic load rating identified by the manufacturer, and P is the load experienced by the bearing. In the case of varying loads, P represents an aggregate of the various loads.

$$L = (C/P)^3$$

Because the life of the bearing is shortened as the third power of the load applied to the bearing relative to its rated load, it is very important that a bearing be properly sized for the job at hand. If the linear bearing is not stiff enough, the

Figure 2-20:
Mounting of linear guideways to column of vertical machining center. Note that the rails are mounted to ground (not machined) surfaces, and that the rail mounting surface is not raised up significantly beyond the main body of the casting.

life of the machine tool will be significantly reduced. This holds true not only for cutting loads, but for the loads placed upon the bearing by acceleration and deceleration of machine axes.

For high performance machining centers, particularly those cutting metal, barrel roller linear bearings are recommended. Ball-based linear bearings provide a cost effective (and lower performance) alternative to roller ways when working in materials such as graphite and plastics, or where very light cuts are being taken in free machining metals. In such applications cutting forces are typically low, and the need for low friction to enable fast reversals is paramount. Hydrodynamic way systems are not recommended for high performance machining when 3D high speed contouring is required.

Hydrostatic Bearings

Rolling element bearings represent the practical state of the art in way system technology. They are cost effective, stiff, have relatively low friction, and are easy to maintain. But, in the future, hydrostatic way systems may become increasingly prevalent in high performance machine tools. Hydrostatic ways use an oil film like the hydrodynamic way systems. But, unlike hydrodynamic ways, hydrostatic bearings are self-compensating. The oil flow is under constant closed loop control, allowing the system to compensate for changes in the thickness of the oil film. Hydrostatic way systems, while expensive, overcome the principle weaknesses of hydrodynamic ways (lower accuracy and a lack of stiffness), while providing a high degree of damping. Hydrostatic ways are currently employed on a limited number high performance machines, such as the Weldon 1632 grinder and the Moore Special Tool's Nanotech 150 aspheric grinder.

Unfortunately, the expense associated with hydrostatics will limit their widespread adoption for high performance machining in the near term. Nonetheless, hydrostatics are a technology which may be adopted in the years ahead if improved damping systems are not developed to augment rolling element linear bearings. An innovative design called the HydroRail™ has been developed by Aesop, Inc. and M.I.T. (Figure 2-21). The HydroRail promises to reduce the cost of hydrostatic bearings by building them into the profile of a conventional rolling element linear bearing system. This allows the hydrostatic way system to be provided as optional equipment on machines normally outfitted with roller bearings. Developers of this concept believe that the HydroRail, if produced in large quantities, could be manufactured for less than two or three times the cost of current roller ways, including the necessary high pressure oil pumps and oil scavenging equipment. The technology is also said to be more robust than conventional hydrostatics, and should require less maintenance. Table 2-5 compares the general properties of the four different way system types discussed.

Characteristic	Hydrodynamic	Ball Linear Way	Roller Linear Way	Hydrostatic
Stiffness[†]	Low	Medium	High	High
Geometric Accuracy	Medium	High	High	Very High
Friction	High	Low	Low	Almost Zero
Damping	High	Low	Low	Very High
Cost	Medium	Low	Medium	High
Maintenance Requirements	Medium	Low	Low	Medium –High
Longevity	High	Medium	Medium	High

[†]Stiffness measure includes the effects of intrinsic play.

Table 2-5:
Comparison of properties of popular way system types. The comparison applies to high performance components. Lower grade components have correspondingly lower performance characteristics.

Geometric Accuracy

Geometric accuracy is the most critical element of machine geometry as it relates to high performance machining. Unfortunately, the geometric accuracy of machine tools is often overlooked by buyers, who assume that similar levels of accuracy are achieved by most, if not all, builders. This is not the case, and much of the cost difference between machines is related to the level of geometric accuracy which they achieve. High levels of geometric accuracy are time consuming and expensive to establish, requiring skilled labor and high quality components.

Geometric accuracy is measured in terms of the magnitude of different classes of geometric errors such as squareness, straightness, parallelism, and flatness. Note that in each case, these errors are angular in nature. Linear, or translational, errors do not affect geometric accuracy. If a VMC column is 0.002" higher than intended with respect to the machine table, the geometric accuracy of the machine is not affected, and the "error" is eliminated during the process of setting up part zero. If, on the other hand, the column has an error in squareness with respect to the X-Y plane of 0.002", a very serious problem exists!

Figure 2-21:
Prototype test bed of HydroRails™, with 1,000 lb axial load.
Even with this load, the slide moves along the rails with almost
no axial force because friction is minimized. The rails have a
profile similar to popular rolling element rails, and hydraulic
oil is pumped into the cartridges to create a fluid film bearing.
(Courtesy of Aesop, Inc., and MIT).

The Role of Angular Errors

As previously discussed in the context of axis stackup, the effect of angular errors increases with distance from the source of the error. If the distance from the source of the error doubles, the magnitude of the error also doubles. This differs significantly from translational errors, which simply add to one another, and represents the principal difficulty in producing accurate machine tools.

Consider an error in squareness between the column and Y-axis of a c-frame machining center with 16" of Z-axis travel. Figure 2-22 illustrates the

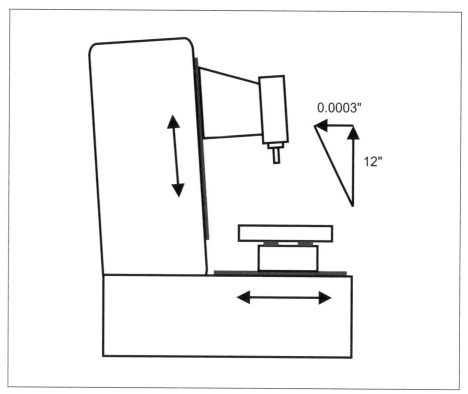

Figure 2-22:
C-frame VMC with Y-Z squareness error of 0.0003" per foot.

error in squareness, which amounts to 0.0003" in the Y-Z plane per foot of Z-axis travel (measured from the table in the positive Z direction). The impact of this error upon overall machine quality is twofold. First, the angle between tool and worktable will be in error by an amount θ_{error}.

$$\theta_{error} = \tan^{-1}(0.0003/12)$$
$$\theta_{error} = 0.0014° = 5.04 \text{ arc seconds}$$

In this example, the angle does not change with Z-axis position. If the Z-axis was not straight, the angle would change as the spindle moved in the +Z direction. When the Z-axis is at full travel, a Y-axis positioning error is also created.

$$Y_{error} = 16" \cdot \tan(0.0014°)$$
$$Y_{error} = 0.00039"$$

When the Z-axis is 8" above the table, the magnitude of the error is reduced significantly to

$$Y_{error} = 0.0002".$$

In either case, the error is significant when part tolerances of ±0.0002" to ±0.0005" are sought.

Geometric Accuracy Guidelines

Very few machine tool builders publicize the geometric accuracy of their products. Because it is so critical to machine tool performance, guidelines are provided for evaluating prospective machines in Table 2-6. These values apply principally to vertical machining centers, although they relate to horizontal machining centers as well. If the machine tool builder cannot readily provide geometric accuracy values — beware! When purchasing a machine tool it is wise to stipulate the desired geometric accuracy as part of the purchase order. Highly capable machine tool builders routinely achieve tighter tolerances than those shown in Table 2-6, and can often manufacture to even tighter specifications to meet specific customer needs (for an added charge, of course).

Geometric Accuracy Specification	Minimum Requirements for High Performance Machining (small- to mid-sized components)
Squareness (X-Y, X-Z, Y-Z)	0.0002" / 12", 0.0004" over full travel
Straightness (all axes, pitch, yaw, roll)	0.0002"/12", 0.0004" over full travel
Table Flatness	0.0004"/12", 0.001" over complete surface
Table Rise and Fall	0.0004"/12", 0.001" over complete surface
Spindle Tram to Table	0.0005" TIR on a 12" sweep
Spindle Parallel to X-Z, Y-Z Planes	±0.0002" over 6"
Ball Bar (12"∅, 20 IPM, all three planes)	less than 0.0003" TIR

Table 2-6:
Minimum geometric accuracy requirements for high performance machining centers. These values are not "±" unless expressly labeled as such.

In reviewing these guidelines, it is important to keep in mind the amplification of angular errors with distance. The larger the parts being machined, the more critical the geometric accuracies become. In all cases, buyers can perform their own calculations to determine the net effect of all errors upon positioning accuracy for a given part or family of parts. First calculate the effect of each error at the worst case tool position. The effects of each error can be added together to calculate a worst-case total error due to geometric inaccuracies, but this will overstate the total error because many geometric errors cancel each other out, depending upon their relative orientation, and not every error is likely to be at the limit of the machine builder's specification.

Results from a 12"∅ ball bar test are included in Table 2-6. This test reflects motion control inadequacies and errors such as backlash, in addition to geometric inaccuracies. As a composite measure of overall machine performance it is quite useful, and will be discussed in depth in Chapter 3.

Building Geometric Accuracy into Machine Tools

The subject of how to build accuracy into machine tools is generally beyond the scope of this text. But a brief overview of some of the more important elements is provided to aid in the evaluation of machine quality.

Construction Techniques

To provide the qualities listed in Table 2-6, it is generally required that all reference surfaces be precision ground, as well as hand scraped or lapped depending upon the geometry in question. These production steps, while time consuming and expensive, ensure that the assembled components are properly aligned.

Many general machine tools forego the grinding steps by affixing rails and other components directly to machined surfaces. This is unlikely to provide the geometric accuracies necessary for a high performance machine tool. Linear rails, for example, are not highly stiff in and of themselves, and provide adequate stiffness only when mounted to a rigid machine structure. So, when the rails are mounted to a machined base, they deform to match the surface to which they are mounted. If the rail mounting surfaces are twisted, the rails will twist. In other cases, such as the assembly of axis drive housings, misalignment does not directly affect geometric accuracy. But because the drive housing establishes alignment between the ball screw and the way system, angular misalignment causes uneven loads on the screw during use, resulting in premature wear and failure.

An alternative to grinding all surfaces is to machine the reference surfaces and to replicate the required geometric accuracy by casting components in place using precision reference fixtures and compounds such as Diamant® Moglice (for sliding members) and Diamant® DWH for static structural elements. This methodology depends upon the reference fixtures, rather than the machine tool components themselves, to establish machine accuracy. While this technique cannot totally replace the role of grinding and hand scraping, it has proven effective in the mounting of rails, ball screw drive housings, and the joining of major machine castings, such as the base to column.

The benefits of using Moglice, DWH, or similar replicating mediums are easier machine assembly with less labor, and increased damping relative to metal-to-metal joints. The drawbacks are that epoxy joints are less stiff, require time to harden (increasing manufacturing lead times), and are susceptible to air bubbles and porosity if improperly applied. Firms using such replicating compounds have largely overcome the manufacturing process difficulties, making the choice between grinding/scraping/lapping and replicating an issue of stiffness versus damping tradeoffs, and manufacturing preference.

One final consideration when evaluating various construction methods is that epoxy joints can be harder to work with in the field. This is particularly important when dealing with the replacement of linear ways or other machine elements. When the worn way or other element is removed, the polymer – epoxy joint can be damaged despite the use of release agents; this will require geometric accuracy of the machine to be reestablished in the field. This is a time-consuming and very difficult process away from the machine tool factory. Some of the builders working with these compounds have developed innovative practices for reducing the difficulty of in-field repairs. If the ways or ball screws need to be replaced on a ground/scraped/lapped geometry, reestablishing geometric accuracy in the field is easier because the accuracy is built into the reference surfaces to which the components are mounted.

Compensating for Geometric Inaccuracy

Generally speaking, there is no substitute for a high degree of geometric accuracy in a machine tool. The nature of a 3-axis machine tool makes it difficult to compensate for most geometric inaccuracies. This is because the axis motions

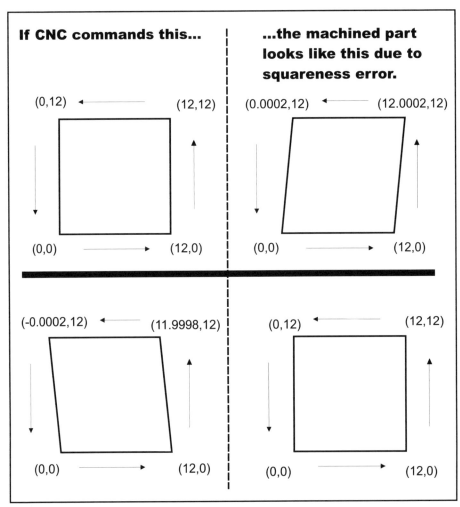

Figure 2-23:
Relationship between desired geometry and machined results on a VMC with an X-Y squareness error of 0.0002" per foot. Embedding information about this error in the CNC enables corrections to be made automatically during machining.

(X, Y, Z) cannot adjust for errors in tool orientation, nor for most other angular errors. Only the effects of positioning errors can be adjusted for. Returning to the aforementioned example of Z-axis squareness in a machining center, CNC based compensation could adjust for the Y-axis positioning error, but any form machined would possess an angular error. A fourth axis rotating about "X" would be required to compensate for squareness errors in the Y-Z plane.

One type of geometric inaccuracy that can be reliably compensated for is squareness errors that do not affect the tool carrying axis (typically Z in machining centers). In 3-axis machining centers, errors in X-Y squareness can be corrected. By creating a representation of the error in the CNC, each axis move is adjusted in real-time to eliminate the skew between the X- and Y-axes. Unfortunately, these error corrections can introduce additional errors in machine tools with inadequate motion control systems. Consider a VMC, on which the X-axis is out of square relative to the Y-axis by 0.0002" over 12". Normally, to cut a 12" square counterclockwise at 50 IPM, each axis would move independently. The machine movements would be from (0,0) to (12,0) to (12,12) to (0,12) and back to (0,0), creating the incorrect geometry shown in Figure 2-23. To create a perfect square, the CNC compensation will command the machine to move from (0,0) to (12,-0.0002) to (12,12) to (0,0.0002) to (0,0). The 0.0002" moves created by the compensation require a Y-axis feed rate of only 0.004 IPM. Such slow motion requires exceptional motion control performance at low speeds to overcome high friction effects, and to properly regulate the feed rate. In most machine tools, the capabilities necessary to accurately perform such compensation are not present.

While a high performance CNC can provide geometry compensation to improve accuracy, the best approach to minimizing geometric inaccuracies is to start with an intrinsically good machine geometry, which is stable, and built to a high quality standard.

4- and 5-Axis Considerations

4- and 5-axis machine tools are more difficult to manufacture to high performance standards. While many 4-axis parts require tolerances within the ±0.0002" to ±0.0005" band, 5-axis applications, particularly those related to turbo-machinery, are more likely to require tolerances in the ±0.001" or ±0.002" range. This is still difficult to achieve when considering complex airfoils produced in hard-to-machine materials, such as the titanium blade machined from bar stock in Figure 2-24. Special considerations in machine construction and geometric accuracy must be considered when pursuing high performance machining of 4- or 5-axis components.

Stiffness and Damping

Stiffness is reduced with each additional axis of motion added to a machine tool. The amount by which the stiffness is reduced is strongly a function of the design of the 4th and/or 5th rotary axis, and their placement relative to the other

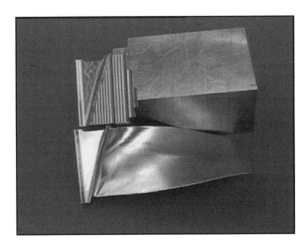

Figure 2-24:
This titanium blade, including the root and platform, was machined in two setups on a BostoMatic® 505 × 5-axis machining center from a solid billet. The part is shown after the first operation, and after the second operation, during which the airfoil is produced.

axes. Reduced stiffness is of particular concern with respect to 5-axis machines, due to the long, slender tooling that must often be employed to produce complex contours in components such as impellers. If stiffness is inadequate, significant vibration can develop during 5-axis cutting with long cutters.

Damping in 5-axis applications is also critical because of the difficult to machine materials which must be processed, such as titanium, inconel, and nickel-based alloys. The hardness of many of these materials tends to induce chatter and vibration during cutting.

Comparison of Popular 5-Axis Configurations

In 5-axis machine tools, a number of different geometries have evolved, including compound rotary tables, compound spindle heads, pendulum head with rotary table, and tilting spindle with rotary table.

Compound Rotary Tables

Compound tables (Figure 2-25) are the most straightforward and economical method of achieving 5-axis machining. While these tables can be installed upon 3-axis machine tools, they are less stiff and possess higher angular errors than more integrated approaches. Because the rotary axes are stacked on top of one another, angular errors are magnified. Also, the large stackup between workpiece and rotary axes when using a double tilt rotary means that high torque loads are placed upon the gear sets, reducing life and increasing deflection. The nature of the compound rotary also requires large axis travels to maintain contact between the workpiece and tool tip. This further increases errors, and limits effective material removal rates. Finally, a large machine tool is required relative to the part size when using a compound rotary table. Compound rotary tables are best suited to 5-axis positioning (versus contouring) applications, and 5-axis contouring of less demanding small components.

Figure 2-25:
This compound rotary table produced by Nikken Kosakusho Works, Ltd. is one of the better such products on the market. It utilizes a powerful brake system to facilitate 5-sided part machining and is accurate to 20 arc-seconds.

2-Axis Spindle Heads

2-axis (sometimes called "nutating") spindle heads (Figure 2-26) are typically employed on gantry type machining centers, and possess the same weaknesses as double-tilt rotary tables, including lower accuracy and stiffness than other designs. Further, the rotational range of these heads is often limited. In a typical VMC arrangement, the C-axis will typically have unlimited range of motion, while the carried (A) axis might be limited to ±90° of motion from the vertical position. The principal strength of this design is that it provides good access to large and deep cavities, and is therefore used extensively in the production of very large mold and die components, particularly in the automotive sector. 2-axis heads are not well suited to relatively long, slender parts, such as blades and propellers, where 360° access to the part is required. 2-axis spindle heads are exceptionally well suited to parts where machining is required in a wide range of orientations, such as mold cavities, and large dies.

Single Axis Spindle Heads (Pendulum Type)

Single-axis spindle heads, when combined with a rotary table, can provide better accuracy than double-tilt tables or multi-axis spindle heads because the ro-

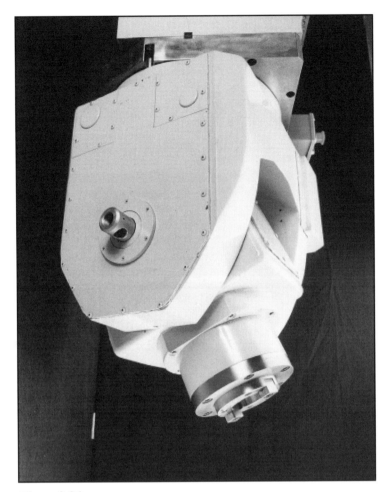

Figure 2-26:
2-axis spindle head manufactured by Dayton Machine Tool Company.

tary axes are not stacked atop one another. When utilized with a VMC, this means that the axes are typically distributed in a three axis set (X, Y, and A, or C), and a two axis pair (Z and B or A). The principal weakness of this design is that the center of rotation of the spindle head (as with 2-axis heads) is located relatively far from the tool tip (typically 8" or more), causing angular errors and decreasing overall system stiffness. The range of angular motion is often limited, thus limiting the range of applications to which this design can be successfully applied. Nonetheless, this geometry has advantages over previously discussed designs with respect to high performance machining a range of components such as impellers, blades, and other parts where the part itself can be rotated to present different faces to the spindle.

Tilting Heads

The tilting spindle combined with a single axis rotary table is the ideal choice for 5-axis machining of many small- to mid-sized components, and is applicable to both prismatic and long, slender parts. Illustrated in Figure 2-27, the B-axis is designed so that the spindle rotates around the tool tip. This minimizes angular errors, and keeps torsional loads on the B-axis at a minimum. Even when the tool tip is not exactly aligned with the center of B-axis rotation, the distance between the tool tip and center of rotation is usually less than 2" or 3", compared with 8 – 12" for other designs. As a result, angular errors are reduced by 75% or more.

The tilting spindle design further enhances accuracy by ensuring that linear axis motions are kept to a minimum when large B-axis angular motions are required. Figure 2-28 illustrates this point when machining an impeller. Because the distance R between the center of B-axis rotation and the tool tip is small, the distance L which the X-axis must move for a 90° B-axis move is also small. Figure 2-28 also shows that the distance L which the linear axis must move is significantly longer when working with a double-tilt table (likewise a compound rotary spindle head).

Figure 2-27:
The tilting head spindle design provides high stiffness while minimizing angular errors and axis motions. This is achieved by rotating the B-axis at, or near, the tool tip. (Courtesy of Boston Digital Corporation.)

Other benefits of the tilting spindle design include the separation of the two rotary axes to minimize stackup, and the ability of the spindle head to rotate ±100° from the vertical. This gives the machine a higher degree of flexibility than tilting heads or double-tilt tables, which cannot easily present the sides of parts to the spindle, making it difficult or impossible to machine undercuts into parts. This is particularly important when machining components such as tire patterns, complex electrodes, or turbo-machinery components.

The tilting spindle head is less well suited to the machining of cavities than the 2-axis spindle head because it is unable to access very deep cavities in large

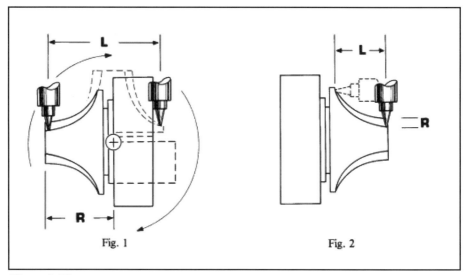

Fig. 1   Fig. 2

Figure 2-28:
The linear distances L which must be traveled when using compound rotary designs
(Fig. 1) versus a tilting head (Fig. 2) are illustrated. The distance between the tool tip
and the center of rotation R is also represented.

diameter parts. This restriction exists because of the limited throat distance between the spindle centerline and the face of the B-axis gear set. As a result, the
tilting spindle head design is best suited to small- to mid-sized concave parts,
and a wider range of convex parts.

Effect of 5-Axis Design Upon Machine Performance

Figures 2-29, 2-30, and 2-31 illustrate the relative merits of typical 5-axis
designs. Each figure illustrates the distance through which the tool – part interface will move to accommodate a 5° angular motion of one rotary axis. Rotation
of the second axis would add additional movements to the part or tool. On the
tilting spindle machine pictured in Figure 2-29, the tool extends 0.5" below the
center of B-axis rotation. Figure 2-30 illustrates a pendulum type spindle, where
the center of rotation is 12.2" from gauge line. The tool length from gauge line
is the same for Figures 2-29 and 2-30. Two axis heads demonstrate similar performance to the pendulum type in this regard. Figure 2-31 illustrates one axis of
a compound rotary table, where tool length does not come into play. Performance
of this rotary is similar to a range of part carrying compound rotaries, even if the
orientation of the rotating axes (e.g., B or C) differs. Table 2-7 compares the
linear moves required for each 5° rotation. In each case, the distance moved also
relates to the amount of axis velocity needed to maintain tool-part contact, and
the multiplication of angular errors.

Table 2-7 indicates that angular errors are multiplied by a factor of over
200 for both the pendulum and double-tilt rotary compared to the tilting spindle
design. Figures 2-29 through 2-31 indicate the critical importance of minimizing the distance between centers of rotation and the tool-part interface. Even if

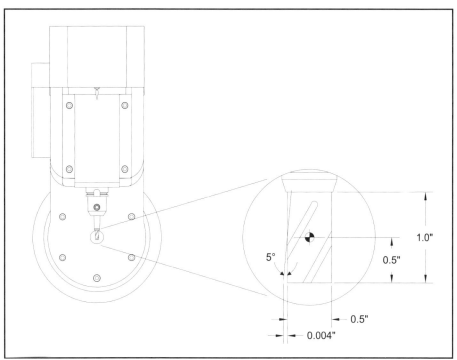

Figure 2-29:
The tilting spindle 5-axis concert requires minimal tool movement along the X-axis (.0004") for a 5° rotation of the B-axis when working with a tool that measures 5" long from gauge line and extends past the center of rotation by 0.5". Rotation about the tool tip optimizes accuracy of the system.

5-Axis Design	Displacement due to 5° move of one rotary axis	Relative velocities and multiplication of angular errors
Tilting Spindle	0.004"	1
Single Axis Spindle Head	1.0"	250
Double-tilt Rotary	1.6"	400

Table 2-7:
Displacement of tool-part interface for a 5° rotation of the axis furthest from the part in various 5-axis machine geometries. Required axis velocities and the multiplication of angular errors grow with increasing displacement.

the B-axis of the tilting spindle design was ten times less accurate than the other models, it would make significantly more accurate parts, would require lower axis feed rates to achieve the same surface speed over the part surface, and would make the same parts with smaller axis travels.

The importance of minimizing the distance between axes of rotation and the tool – part interface can not be overemphasized. Consider a double-tilt ro-

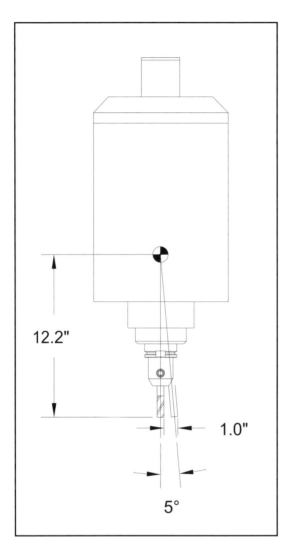

12.2"

1.0"

5°

Figure 2-30:
The pendulum type spindle
head requires increased X-axis
motion (1") to maintain tool –
part contact compared to the
tilting spindle for a 5° rotation
of the B-axis. Extra motion is
required because the center of
rotation is located a considerable
distance from the tool tip. In
this example, the tool measures
5" from gauge line. The extended
swing required by this design
degrades overall accuracy.

tary on which the tilt axis (rotation about the X-axis) is accurate to ±5 arc seconds, and the distance between the face of the rotary and the tilt axis is 4". If a 4" high part is placed on top of this rotary axis, the displacement error along the Y-axis will be ±0.0002". At this stage, only one source of positioning error has been considered. If the rotary axis was accurate to only ±10 arc seconds, as is the case with conventional rotary axes, the error would amount to ±0.0004". Add errors due to positioning of the remaining four axes and it is likely that the error will grow to ±0.001" before considering dynamic errors, thermal effects, tool run-out and deflection, etc.

The Role of Angular Errors in 4-Axis Machining

The importance of minimizing the multiplication of angular errors is important in 4-axis applications also. Bolt-on rotary axes for machining centers

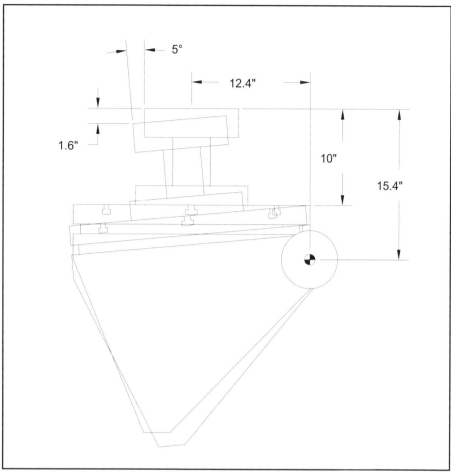

Figure 2-31:
A machine with a pivoting work table. This design rotates along the X-axis. The center of rotation is toward the rear of the table, and the part stacks up several inches above the table. As a result, angular errors are greatly magnified by this design. The workpiece sweeps through 1.6" due to a 5° rotation of the A-axis.

(Figure 2-32) must possess a high degree of accuracy, particularly if machining is going to take place more than a few inches from the center of rotation of the 4th axis. Rotary die manufacture, for example, requires that large diameter cylinders be mounted to an A-axis and a heavy duty outboard support. To support high performance machining, rotary axes with accuracies of better than ±10 arc seconds should be sought. For larger parts, or where accuracies towards the ±0.0002" mark are sought, rotary axes should be accurate to better than ±5 arc seconds. The positioning error due to angular errors in a rotary axis (any orientation — A, B, or C) can be calculated as follows.

R = distance between center of rotation and tool – part interface [inch]

q = accuracy of rotary axis [arc-seconds]

Error = $R \cdot \tan(q/3{,}600)$ [inch]

Figure 2-32:
Typical configuration of a bolt-on 4th axis for A- or C-axis
configurations. This model provides a 320 mm face plate.
(Courtesy of HPI Nikken.)

Considerations when Machining Heavy 4-Axis Parts

Another consideration when machining heavy components, particularly in an
A-axis configuration, is that the part can sag under its own weight. Deflection of
the machine table and saddle can cause a crowning effect to be superimposed on
top of this sag; for example, 2,200 lb steel cylinder 39" long, supported at both
ends on a high performance VMC deflected by 0.0007" along its length due to
its own weight and distortion of the machine table (Figure 2-33). Large cylinders such as these are used to manufacture cookies and biscuits, among other
things. Cavities are machined into the cylinder with the shape of the cookie. Two
such cylinders are then used together in baking machinery to rapidly form the
cookies from raw dough fed into the machine. If the depths of each cavity on the
roll are not held relatively precisely, the cookies will not weigh the same amount,
nor will they cook evenly. Similar concerns affect the production of large rotary
cutting dies for producing cardboard boxes and other materials. If the depth and
land of the cutting edges machined into the cylinder are not consistent, the rolls
will not properly cut the material run through them.

To support high performance machining of large components such as these,
CNC-based beam compensation can be used to map the Z-axis sag of the cylinder as a function of X-axis position. As the machine cuts the cavities or knife
edges, the Z-axis position is automatically adjusted to account for deflection in
the roll. This allows more accurate features to be machined. The error in the
aforementioned cylinder was reduced to a maximum of 0.00035" (a 50%

Figure 2-33:
This rotary die weighs in at 2,300 lbs. The machine is outfitted
with a 42,000 RPM spindle for sharpening lands on the die.

reduction). But, as discussed previously, this is an imperfect solution. While the
CNC can correct for displacement errors, it cannot correct for the angular errors
in the features machined along the roll. These angular errors are caused by the
changing slope of the roll due to its sag. These errors can not be corrected because a 4-axis VMC (X-,Y-, Z-, A-axes) does not possess a B-axis, which would
be necessary to adjust for the angular errors. Fortunately, in this example, such
errors were small compared to the displacement errors, and could be ignored.

Chapter 3

Motion Control (CNC) and Drive Train

Overview

The importance of the CNC and drive train to high performance machining is often lost in the simplistic machine specifications provided by machine tool builders. The information provided by most manufacturers in their brochures only quantifies positional accuracy, CNC block processing rates, and axis feed rates. These measures are inadequate to describe the performance of a machine tool.

Today, the machine tool landscape is rapidly changing; and with increased choice and more demanding performance requirements, consumers need better information to evaluate machinery. A high quality, geometrically accurate machine structure is only the start to achieving high performance machining. Increasingly, the CNC and drive train are the key elements to achieving high performance. This chapter discusses the requirements for high performance machining with respect to positioning accuracy, drive train, and CNC motion control.

Positioning Accuracy and Repeatability

Positioning accuracy and repeatability have long been the basis for evaluating the quality of a machine tool. A survey of machine tool brochures identified the following positional accuracy and repeatability values. The results are shown in Table 3-1.

Table 3-1 is interesting for a number of reasons. First, two standards (ISO and JIS) are cited most often, while a number of builders do not cite any standard by which the measurements were made. Second, machines 5 and 6 are actually the same machine, measured using two different methods. Machines 3 and 4 are likewise a single machine, with the results again presented via two different measurement methods. The fact that the "accuracies" and "repeatabilities" can differ so significantly for the same machine when measured differently calls into question the validity of one, or both, measurement methods. Further, it is disturbing that some builders provide accuracy and repeatability values without indicating how they were determined. This makes it impossible to compare the performance of one machine brand to another, and casts serious doubt over the relevance of such builders' figures to the real world.

The JIS B6201 (Japanese Industrial Standard) method of determining accuracies and repeatability works as follows. Each machine axis is commanded

Machine	Approximate Price	Accuracy	Repeatability	Standard
1	$60,000	±0.0002"	±0.0001"	No Std.
2	$60,000	±0.0002"	±0.0001"	No Std.
3	$85,000	±0.0002"	±0.0001"	ISO
4	$85,000	±0.0001"	±0.0001"	JIS
5	$150,000	±0.0001"	±0.000075"	ISO
6	$150,000	±0.00006"	±0.00004"	JIS
7	$150,000	±0.0002"	±0.00004"	JIS
8	$220,000	±0.00006"	±0.00004"	JIS
9	$500,000	±0.00004"	±0.00004"	JIS

Table 3-1:
Positioning accuracies and repeatabilities per linear axis for a range of machining centers of similar travel. The approximate price of each machine, and the standard of measurement listed in the brochure, are also provided. All values are for full stroke.

to as few as three points unidirectionally along its length: one at each end and a third at the midpoint of travel. The machine stops at each location, and the actual position of the machine is measured using a laser interferometer and compared to the positional readout of the CNC. The difference is a positioning error. The largest of the three positioning errors, represented as ±½ the measured value, becomes the positioning accuracy for that axis. Repeatability is measured by positioning seven times to each of three different points along the machine axis. The repeatability is recorded as ± ½ the maximum recorded deviation across all 21 measurements.

The ISO 230-2 (International Standards Organization) method of determining accuracies and repeatability is more involved. For each axis, error measurements are made in at least five locations. Multiple runs back and forth along the axis are made, so that positioning error is measured at each point at least five times in each direction for bi-directional tests. A ±3σ statistical confidence band is then calculated using the error data, so that there is more than a 99% probability that the accuracy and repeatability data presented will hold true if additional measurements are taken.

Actual machine positioning performance in the field is better approximated by the ISO method than the JIS method. First, with ISO many more measurements are made, and over a longer period of time. This takes into account thermal drift, which is experienced under actual use, and better accounts for errors in measurement. Second, the bi-directional nature of ISO means that the effect of mechanical backlash, and variations in the ball screw of the machine, are better represented. Finally, the statistical nature of ISO means that it is very likely that ISO accuracies and repeatabilities can be achieved in the field by the machine tool user *for point-to-point positioning.* The nonstatistical nature of the JIS method makes it almost impossible for users to achieve JIS accuracies and repeatabilities in the field. The low number of data points, and the lack of accommodation for random "noise" and thermal effects, makes the JIS figures a theoretical optimum, not a practical measure of real-world performance. The differences between the two methods are summarized in Table 3-2.

Characteristic	ISO 230-2	JIS B6201
Number of Measurement Locations	5	3
Minimum Number of Measurements for Accuracy Calculations	50	3
Minimum Number of Measurements for Repeatability Calculations	50	21
Direction	bi-directional	uni-directional
Statistical Confidence Band	$\pm 3\sigma$	none

Table 3-2:
Comparison of minimum requirements of JIS and ISO measurement methods upon a 40" long machine axis.

While the positioning accuracy values obtained using ISO provide valuable information, it is important to remember that the results apply to point-to-point positioning. Neither measurement method describes machine accuracy during contouring. If a machine is intended to locate bores and similar features (e.g., a jig borer), the ISO results are meaningful. But ISO results may not be achieved during high speed 3D contouring. While high performance machine tools will approach ISO accuracies during contouring, the accuracy of most machine tools drops off dramatically with increasing feed rates. This phenomenon will be discussed in greater depth later in the chapter.

ISO and JIS positioning data provided in brochures include lead screw and backlash compensation, installed in the CNC by the machine tool builder. After taking initial data on machine accuracy without compensation, data are loaded into the CNC to adjust for errors in the pitch of the screw, and the backlash observed during axis reversals. While the use of compensation improves the accuracy and repeatability results, the role of backlash cannot be corrected for during contouring as it can during these positioning tests. Further, as the machine ages, the amount of backlash will increase.

When positioning, each axis comes to a full stop at the end of its move. As such, the system has time to "catch up" and eliminate any backlash in the ball screw before the next move when equipped with a linear encoder. In contouring, there is no time to speed through the backlash, as the other axes are still in motion. This becomes apparent when cutting a circle. At each axis reversal location (0°, 90°, 180°, 270°), a deviation from the desired circle due to backlash will be seen.

Figure 3-1 illustrates the effect of backlash in a highly exaggerated manner for a tool path programmed to cut a circle of radius 3, beginning at the point (3,0) on a machine with backlash of 0.25 in each axis's screw. Initially, we as-

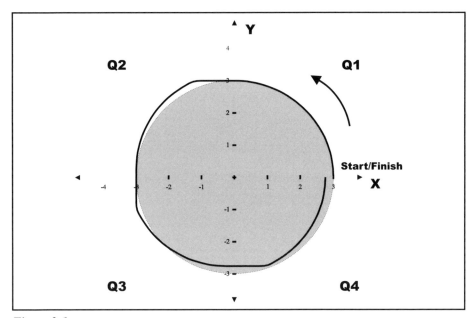

Figure 3-1:
The effects of mechanical backlash can be corrected in the CNC with respect to their effect on point-to-point positioning. But, during contouring, mechanical backlash is more difficult to compensate for. The uncompensated effects of 0.25 of backlash in the X- and Y-axes upon a circle with diameter 6 are illustrated. In reality, the magnitude of backlash is several orders of magnitude less than depicted here.

sume that the ball screw nuts are in full contact with the thread. As a result, the arc in quadrant 1 (Q1) follows the desired path, indicated by the gray shaded circle. At the point (0,3), the Y-axis screw reverses its direction of motion. As it does so, 0.25 of backlash must be taken up before the Y-axis commences moving. The X-axis continues in the same (negative) direction, so no impact of X-axis backlash is seen at this point. The Y-axis backlash creates a "flat" in the tool path, and the mill deviates from the desired geometry. As the machine reaches (-3,0), the X-axis reverses. This also creates a flat in Q3 because the Y-axis continues to move while the X-axis stops until 0.25 worth of backlash is taken up by the X-axis screw. As the tool path approaches (0,-3), another flat is machined, although now the local radius of the circle is 2.75 (= 3 - 0.25). Finally, as the tool path comes full circle, the final position is in error by 0.25 in X; the amount of backlash in that axis. This simple example illustrates the significant impact of mechanical backlash upon part accuracy during contouring.

Stopping the nonreversing axis to allow backlash to be taken up in the reversing axis would interfere with the cutting process and introduce other, friction related, errors. Even when linear encoders and sophisticated motion algorithms are used, the adverse effects of mechanical backlash cannot be fully eliminated. As a result of backlash (among other things), machines with similar positioning accuracy and repeatability values will perform at significantly different levels when contouring.

When evaluating the applicability of machine tools to high performance machining, ask the builder to provide information about the standard used to determine positioning accuracies, and also seek data on the amount of mechanical backlash present in the ball screws. Positioning accuracy and repeatability figures are most useful when evaluating a machine tool's ability to position point to point. As the proportion of contour machining increases, it is important to augment these data with further information, including the results of ball bar tests.

A Note on Repeatability

Accuracy can be loosely defined as the ability of a machine tool to go to the location commanded. Repeatability can be thought of as the ability of a machine tool to go to the same place over and over again, even if it is not the commanded location. In the final analysis, accuracy is what determines whether a machined part is produced to tolerance. But it is repeatability that dictates the ability of the machine tool builder, or user, to make corrections for inaccuracy.

A highly repeatable machine tool can be adjusted or compensated so as to be more accurate. If a machine always moves 0.2" farther than the commanded position, it is fairly inaccurate (there is an error of 0.2") but highly repeatable (it always goes long by 0.2"). By adjusting the commanded position to 0.2" less than the desired position, it is possible to have the machine always move to the correct location. In this way, a highly repeatable machine can be made more accurate. While this example is very simplistic, and improving overall accuracy is much more involved, it demonstrates the value of a highly repeatable machine tool. A highly repeatable machine provides the opportunity for the resourceful machinist to make parts better than the stated accuracy of the machine, particularly during large production runs, when data can be collected, and meaningful adjustments can be made to part programs. It is important to note that this process of adjusting machine performance is extremely time consuming and difficult — it is better to start with an accurate machine.

Drive Train

The drive train of a high performance machine tool typically consists of the axis motors, couplings, ball screws, and their interface to the machine slides. The drive train plays a critical role in establishing the positioning accuracy and dynamic (cutting) performance of a machine tool because it links the CNC and the machine slides. Very often, the full utilization of a CNC's processing power is limited by the stiffness, damping, and geometric accuracy of the machine's drive train. The CNC could push the machine harder and faster, but the dynamics of the drive train limit performance. When comparing high performance machine tools, it is important to evaluate the various components in the drive train, and the care with which they have been assembled.

Ball Screws

Ball screws are the principal axis drive mechanism used in high performance machine tools today. Ball screws utilize a series of steel balls and recirculators built into the nut to convert rotary motion into the linear motion needed to drive machine axes. This conversion process is extremely efficient in a ball screw, requiring only about 30% of the torque needed to drive the lead screws found in conventional knee mills. Static and rolling friction in ball screws are also low, minimizing stick-slip. Finally, the use of preload minimizes axial play (back-lash) in the ball screw as compared to lead screws, which have sliding contact between the nut and screw. When evaluating high performance machine tools, it is important to understand a number of ball screw characteristics including construction, accuracy, stiffness, critical speed, and longevity.

The ball screw provides mechanical advantage as it transforms rotary motion into linear motion. The lower the lead of the screw, the higher the mechanical advantage. By the same token, the lower the lead, the lower the axis velocity for a given servo motor speed. For example, a screw with a 5 mm lead can travel at 10 meters per minute (about 400 IPM) if the servo motor is capable of 2,000 RPM. A screw with a 10 mm lead will travel 20 m per minute (792 IPM) given the same servo motor RPM, but will require twice the motor torque to provide the same axis thrust. For high performance machining, a low lead is recommended to ensure that a high degree of accuracy and controllability of the system is achieved. A ball screw with lead of 8 mm or less should be sought for mid-sized VMCs. On smaller units, leads approaching 5 mm should be employed as the need for high rapid rates is reduced. Suitably fast servo motors are necessary to achieve high axis feed rates when using low leads such as these.

Ball screws come in a wide range of configurations, some of which are more suitable for high performance machine tools. Seek ball screws which are

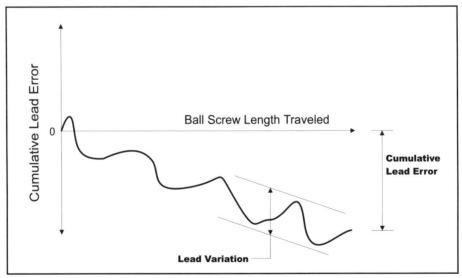

Figure 3-2:
Cumulative lead error and lead variation are plotted for a ball screw as a function of distance traveled. It is easier to create a compensation table in the CNC for cumulative lead error than it is for lead variation.

ground rather than rolled, and ensure that the machine is fitted with Class 5 screws or better. The class of the screw identifies the accuracy of its lead over the screw's length. While CNCs can compensate for error in the lead of the screw, such compensation is never perfect, and better adjusts for what is termed "cumulative lead error" rather than "lead variation." Figure 3-2 illustrates the two errors. The cumulative lead error is addressed fairly easily with a limited amount of compensation data within the CNC. Lead variation, on the other hand, is periodic over the length of the screw, oscillating around the cumulative representative lead. When the lead error for a ball screw is compensated within a CNC, a portion of the lead variation error remains because a very large amount of compensation data would be required to completely correct for it. The magnitude of the lead variation varies significantly with different classes of ball screws. A 20" long class 5 ball screw can have a lead variation of about 0.0008". A similar class 0 screw would have only about 0.0001" of lead variation. The amount of lead variation tends to increase with the overall length of the screw.

The construction of the ball screw is also important. To recirculate the balls through the nut, ball screws are either built with external recirculating tubes, or with internal deflectors which pass the balls from one thread of the screw to the preceding thread. Figure 3-3 illustrates a precision ball screw built with deflectors. Internal recirculating screws generally provide higher maximum speeds and smoother operation, and are preferred for high performance machining applications. The preload of the screw, which reduces the backlash caused by clearance between the steel balls and the grooves in the screw, is also impor-

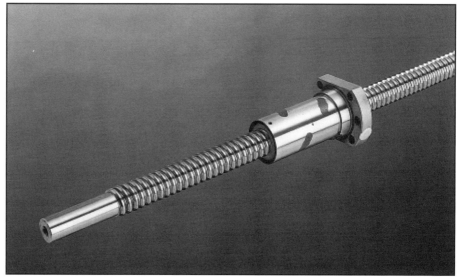

Figure 3-3:
A precision ball screw with internal ball deflectors. A low lead, precision ground screw with minimal backlash is essential to high performance machining. (Courtesy of Schneeberger, Inc.)

tant, and may be set through a number of mechanisms. Ball screws are often preloaded using two nuts, which are either spring loaded or spaced in opposition to one another. Oversize balls can also be used to create preload, as can the use of a ground-in lead offset. A higher preload is more effectively achieved via these last two methods rather than a spring preload, and results in more accurate machining by minimizing backlash.[1]

Ball screws typically do not require the continuous application of lubricant. Intermittent lubrication with grease or oil is adequate to ensure low friction and long life. The benefit of oil lubrication is the self-cleaning action created as the oil flushes the ball nut. Unfortunately, tramp oil is created which can contaminate coolants. The use of grease lubrication, which can be applied as infrequently as every 1,000 hours of use, creates minimal waste, and costs less to apply, as there is no automatic lubricator. Grease-lubricated screws can provide service lives as long as comparably constructed oil-lubricated screws when properly shielded against contaminants. Even in graphite machining applications, grease lubrication appears to work adequately, given sufficient sealing of the ball nut. This is often achieved by the addition of special wipers, which scrape the threads of the screw clean as the screw rotates, or through the use of specialized ball screw covers.

The life, maximum speed, and stiffness of a ball screw are all strongly influenced by the diameter and length of the screw, the way it is mounted, and the accuracy of its overall construction. Ball screw life, L, in terms of distance traveled, is guided by the following relationship.

$$L \cong \{[C/(F \cdot f)]^3 \cdot \lambda \cdot 10^6\} / (60 \cdot n) \text{ [hours]}$$

L is the number of hours of life, C is the basic dynamic load capacity of the screw specified by the manufacturer, F is the axial load, λ is the lead of the screw, f is the load factor, and n is the rotational speed (RPM). f is usually between 1.5 and 3 for screws experiencing impact loads (machine tools), and less for screws running under impact free conditions. The basic dynamic load capacity is a function of the screw's construction, including the number of ball circuits in the screw. Screws of similar dimensional characteristics can have widely different C values. Buyer beware!

Of primary interest is the relationship between the load seen by the screw, F, and life. Note that the life of a given screw drops rapidly with increased load as the cube of the quantity $C/(F \cdot f)$. If F doubles, the life drops by a factor of 8! Because the loads and speeds of a ball screw are never constant, F is calculated by aggregating the various load factors in terms of the proportion of time which they are present. It is therefore very important that the builder has designed the machine to handle the type of work for which it is used. If a machine was developed for graphite machining, the higher loads experienced during the machining of hardened steel may significantly reduce the overall life of the screw. By the same token, if a machine tool builder has sized the ball screws to

---

[1] "Tips on Designing with Miniature Ballscrews," George Jaffe, and Alexander F. Beck (August Steinmeyer GmbH & Co., 1997).

handle both metal and graphite cutting, the screws are likely to last much longer. Generally speaking, ball screws for machine tool use should be designed to handle expected loads for 20,000 hours. Ball screw life is unfortunately not infinite.

The axial load that a ball screw can support before buckling under compression, F, is proportional to a number of factors, as follows:

$$F \cong K \cdot \beta_1 \cdot (E \cdot I / L^2)$$
$$I = (\pi \cdot d^4) / 64.$$

β_1 is a factor for the type of screw mounting, E is the elastic modulus of steel ($30 \cdot 10^6$ psi), I is the inertia of the screw, and L is the length; K is a constant.

With respect to the inertia of the screw, note that it increases as the fourth power of the root diameter of the screw, and that the permissible axial load is similarly related to d. A 32-mm-diameter ball screw will support loads 2.7 times higher than a 25-mm-diameter screw of identical construction and length, even though the 32 mm screw is only 28% larger in diameter. The length of the ball screw also has a large impact upon overall load capacity. Doubling the length of a ball screw drops the load bearing capacity to 25% of its original value. This further makes the case for sizing a machine tool to be no bigger than necessary for the job at hand.

The factor β_1 relates to how the ball screw is mounted. Ball screws are typically mounted using one of the configurations identified in Figure 3-4. β_1 varies from 0.25 for a fixed-free mounting to 4 for a fixed-fixed mounting. Thus,

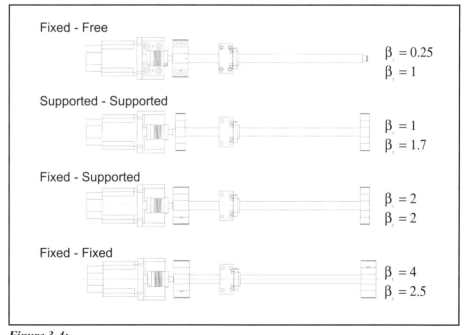

Figure 3-4:
Four ball screw mounting methods, along with their respective values for β_1 and β_2, are illustrated.

a fixed-fixed arrangement can support axial loads $16 \times$ higher than a fixed-free arrangement, given adequate stiffness of the end supports, and all else being equal.

The mounting method of the ball screw also affects the maximum speed that the screw can attain without vibrating (called the critical speed). Vibration occurs because the screw rotates while it is simultaneously bending under its own weight. Because some of the screw's mass is now off-center, an imbalance condition is created, which in turn leads to vibration. When the rotation of the screw approaches the natural frequency caused by this effect, the system becomes difficult to control, and machine performance suffers. The critical speed, S, is related to a number of ball screw characteristics as follows.

$$S \cong [(K \cdot \beta_2{}^2) \cdot (E \cdot I / (g \cdot A))^{0.5}] / L^2$$

K is a constant. β_2 relates to the screw mounting method, E is the elastic modulus of steel, I is the inertia of the screw, g is the density of steel, A is the minimum cross-sectional area of the screw, and L is the screw length. Values of β_2 range from 1 for a fixed-free mounted screw, to 2 for a fixed-supported unit, to 2.5 for a fixed-fixed screw. The effect of mounting, while important, is overshadowed by the importance of ball screw diameter which, through the inertia, contributes to increased critical speed as d^4.

Generally speaking, if two machines have screws of the same diameter, the machine with a more fully supported ball screw will have better performance. But a larger diameter ball screw with a fixed-free or fixed-supported arrangement will often provide better performance than a more rigidly mounted screw of lesser diameter. The use of fixed-fixed or fixed-supported ball screws also requires a higher level of precision in the assembly, as any misalignment between the two ends of the screw will lead to runout, uneven driving torque, and premature failure of the screw.

Different screw geometries and mounting methods can be qualitatively compared using the above equations for critical speed and life. For example, consider the two ball screws in Table 3-3.

Ball Screw Characteristic	Screw 1	Screw 2
Root Diameter [in]	1	2
Length [in]	24	20
Mounting Method	fixed-fixed	fixed-free
β_1 (depends on mounting)	4	0.25
β_2 (depends on mounting)	2.5	1

Table 3-3:
Characteristics of ball screws used in high performance machining centers.

If we assume that all other characteristics of the screw are equivalent — a relatively safe assumption for material properties E and g, but one that assumes the same value for the screw's basic load capacity, C — we can compare the maximum axial loads and critical speed for the two screws as follows.

$$F_1 = \text{axial load for screw 1}$$

$$F_2 = \text{axial load for screw 2}$$

$$S_1 = \text{critical speed for screw 1}$$

$$S_2 = \text{critical speed for screw 2}$$

$$F_1/ F_2 \cong (\beta_1 \cdot d^4/L^2)_{\text{Screw1}} \div (\beta_1 \cdot d^4/L^2)_{\text{Screw2}}$$

$$S_1/ S_2 \cong (\beta_2{}^2 \cdot d^2/L^2)_{\text{Screw1}} \div (\beta_2{}^2 \cdot d^2/L^2)_{\text{Screw2}}$$

$$F_1/ F_2 \cong 0.007 \div 0.01 \ @ \ 0.7$$

$$S_1/ S_2 \cong 0.011 \div 0.01 \ @ \ 1.1$$

So, in this case, screw 2 can handle approximately 43% higher loads than screw 1, even though it is not fixed-fixed. But, screw 1 can run approximately 10% faster than screw 2, due to the benefits of its mounting arrangement. Although such calculations do not provide concrete values (depending upon the actual application, both screws may be adequate or inadequate), and don't account for issues such as alignment, stiffness of the mounting arrangement, etc., they do provide some insight into the relative merits of one ball screw arrangement to another.

When evaluating the quality of a high performance machine tool, evaluate the characteristics of the ball screws. Seek the largest diameter ball screw and stiffest mounting method that still provides the required dynamic performance. Also look for a low lead, and an assembly for which runout at both ends of the screw is at a minimum. Don't hesitate to ask the machine tool builder to identify the class of the screw, and the life expectancy around which they design the ball screw assembly.

Servo Motors, Drives, and Couplings

Most consumers pay little attention to the servo motors used on machine tools. While users can't always specify the motors employed on a machine, it is important to understand some of the characteristics desired for high performance machining. Likewise, the drives used to control the motors, and the couplings which connect the motor to the ball screw, are important too.

Two types of motors dominate the field for axis servos — conventional DC motors and DC brushless motors. While AC induction motors are also used, most people are actually referring to DC brushless motors when they mention AC servos. Conventional DC motors are often constructed with permanent magnets in what is termed the "field" (nonrotating element), and an array of independent conductors, called windings, in the rotating armature. Alternately, the field will also contain windings. Electricity is passed to the armature through physical contact between brushes in the motor frame and the commutator (connected to the armature). Current flow through the armature windings causes a magnetic field to be created around the conductor. When this field is located within another magnetic field at right angles to the conductor field, forces are applied to the conductor (Figure 3-5). These forces in turn create torque on the motor shaft, causing rotation. As the motor rotates, commutation causes current to run through different sets of windings so that torque is continuously applied to the motor shaft.

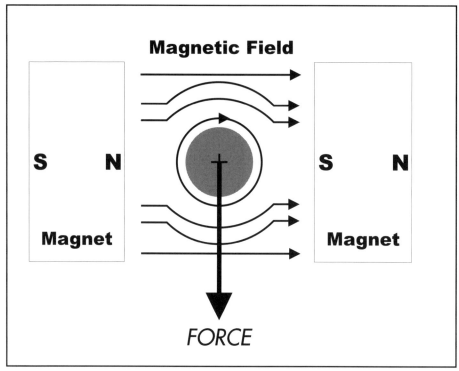

Figure 3-5:
The magnetic field around the conductor interacts with the field due to the magnets which create a net force on the conductor. When the conductor is mounted to a shaft (not shown) a torque is created, causing rotation of the motor.

The DC brushless motors do not contain brushes or commutators. Instead, electronic switching in the servo drive causes rotation by controlling the flow of current to windings in the stator. In this design, the rotor contains permanent magnets. Again, the flow of current through the magnetic field causes torque to be generated on the motor shaft. The drive switches the current between different circuits within the motor to continually generate the torque necessary to keep the motor rotating.

Although DC motors with brushes (commonly called "DC motors") have long dominated servo motor applications, the DC brushless motor has become the motor of choice for most machine tool applications, principally because there are no mechanical brushes to be replaced, and there are no commutator surfaces to wear. The mechanical system of commutation in DC motors places restrictions on their maximum rotational speed, and the motors tend to have higher inertias. Also, because arcing takes place in DC motors, they are unsafe for a range of hazardous applications. While DC brushless motors can run faster (translating into higher feed rates) and have fewer wear parts, the technology is more expensive and sophisticated than conventional DC motors.

Based upon machine tool literature, it is very difficult to compare the servo motor/drive performance of different machines. Most literature identifies only the type of motor (e.g., DC or DC brushless) and the continuous and maximum torque that the motor can apply. Other important information, for the sake of brevity, is often neglected.

In and of itself, the motor type says little about motor performance, other than to identify the motor's maintenance requirements. Torque figures, in conjunction with the ball screw lead, dictate the amount of thrust available to accelerate and decelerate the machine axes. When evaluating maximum torque values, be sure to identify the duty rating used. How the duty rating is defined — "instantaneous" or "30% duty cycle," for example — dictates whether the duty rating is meaningful or just a case of "creative advertising."

A number of motor characteristics beyond the torque rating and motor type should be evaluated when purchasing a high performance machine tool. These characteristics include the following: torque ripple, speed variation, encoder resolution, bearing quality, and operating temperature. Although it is not always possible to quantitatively evaluate each characteristic, a general comparison between machines is worthwhile. Evaluating a machine's servo motors is much more important than it was a few years ago because of the greater demands being placed upon machine tools. Also, the number of motor brands being used on machine tools is increasing as the dominance of large CNC/servo manufacturers erodes. In the past, most machine tools were equipped with one of a handful of CNC/servo motor combinations, and it was therefore likely that two machines being considered had the same motors. This is no longer true.

When operating at low speeds, servo motors may not rotate smoothly because the armature tends to favor certain positions in the magnetic field over others. The resulting variation in torque (and by association speed) adversely affects surface finishes when machining. In conventional DC motors, this cogging effect can be combated by adding additional windings to the armature or by skewing the windings. To reduce cogging in brushless DC motors, additional magnets (poles) are added to the armature, and/or skewed laminations are employed. Additional torque ripple can be introduced by the servo drives, depending upon the method by which the drive generates the sinusoidal output to drive the motor.

Many servo motors exhibit torque ripple of 5% or more. Ideally, this value should be below 2.5% – 3% for high performance machining. Generally speaking, torque ripple is more of a problem in DC brushless motors, although new drive technology has allowed some servo motor manufacturers to reduce torque ripple to less than 1%. When evaluating high performance machine tools, it is important to evaluate the smoothness of motion at low speeds. This can be checked by measuring the surface finish achieved during test cuts at low feed rates. Excessive torque ripple will manifest itself as a very regular surface finish defect in the part. Too often, machine tool buyers focus exclusively on machine performance at high feed rates. Low-speed performance must not be neglected because it impacts most machining operations.

It is important to know the resolution of the encoder mounted to the rear of the servo motor. The encoder is used by the servo drive to control the speed of the motor, and also by the CNC to accurately position the machine. Many servo motors are outfitted with 2,000 or 4,000 line encoders. For high performance machining, at least 5,000 line encoders are recommended. Rotary encoders are discussed in greater depth below.

Construction of the motor is critical to its longevity. Unfortunately, it is also difficult for the machine tool buyer to evaluate. Servo motors should be sealed against both airborne and liquid contaminants. A stiff motor frame with high quality bearings should be supplied to minimize runout of the motor shaft, and to ensure a long operating life. Excessive runout will adversely affect the smooth running of the axis drive train (motor–coupling–ball screw) by creating loads which vary with the angular position of the motor. These loads can cause variations in torque and motor speed which are difficult to compensate for within the servo drive and CNC. As a result, axis motion is adversely affected, and surface finish deteriorates. As a rule of thumb, axial and radial runout of the motor shaft should be less than 0.0005" TIR. Runout of the ball screw should also be restricted to no more than 0.001" TIR to prevent periodic loads from being placed on the motor. These loads can adversely affect the servo tuning of the machine. Compared to the motor shaft, runout of the ball screw shaft is typically higher because of the complexity of the drive-train assembly.

The thermal properties of the motor are also critical to high performance machining. Today, the trend is to utilize motors that are increasingly compact and run at higher speeds. The result is often motors that run hotter. Because servo motors are typically embedded deep within a machine tool, the heat thrown off by the motor can adversely affect geometric accuracy. This heat transfers into the ball screw and ball screw support bearings causing local growth, and affecting bearing preload. Machine castings and other structural elements are similarly affected by heat transfer from the motor.

One characteristic of the drive train which warrants close inspection is the coupling between the servo motor and the ball screw. Couplings are either direct (whereby a solid sleeve or bellows coupling is used to link the motor and screw) or indirect (which typically involves a belt). Figure 3-6 illustrates the two coupling methods.

Use of a belt to couple the servo motor and ball screw causes several problems for high performance machining, adversely affecting accuracy, stiffness, and controllability. A belt-driven system cannot be tuned as tightly as a direct coupled system because the belt does not respond well to high frequency commands. The belt acts as a low-pass filter, damping out high-frequency motor motion rather than transferring it onto the screw. This characteristic of the belt does provide a benefit — it reduces the effect of motor torque ripple upon surface finish. When using belt drives, the axis encoder is often mounted to the motor rather than to the screw itself. This arrangement reduces accuracy be-

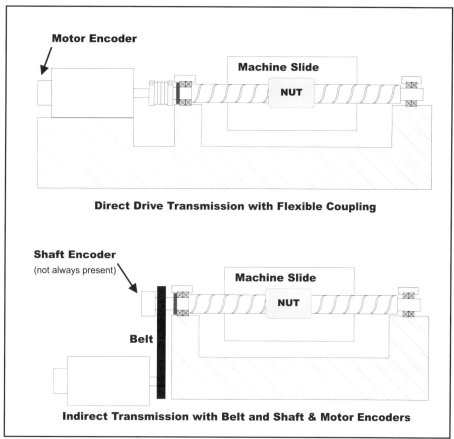

Figure 3-6:

Linear axes in machine tools typically employ a bellows coupling or belt to connect the servo motor to the ball screw. When using a belt drive, the presence of an encoder on the ball screw shaft is necessary to partially compensate for the inaccuracies introduced by the belt.

cause of the play (lost motion) in the belt. A further benefit of belt coupling is that the assembly is much more forgiving of misalignment between the motor shaft and ball screw.

Direct couplings are either solid steel or, more often, constructed with steel bellows. While solid couplings provide the highest degree of accuracy and stiffness, they are unforgiving of misalignment between the servo motor and screw. If not well aligned, a solid coupling can introduce undesirable load variations into the servo system, reducing bearing life and machine accuracy. Bellows type couplings represent the best compromise for high performance machine tools. These couplings provide high torsional rigidity, while accommodating moderate misalignment between the motor shaft and the end of the ball screw. Nonetheless, for the most demanding applications, solid couplings provide the best dynamic performance because they are very stiff. Unfortunately, the drawbacks associated with solid couplings, i.e., principally high radial loads due to any misalignment, make their widespread application problematic.

Feedback Devices

The quality of the feedback devices used in the drive train is critical to overall machine performance in terms of positioning, contouring, and surface finish. The feedback devices are the CNC's window on machine activity. As such, the motion control performance of the CNC is only as good as the feedback device providing it information.

Rotary Encoders

In conventional machine tools, information about the position of each linear axis is provided from an incremental or absolute rotary encoder mounted to the rear of the drive motor (Figure 3-7). Incremental rotary encoders utilize a photoelectric scan of a graduated disk to generate electric signals as the encoder rotates. The CNC counts these signals to establish distance traveled and/or the speed of travel. This information must be used in conjunction with a reference position (such as an axis limit switch) to establish true position. Absolute rotary encoders scan a pattern on a disk to establish an actual angular position. No external reference such as a limit switch is required. The actual position data are sent to the CNC for use in the control loop.

Figure 3-7:
Rotary encoders, such as these from Heidenhain Corporation, are used to track the number of ball screw revolutions in machine tools. Similar units are also used in spindles and other rotary devices. (Courtesy of Heidenhain Corporation.)

As a general rule, motor encoder resolution should be as high as possible so that the CNC receives good feedback about the location of the machine axes. For incremental encoders, the resolution is measured in terms of lines per revolution, while for absolute encoders, resolution is provided in terms of arc-seconds or bits. The resolution of the encoder must be combined with information about the lead of the ball screw to determine the accuracy of the feedback system in terms of axis motion. For an incremental encoder the axial accuracy, A_{axial}, in terms of the lead, L, of the screw, and the rotary resolution of the encoder (lines per revolution), $r_{encoder}$, is as follows.

$$A_{encoder} = \pm (18° \text{ mech.} \cdot 3600) / r_{encoder} \qquad \text{[arc-seconds]}\,[2]$$

$$A_{Axial} = \pm L \cdot (A_{encoder}/360°) \cdot (3,600)^{-1} \qquad \text{[inch]}$$

For a ball screw with a 0.2" lead, and an incremental encoder resolution of 5,000 lines, the axial resolution provided by the measuring device is about ± 0.000002".[3] More commonplace machine tools utilize 2,000 line encoders, and to achieve high feed rates use leads of at least 0.4". On such machines, the axial resolution provided by the encoder is ±0.00001". Illustrated in this manner, the tradeoff between high speed (facilitated by a large lead) and accuracy (low lead) is apparent. This trade off is mandated further by the CNC itself, which is limited in terms of the maximum input frequency of encoder data. The 0.2" lead ball screw and 5,000 line encoder will generate a pulse stream with frequency of 333 kHz at 800 IPM. Some CNCs are limited to input frequencies of 350 kHz, so increasing the feed rate (or rapid rate) much above this level will lead to a loss of positioning accuracy, if not system shutdown. A high performance CNC should be capable of handling encoder input frequencies of at least 1 MHz.

A high encoder resolution is very important when moving at slow speeds. To accurately calculate the velocity for each axis as part of the control loop, the CNC needs high-frequency position data. When using lower resolution encoders, the velocity calculations become less accurate, decreasing the quality of the surface finish.

Linear Encoders

The use of only rotary encoders to determine the position of the machine's linear axes detracts from the overall machine performance for a number of reasons. Rotary encoders depend upon the ball screw to act as a length standard. To accurately determine axis position using a motor encoder, the ball screw must remain geometrically stable. In other words, the lead of the ball screw must not change with time. In use, temperature changes in the ball screw cause the ball screw to grow, thus changing the lead. Even in cases where the ball screw is fully supported at both ends, thermal growth is not reduced

---

[2] Heidenhein Incremental Rotary Encoder Catalog (4/97).

[3] This does not mean that the machine's resolution will be this good! System resolution, due to mechanical and electrical inadequacies, will be significantly worse.

substantially. Given a reasonable temperature rise in a ball screw of 18°F, the ball screw support bearings would need to provide a stiffness of 5,800 lb•f to prevent an overall change in length of a 40-mm-diameter screw.[4] Likewise, localized thermal expansion of the ball screw will affect the lead of the screw, and its accuracy, despite the screw being fully supported.

Over time, the amount of backlash in the ball screw will increase. The motor encoder cannot recognize changes in backlash because it counts only the number of ball screw revolutions. If the screw rotates and the axis slide doesn't move, as when reversing direction in the presence of backlash, the motor encoder still assumes that the slide position changed. The result is a positioning error.

Other error sources not picked up when using motor encoders include deformation of the drive train due to cutting forces, friction, or acceleration; these effects are increasingly important in the context of high performance machining. Even with a low acceleration of 0.2 g, a 1,100 lb slide will cause a 40 mm ball screw to deform between 0.0002" and 0.0004" depending upon the manner of support.[5]

The problems associated with using a motor encoder to provide feedback to the CNC can be addressed through the use of linear encoders (also known as linear scales). Typical linear encoders for high precision applications use a graduated glass scale and an interferential measuring principle to accurately measure distances. The scale and read head are mounted directly to the machine axis and structure, respectively, providing a true measurement of axis position. By measuring the position of the machine axis directly, backlash in the drive mechanism is included in the control loop. Figure 3-8 illustrates the assembly of a glass scale on a machine axis.

Linear scale performance is measured in terms of its accuracy and measuring step, which is a measure of repeatability. Typical values for a high performance sealed scale are an accuracy of ±0.00012" (3 µm) and a measuring step of 0.00002" (0.5 µm) or 0.000004" (0.1 µm). Unsealed ultra-high-precision versions from Heidenhein, which are not protected against contaminants like coolant, chips, or graphite dust, provide accuracies in the range of ±0.000008" (0.2 µm). Interestingly, the accuracy of the sealed scale is perilously close to the accuracy value sought in the machine tool axis itself. But, because the repeatability of the scale is 0.5 or 0.1 µm, the errors in the scale can be mapped and corrected as part of the positional accuracy measurement process previously described. Using a laser interferometer, and measuring a large number of points along the machine axis, the effective accuracy of the axis can be improved to a level between the uncompensated accuracy (±0.00012") of the linear encoder and its measuring step. The importance of repeatability — the ability to move to the same position over and over again — as compared to accuracy, which is the ability to move to the desired position, is now clear. A

---

[4]"Position Measurement of Machine Tools," Jan Braasch, Dr. Ing. (Heidenhein Corporation).

[5]"Position Measurement of Machine Tools," Jan Braasch, Dr. Ing. (Heidenhein Corporation).

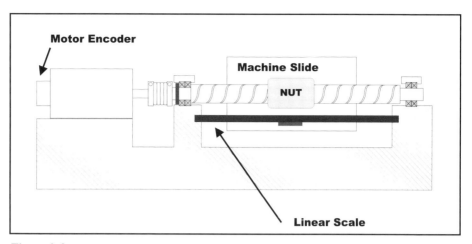

Figure 3-8:
Linear scales directly measure motion of each machine slide. By directly mounting the scale to the moving slide, inaccuracies in the ball screw do not affect the position data fed to the CNC as when using only a motor encoder.

highly repeatable machine (or linear encoder) enables compensation for inaccuracy to be made.

For linear encoders to provide optimum accuracy, their mounting to the machine requires close attention. The surfaces to which the scale and read head are mounted should be precision ground to prevent the scale from twisting. A distorted scale reduces the accuracy of the measurements, and leads to damage of the unit. To optimize precision, the scale must be mounted parallel to and in between the axis guideways, and should be located as close to the axis drive train and tool – work interface as possible. Figure 3-9 illustrates alternative

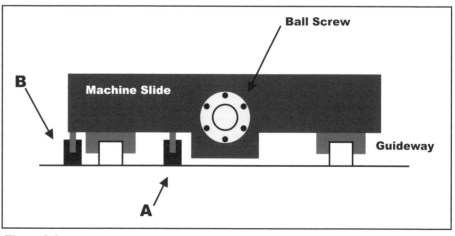

Figure 3-9:
Mounting linear scales between the guideways, and as close to the ball screw as possible (position "A"), improves accuracy and affords maximum protection against contamination and physical damage.

mounting locations for a scale. Location A is superior to location B because it is less susceptible to yaw errors in the slide. Position A is also better protected against chips and other contaminants.

Most machine tools use either linear encoders or rotary encoders to provide position feedback. A superior approach utilizes both feedback devices. The scales are used to provide position feedback to the control loop, and the encoder is used to provide velocity feedback. This is necessary because at low velocity, the CNC gets only a few counts per servo update cycle from the linear encoder. For example, at 1 IPM with a 0.5 µm glass scale and a servo update cycle of 0.9 ms, the CNC doesn't read more than one position count per servo update. This is not a significant problem for position feedback, but it is very important when the velocity is calculated because converting position data from the scale to velocity is very noise sensitive. Even one count of error caused by noise generates a relatively large error in the velocity signal at low speed. Errors in the velocity signal in turn cause significant degradation of surface finish. While a filter algorithm can be used in the CNC to eliminate noise, this reduces the bandwidth of the servo loop, and reduces machine performance. By using the rotary encoder feedback to provide velocity data, improved surface finish is achieved without degrading the accuracy or bandwidth of the machine.

Linear Motors

Linear motors are essentially rotary motors unrolled into a flat form. Figure 3-10 illustrates a range of linear motors. Manufacturers of linear motors tout them as a replacement for ball screws in machine tools, assembly machines, and other machinery. Linear motor technology is of interest because very high feed rates and accelerations can be achieved. Feed rates to 12,000 IPM are reported, along with accelerations up to $3 - 5$ g for more powerful linear motors suitable for machine tool applications. These incredible figures compare to maximum (ideal) feed rates for ball screw technology of approximately 1,800 IPM. Further, linear motors are reported to be significantly stiffer than ball screw drives, with stiffnesses over 1,000,000 lb•f/in in some cases.[6] This enhanced stiffness enables more aggressive motion algorithms to be used within CNCs.

Linear motors are built in two basic forms: iron-less and iron-core. To achieve the thrust values required for machine tools, iron-core motors are typically required. The linear motor assembly consists of a magnet way, which is usually mounted to a fixed component of a machine tool (e.g., base, column), and a coil assembly, typically mounted to a machine slide. A feedback device for commutation is also required as part of the assembly (this can be a linear scale). A linear motor can eliminate a wide range of components typically associated with a ball screw drive, including the ball screw itself, support bearings and bearing blocks, and the motor – screw coupling.

While the advantages of linear motors, principally high accelerations and feed rates, and no wear parts, are significant, there are drawbacks to linear mo-

---

[6] Kollmorgen Platinum™ DL brochure.

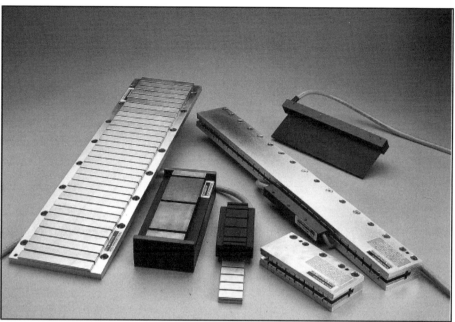

Figure 3-10:
A range of iron core and iron-less Platinum ™ DDL linear motors from Kollmorgen.

tors as well. First, linear motors do not provide mechanical advantage like a ball screw. As a result, the axial forces they create are limited compared to ball screw drives. Large linear motors may provide axial forces of approximately 2,000 to 3,000 lb, which is less than can be achieved using ball screw drive systems and rotary motors, but adequate for the majority of high performance machining applications. Iron-core linear motors are also prone to cogging depending upon the construction method, which can adversely affect surface finishes at low speeds. Some linear motor manufacturers, such as Kollmorgen, report successfully combating cogging through innovative motor and drive design.

The two greatest drawbacks to using linear motors are the high attractive magnetic forces created between the coils and magnets in an iron-core motor, and the large amount of heat that must be removed from the motors.

Attractive forces between the magnet way and coil assembly in an iron-core linear motor are about 5X greater than the axial thrust provided. The attractive forces for a linear motor providing 1,800 lb of axial thrust can exceed 8,500 lb. These huge forces require exceptionally stiff machine structures to resist deformation in the direction of the attractive force. Any deformation caused by these attractive forces seriously affects overall machine geometry, particularly on machine tables, where the table surface can be "sucked down" toward the linear motor assembly. Producing structures which can resist these high loads and which are not exceedingly heavy (thereby reducing the accelerations which can be achieved) is an area of ongoing development. These high attractive forces also require exceptionally stiff way systems to resist deflection. When one considers that many mid-sized (e.g., 22"×16"×20") VMCs have part weight restrictions of less than 2,500 lb, and that such a machine built with ball screw drives may typically provide peak axial thrusts of 2,000 to 3,000 lb (albeit all of which is not available for useful work), the magnitude of these attractive forces is significant. A final side effect of these attractive forces is that ferrous chips created during machining will be attracted to the linear motor. It is therefore extremely important that the way system be well sealed in linear motor applications.

Linear motors generate significant amounts of heat during operation. This is problematic because linear motors are attached directly to machine slides. As a result, heat is generated very close to the work area, rather than in a rotary motor somewhat more isolated from the work area, as in a ball screw drive machine. The aforementioned linear motor, which produces 1,800 lb of axial thrust, also dissipates heat at the rate of 6.7 HP. This is as much power as a mid-sized high speed motorized milling spindle generates in total, and can significantly increase the temperature of a machine structure. When three axes are considered in total, energy can be released by the linear motor as heat into the machine structure at the rate of up to 20 HP. All of this energy must be removed from the linear motor before it enters the structure to prevent significant dimensional shifts, warpage of the machine, and the loss of geometric accuracy. Cooling must be provided to the coil assembly, magnetic way, and machine structure to maintain a constant machine temperature. In practice, this further complicates the design of machine structures intended for use with linear motors in all but the most light-duty or low accuracy applications. As will be discussed in Chapter 5, ensuring that almost all of this thermal energy is removed from the machine tool is critical (and extremely difficult to achieve) if tolerances between ±0.0005" and ±0.0002" are to be maintained.

Linear motors promise to provide very high accelerations and feed for high performance machine tools in the future. At present, the higher cost of linear motors, and the cost of adequate structures and cooling systems, means they are not practical for most high performance machining applications. Those machines outfitted with linear motors today are expensive ($1M+), and are intended for operations such as drilling, boring, and face milling engine components, rather than the precision machining of contoured components.

While linear motors will find their place in the realm of machining, it will be many years (if ever) before they are used more widely than ball screw drive trains. The evolution of machine tools to linear motors is not imminent because the practical limits of ball screw technology have not yet been realized. Most shops are still far from machining at the 1,000 + IPM that advanced ball screw technology can support.

Counterbalances

An important element in the performance of machine tools is the counterbalance. Most machining centers utilize a balancing weight to aid Z-axis (in VMCs) or Y-axis (in HMCs) motion against gravity. Counterbalances often consist of weights inside the column which are connected to the slide via cables or chains run over pulleys. Alternative counterbalance designs balance the load of the moving elements using inert gas or hydraulic cylinders.

Counterbalances allow a smaller ball screw and motor to drive the vertical axis upwards. Given the weight of spindle assemblies and cast slides, the reduction in motor size and ball screw diameter (and therefore cost) can be significant. The application of equal loads to the drive train when moving up and down extends the life of a given ball screw. The use of a counterbalance also prevents the Z- or Y-axis slide from "unwinding" the screw and moving toward the workpiece when mill power is off, which is an important safety feature.

The disadvantage of counterbalances is that they negatively affect the dynamics of the drive train. Mechanical, hydraulic, or inert gas counterweights induce Z-axis vibration during high speed reversals in VMCs, as when producing electrodes, mold cavities, or turbo-machinery blades. These vibrations occur because counterbalances have natural frequencies and dynamic properties only loosely coupled to the vertical axis drive train. The CNC controls the drive train, but not the counterbalance, and so the varying loads applied to the drive train by the counterbalance act as disturbances that are difficult for the CNC system to reject. These disturbances show up in parts as defects in surface finish at points where Z-axis reversals occur. When working with small end mills and hard workpiece materials, these vibrations can reduce tool life and lead to tool breakage as well.

For high performance machining, it is recommended that no counterbalance be employed. Instead, higher power servo motors and stiffer ball screws should be used. When properly sized, the life of the screw can be extended, and the axis will be better controlled by the CNC. Not only will imperfections in the surface finish be avoided, but the CNC can be tuned to provide improved motion control without concern that the high-frequency command signals it issues will excite vibration in the counterbalance. A "normally on" brake motor and electronic "heartbeat" circuit are used to lock the Z-axis in place in the event of power loss or CNC glitch, thus ensuring user safety. A test performed on a VMC with and without a mechanical counterweight improved the surface finish in a steel clutch dog by removing intermittent ripples, 0.00005" deep, in the surface of the part.

Motion Control (CNC)

The subject of computer numerical controls (CNCs) is itself so expansive that it could fill several volumes of text. From the debate over the merits of PC-CNCs to the discussion of so-called "open CNCs" and "software CNCs," much can be said about the ease of upgrading, ease of programming, ease of configuring, ease of repair, and so on. These are important elements of a CNC, no doubt, but unfortunately get more attention than the most critical elements of the CNC, such as the motion algorithms themselves. Our focus here will be on the performance requirements of CNCs as related to high performance machining. We will discuss elements of CNC performance that directly impact the ability to machine contoured, complex parts accurately and quickly.

Block Processing

One of the more popular ways to measure CNC performance is block processing time. Almost every CNC on the market today notes that it can process 1,000 blocks per second (BPS). But what does this mean?

The block processing rate should be a measure of how many programmed moves (per second) the CNC can translate from G-code, feed to the servo algorithms, and execute in the servo loop. Using the BPS number for a CNC, and knowing the length of the programmed line segments and feed rates, the programmer can then determine if the CNC will hesitate during machining.

To approximate the block processing rate necessary for a specific application the following calculation can be performed.

L = length of typical programmed segment	[inch]
F = programmed feed rate	[inch/minute]
$T = 60 \cdot (L \div F)$	[second]
$BPS_{Required} = 1 \div T$	[1/second]

For example, if a program is to be produced with segments 0.001" long, and a programmed feed rate of 70 IPM is desired, $BPS_{Required} = 1,167$ blocks per second. For high precision parts, where small programmed line segments are required, the block processing requirements can become quite large. Fortunately, most CAM systems optimize the length of the programmed segments to correspond to a desired chordal deviation. As a result, there are areas in the program where the required BPS drops significantly, for example, in long straight sections of the part.

Unfortunately, like positional accuracy figures, interpreting published BPS values is not straightforward. Some important issues to be aware of when comparing BPS figures are provided.

- *Line size.* Some BPS values are determined with a limit to the number of characters that can appear on each line of the program.
- *Programming resolution.* Some BPS figures are calculated with a limit to the resolution of the programmed axis coordinates (e.g., 4-place versus 6-place programming).
- *Multitasking.* Some CNC builders shut down all multi-tasking when calculating BPS figures.
- *Preprocessing.* To achieve some BPS values, extensive preprocessing of the part program is required either on-line or, in the worst case, off-line.
- *Buffer size.* Some CNCs can only support the full BPS value for a few minutes (or seconds), because they depend upon a combination of preprocessing and buffer storage between interpolation and servo loop calculations. These CNCs will hesitate when machining long, data intensive part programs.
- *Feed rate modification.* Some CNCs will reduce the programmed feed rate without informing the user to ensure that the CNC does not hesitate

when data starvation is imminent. Such behind-the-scenes machinations modify part programs without user consent, and should be avoided.

- *Number of axes.* Many block processing rates fall off quickly when 4th or 5th axes are added to the CNC. Decreases of up to 40% are not uncommon.
- *Data storage.* Many CNCs cannot store large part programs. As a result, programs need to be drip fed to the CNC using DNC. The true block processing rate is significantly lower when drip feeding than when running from memory on such CNCs.
- *Cutter compensation.* Many BPS figures do not include the time necessary to perform cutter diameter compensation or cutter length compensation.
- *Advanced features.* In many CNCs, advanced features such as thermal compensation, variables, and look-ahead functions decrease block processing rates below advertised values.
- *Interpolation versus servo update.* Many CNC builders are referring only to the time required to translate G-code into data that the servo loop can understand (e.g., interpolation) when they define BPS. The time for both elements must be considered. For example, if a CNC can interpolate a line of G-code every 0.9 milliseconds, and updates the servos every 1.5 milliseconds, the true throughput capability of the CNC is 667 ($1 \div 0.0015$) moves per second, not 1,111.
- *Options.* Many CNCs require expensive options to provide the published BPS values.

To establish the true block processing rate for a CNC, or to compare the performance of different CNCs, the best approach is to test the CNC's under true operating conditions. A suggested testing methodology is described as part of the machine evaluation test suite (Chapter 8). For high performance machining a true block processing rate approaching 1,000 BPS with all axes (3, 4, or 5 depending upon the machine) is required. This rate should be sustainable indefinitely, require no preprocessing, and apply to all machine features such as contour optimization, cutter compensation, and thermal compensation, in effect. Finally, the machine should be capable of multitasking at this 1,000+ BPS rate to enable file transfer and editing to take place.

Servo Gain and Servo Lag

All servo systems exhibit a property called "servo lag," which is the amount that actual machine position trails the position commanded by the CNC. Figure 3-11 illustrates a simple case of servo lag. Servo lag is a significant source of inaccuracy when machining contoured surfaces, and at high speeds it may contribute more error than geometric or positional inaccuracies.

Servo lag is an inherent characteristic of closed loop feedback systems, which are used by the CNC to provide motion control. The servo loop works by responding to differences in the commanded position, dictated by the part program, and the machine's actual position. This difference between these posi-

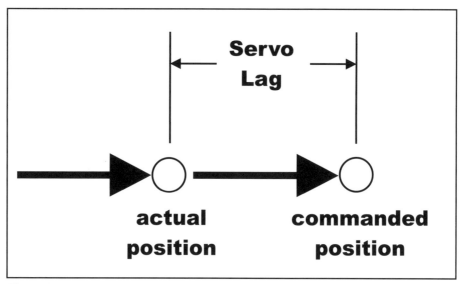

Figure 3-11:
Servo lag is the distance between the commanded position (from the part program) and the actual position of the machine.

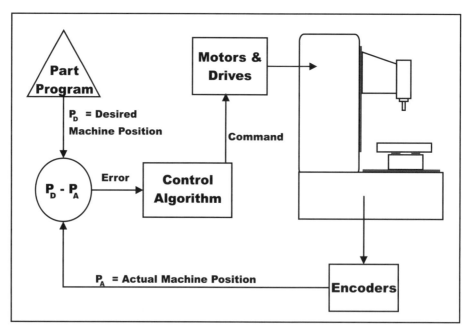

Figure 3-12:
Simplified block diagram of a closed loop position control algorithm.

tions is considered an error by the servo loop, which is designed to bring these errors to zero. Figure 3-12 is a highly simplified schematic of a closed loop control algorithm. The command position, interpolated from the part program by the CNC, is fed into the control loop as P_D. The actual position P_A of the machine is measured by the rotary encoder or linear scale. The difference between P_D and P_A (positioning error) is fed into the algorithm. The algorithm commands the motors to move the machine along the shortest path between the current position and the command position, attempting to make P_A equal P_D. If the difference between P_D and P_A is zero, the machine doesn't move because there is no positioning error; the machine is in the correct location. This process is repeated as many as 1,000 times per second or more depending upon the servo update rate of the CNC.

The value of $(P_D - P_A)$ can be nonzero for two reasons. First, cutting forces and other loads cause the machine to move, creating position errors by changing P_A. In this case, signals are issued by the control loop to bring the machine back to the correct position P_D. Second, the CNC reads the part program and generates new commanded positions P_D necessary to cut the part. By its very nature, the commanded position is located further along the tool path than the current position of the machine. The difference between the command and actual positions is "servo lag."

Figure 3-13 illustrates the effect of servo lag when machining two straight lines joining a half circle. The mill moves at a constant feed rate from point *A* until the command position reaches point *B*. At that point, due to servo lag, the slide will only have reached point B_L. Since the control command is moving

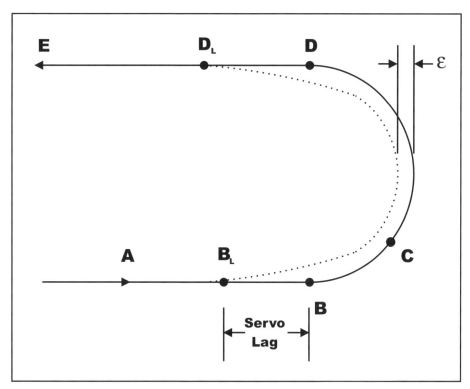

Figure 3-13:
Servo lag causes the actual tool path to deviate from the desired tool path by an amount ε, which is a function of CNC performance and feed rate.

forward at a constant rate, it begins generating commands around the arc toward point D, including the point C. At the next servo update, the actual cutter path deviates from the desired path at B_L, heading toward point C, rather than around the desired arc. The actual path followed is shown by the dotted line. From point B_L to point D_L, the actual path will deviate from the desired path, and that deviation is labeled ε. The higher the feed rate, the larger the error because the command position changes by a greater amount each servo update cycle. For example, if the servo update cycle is 1 millisecond and the feed rate is 100 IPM, the command position advances by 0.0017" along the tool path each update cycle. If the feed rate is 200 IPM, the command position advances by 0.0033" each servo update cycle.

The measure of servo system responsiveness is called "servo gain." The higher the servo gain, the lower the servo lag. Servo gain is limited by the interaction of the control system with the machine tool's natural frequencies. To achieve high gains, and thereby tight cornering performance, the CNC must issue motion commands (which are eventually converted into torque signals to the axis motors) at high frequency. When the frequency of these commands bumps up against machine resonances, the motion control system can become unstable. Machine tool builders use servo tuning to limit the motion control system to a frequency spectrum that the machine tool can handle. Table 3-4 compares the error in radius ε for the tool path illustrated in Figure 3-13 to varying radii and servo gains. Servo gain is measured in units of [IPM/0.001"], and is related to servo lag for straight-line motion by the following formula:

Servo Lag = Feed Rate ÷ (Servo Gain ÷ 0.001").

Feed Rate (IPM)	Radius	Radius Error at Gain 2	Radius Error at Gain 4
10	1.0"	0.000004"	0.000001"
10	0.1"	0.000041"	0.00001"
100	1.0"	0.00042"	0.0001"
100	0.1"	0.00416"	0.00103"
200	1.0"	0.00167"	0.00042"
200	0.1"	0.0146"	0.00403"

Table 3-4:
Error in radius ε for the path illustrated in Figure 3-13 when machined at various feed rates and gains of 2 or 4.

Table 3-4 shows that a high servo gain is critical to achieving accurate contouring. Contouring errors are also experienced when machining geometries other than those of Figure 3-12. The exact magnitude of the error depends upon the relative angle between adjoining motion commands.

The error caused by servo lag when machining 90° corners is illustrated in Figure 3-14. Concentric squares were scribed into a piece of aluminum on a light-duty machine with servo gain of less than 2. The innermost square was

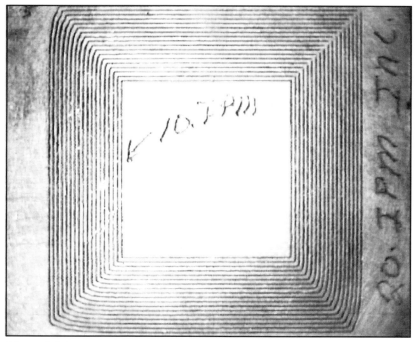

Figure 3-14:
The impact of servo lag is apparent on this set of inscribed squares. Feed rate increases from 10 IPM to 350 IPM in increments of 20 IPM. Servo gain of this table top machine was less than 2.

machined at 10 IPM. Each successive square was machined 20 IPM faster, until a top feed rate of 350 IPM was reached on the outermost path. Note that while the corners are quite close to the desired 90° at low feed rates, the geometry degrades significantly as feed rate increases.

For high performance machining, large gain values are required to minimize contouring errors at high feed rates. On less capable machines, servo gains of 1 or 2 are provided. Users of such machines must employ low feed rates to ensure that corners aren't clipped when 2D or 3D contouring. Many commodity machines utilize CNCs that automatically decrease the feed rate, without notifying the user, to compensate for low servo gains. Even though the CNC display indicates that the programmed feed rate is being maintained, it is apparent, through straightforward calculations, that the CNC is slowing down the machine to prevent large contouring errors. Such feed rate modifications are necessary on these machines, but the display of programmed rather than actual feed rates is misleading. Many machine tool buyers incorrectly conclude that the machine in question can produce complex geometry parts at high feed rates.

High performance machine tools support gains of 4 or more because they possess superior machine dynamics and more responsive algorithms in the CNC. This allows higher feed rates and/or accuracies to be achieved than with commodity machine tools. Despite the better performance, the tradeoff between high feed rates and accuracy does not go away in high performance machine tools. The use of lower feed rates when machining demanding geometries will provide more accurate geometry for a given machine tool. The benefits of high performance machines with gains of 4+ is that they can machine a given geometry, to a specified tolerance level, faster than machine tools with servo gains less than 4.

Relative Importance of Feed Rate versus Acceleration

All machine tool brochures specify the maximum feed rate that can be achieved. On the other hand, data about acceleration are conspicuously absent from most machine tool literature. By themselves, maximum feed rate numbers say little about machine performance. Consider a general purpose VMC (about $80,000) with a maximum feed rate of 350 IPM, a 15 HP spindle, and accuracies of ±0.0002" ISO. As previously discussed, this VMC will not be able to achieve accuracies of ±0.0002" at high axis velocities such as 350 IPM. These high feed rates, then, must be intended for roughing or semi-finish operations. But if a 0.5" deep×1" wide slotting cut in aluminum is made at the full feed rate of 350 IPM, a 50 HP+ spindle would be required, given that the power constant for aluminum, K_P, is approximately 0.32 [HP/(in^3·minute)]! So clearly these feed rates are not useful for extremely high material removal rates given the horsepower available on conventional VMCs. The value of feed rates in excess of 300 IPM on such a machine must be called into question unless very high horsepower spindles are provided.

A machine tool's ability to quickly accelerate is critical when machining complex geometries with many changes in the direction of motion. Acceleration is a measure of how fast a body (in this case, each machine axis) can change its velocity (feed rate). It is measured in units of [distance/s^2], and is often expressed in terms of the acceleration due to gravity, which is 9.81 m/s^2 [32.2 ft/s^2]. To say that a machine is capable of accelerations of 0.3 g means that it can accelerate or decelerate at a rate of 2.94 m/s^2 or 9.67 ft/s^2. The time T it will take a machine tool to reach a specified feed rate can be expressed in terms of its acceleration using the equation,

$$T = (F_{final} - F_{initial})/(\alpha \cdot 386\cdot 60) \qquad \text{[s] English units}$$

$$T = (F_{final} - F_{initial})/(\alpha \cdot 9.81\cdot 60) \qquad \text{[s] metric units}$$

where F_{final} [IPM or mpm] is the final feed rate, $F_{initial}$ the initial feed rate, and α the acceleration in terms of Earth's gravity, "g" (e.g., $\alpha = 1$, if the machine is capable of 1 g acceleration or 32.2 ft/s^2). To use acceleration values independent of "g" (e.g., to use 9.81 m/s^2 instead of 1 g), simply eliminate the "386" and "9.81" multipliers in the denominator. For a VMC with accelerations of 0.2 g to go from zero to 350 IPM will require 0.075 seconds! If the machine is capable of accelerations of 1 g, it will take 0.015 seconds to reach 350 IPM.

Consider a straight line 0.1" long. If the machine enters and exits this move at 200 IPM, it will take only about 0.03 seconds to traverse this distance. But if this move is attached to two other moves (M_{Before} and M_{After}), as part of a larger tool path (Figure 3-15), the time required to complete the move is a function of *both* the programmed feed rate and the capability of the machine to accelerate. Because M_{Before} is oriented 90° to M_1, the machine enters M_1 with zero velocity in the direction of the move. In this case, the time, T [s], to complete the move is

$$T_1 = F_{MAX} / \alpha \quad \text{[s]}$$

$$X_1 = aT_1^2 / 2 \quad \text{[in], [m]}$$

$$\text{if } X_1 < D:$$

$$T = T_1 + [(D - X_1) / F_{MAX}] \text{ [s]}$$

$$\text{if } X_1 > D:$$

$$T = (2 \cdot D / \alpha)^{0.5} \text{ [s]}$$

where T_1 is the time during which the machine accelerates from zero to the programmed feed rate F_{MAX}, and X_1 is the distance traveled while the machine is accelerating to F_{MAX}. D is the total linear distance traveled in time T, and α is the machine's acceleration in terms of in/s² or m/s².[7] Table 3-5 approximates the time required to complete a 0.1" move like that in Figure 3-15 for various machine accelerations and maximum feed rates.

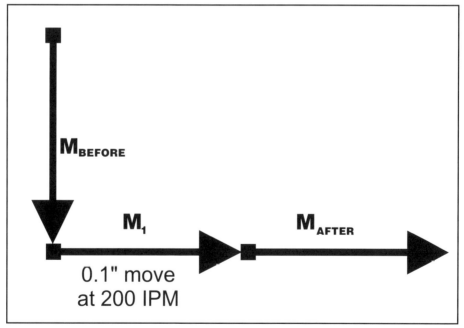

Figure 3-15:
Because M_{before} is at 90° to M_1, the machine enters M_1 at near zero feed rate, increasing the time required to complete the move.

---

[7] To use this equation in terms of "g," replace α with ($\alpha \cdot 384$) when working with English units, and ($\alpha \cdot 9.8$) when working with metric units.

Max. Feed, F_{MAX} [IPM]	Acceleration, α [g], [in/s²]	Time to move 0.1", T [s]	% change in cut time if entire move at 200 IPM
200	0.33g, 128.8	0.0430	+43%
200	0.67g, 257.6	**0.0365**	+22%
200	1.0g, 386.4	**0.0344**	+14%
400	0.33g, 128.8	**0.0394**	+31%
400	0.67g, 257.6	0.0279	-7%
400	1.0g 386.4	0.0236	-21%

Table 3-5:
Time to complete a 0.1" move starting at zero feed rate as a function of machine acceleration and maximum feed rate. If the machine began and finished the move at 200 IPM, it would take 0.03 seconds.

Table 3-5 illustrates that for small moves, such as those typically used when machining 2D or 3D contoured surfaces, acceleration is more important than flat-out feed rate. This effect is magnified as the moves become smaller. A machine with feed rates of 400 IPM and accelerations of only 0.33 g will take longer to machine a 0.1" segment than a machine with a top feed rate of only 200 IPM and accelerations of 0.67 g or 1.0 g. When purchasing a machine tool, it is very important to determine its acceleration capability. The maximum feed rate does not provide enough information to determine the machine's suitability for high performance machining. Figure 3-16 graphically illustrates the (a) acceleration, (b) velocity, and (c) distance traveled for the case where $F_{MAX} = 200$ IPM, $\alpha = 1$ g and the distance traveled is 0.1". Note that while Figure 3-16 illustrates an instantaneous acceleration profile, CNCs smooth the acceleration profile to prevent excessive vibration and wear and tear on the machine tool.

Many moves, such as those illustrated in Figure 3-17, require the machine to both accelerate and decelerate with each programmed segment. In this case, the machine's acceleration is even more important relative to feed rate than in the above example, which required acceleration only at the beginning of the move. The machine test suite (in Chapter 8) includes a test to estimate a machine's acceleration and deceleration characteristics.

From a machine tool builder's standpoint, it is easier to provide high axis feed rates than to provide high accelerations. High accelerations require a better CNC and excellent machine stiffness and damping to avoid vibration. Providing high feed rates with low to moderate accelerations is an easier task because acceleration, not feed rate, puts dynamic loads on the machine's drive train and structure. When looking for high performance machine tools, seek maximum accelerations over 0.5 g. On smaller machines, higher accelerations approaching 1 g, should be provided. As the machine gets larger and the mass of the moving components increases, acceleration typically decreases (otherwise, the

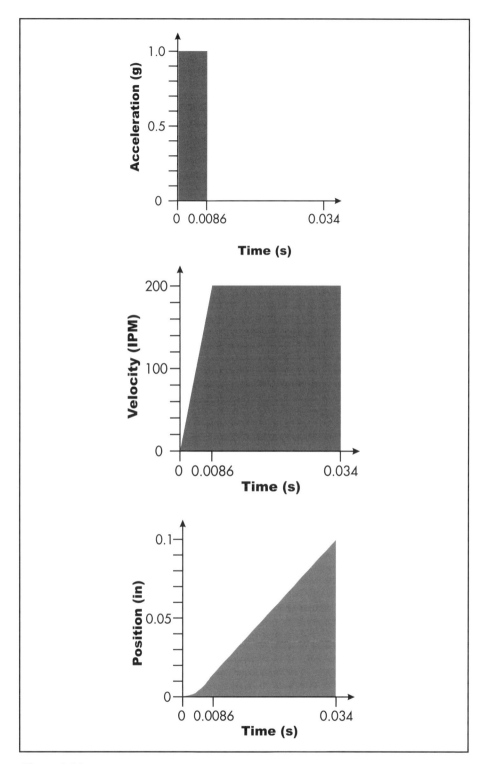

Figure 3-16:
Acceleration, velocity, and position as a function of time to complete the move M_1 as illustrated in Figure 3-15.

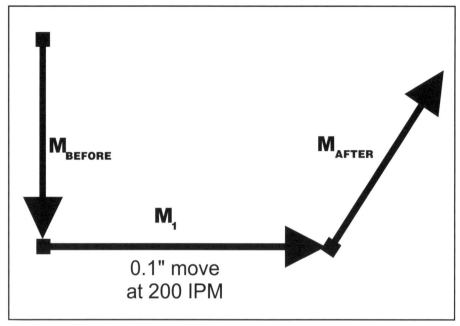

Figure 3-17:
It will take longer to complete move M_1 than in Figure 3-15 because M_{after} is at an angle to M_1. This requires the machine to also decelerate along the axis of M_1, prior to completing M_1.

price of the machine increases dramatically). Comparing accelerations between candidate machines should be a part of every high performance purchasing decision.

The ideal machine possesses high accelerations and high feed rates. Such a machine has less servo lag (because servo gain and acceleration are closely linked), and will cut parts very quickly by achieving high feed rates on small moves. Real-world restrictions — including CNC performance, machine dynamics, reliability, longevity issues, and cost — limit the combination of ultra-high feed rates and accelerations. High accelerations, for example, lead to higher dynamic loads on the machine, which shorten the life of bearings and induce vibration during sudden changes in the direction of motion. High feed rates reduce the life of ball screws linearly, but increased operating loads due to high accelerations reduce ball screw life as the cube of the increased dynamic load.

Advanced CNC Features for High Performance Machining

Several problems were uncovered during this discussion of motion control, including servo lag at high feed rates, limitations of block processing, and the difficulty of cost-effectively supplying both high accelerations and feed rates in a machine tool. A number of relatively new CNC features have been introduced to address these issues. Three of the more noteworthy enhancements relative to high performance machining — feed rate modification software, gain switching, and NURBS — are discussed below.

Feed Rate Modification Software

High performance CNCs can reduce the negative effects of servo lag by "looking ahead" and predicting the effects of servo lag upon the tool path. Based upon this prediction, the feed rate can be reduced to control the amount of servo lag and, consequently reduce the amount of contouring error. The result is more accurate parts, produced at higher feed rates than would otherwise be possible.

These systems, typically called "look ahead" or "contour optimization," are necessary to achieve high performance machining. Figure 3-18 illustrates the benefits of look ahead or contour optimization when machining a 2D contour, although the benefits apply to 3D paths as well. Because the feed rate is

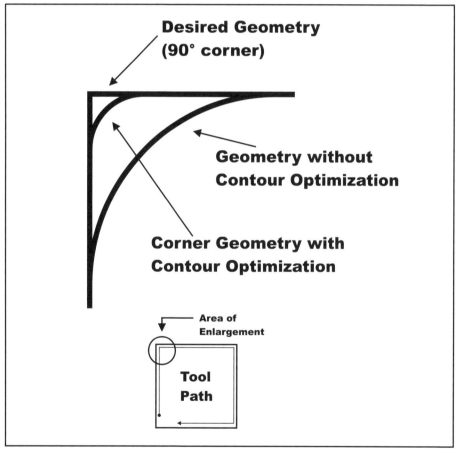

Figure 3-18:
Contour optimization reduces cutter path deviation in curvature (and therefore corners) to a specified tolerance by reducing feed rate in real time when necessary. The CNC increases the feed rate once the cutter exits the corner.

reduced locally to prevent excessive servo lag from distorting the part geometry, a higher overall feed rate can be programmed for the part. This eliminates the need to use a conservative feed rate throughout the program to ensure that good geometry is produced. It also eliminates the need to manually program lower feed rates in areas of the tool path with tight corners.

While several CNC manufacturers supply feed rate modification systems, there are significant differences between the various offerings. The best systems operate in realtime without affecting block processing rates, and allow the user to specify a desired contour tolerance.

Look Ahead

Look ahead systems preprocess the tool path and create a new tool path with modified feed rates. The preprocessing takes place either at an off-line computer, or on the CNC. In either case, the calculations necessary to alter the feed rate are performed outside the servo algorithms themselves. Because the tool path is preprocessed, look ahead systems cannot respond to changes in the feed rate during machining. The modified tool path is stored in a buffer, and if the operator turns the feed rate override knob during machining, the modified tool path will be in error.

Another weakness of many look ahead schemes is that they do not allow the user to specify a particular contour tolerance. These systems provide better, but undefined, performance improvements. Unfortunately, machined parts must be produced to specific tolerances which rarely include " ±better." It is extremely important in high performance machining that control of the machining process be put in the hands of the experienced programmer and machinist. If specific tolerances cannot be set, the look ahead system becomes a black box, making it difficult to properly apply.

Finally, look ahead systems, true to their name, can only look ahead a finite number of blocks. If the programmed segments are very small, and the geometry is varied, the system may not be able to look far enough ahead to properly correct for servo lag. The result is, again, an incorrect tool path and, depending upon the implementation, hesitation of the machine tool.

Contour Optimization

Contour optimization systems modify program feed rates on the fly, as they are resident within the filters of the servo algorithm itself. Calculations are made every servo update cycle. This allows feed rate adjustments made by the operator to affect the machining process. It also eliminates the need for off-line processing, allows program edits to automatically be included in the process, and reduces overall set-up time and manufacturing costs.

The best contour optimization systems enable the user to set a specific contour tolerance, along with a maximum and minimum feed rate. The contour optimization system seeks to maintain the maximum feed rate throughout the program. If the contour tolerance is going to be exceeded, the feed rate is reduced, although never below the minimum feed rate value. This arrangement allows the highest feed rate, which tool and workpiece can handle, to be programmed into the tool path. The minimum feed rate is set to a level below which damage to the workpiece or tool might occur. Programming is greatly simplified as a result of this approach.

Contour optimization can be applied to a wide range of high performance machining tasks. Consider the 24"×6"×6" electrode pictured in Figure 3-19. It was originally machined in 8 hours on a conventional VMC, and required several hours of hand finishing. Tolerance on the electrode was open at ±0.0025". Contour optimization software on a high performance VMC was used with both the roughing and finishing pass. On the roughing pass it allowed a very even stock-on condition to be created at programmed feed rates of approximately 200 IPM. On the finish pass it also allowed high feed rates to be obtained. Total machining time was just under 8 hours, even while quadrupling

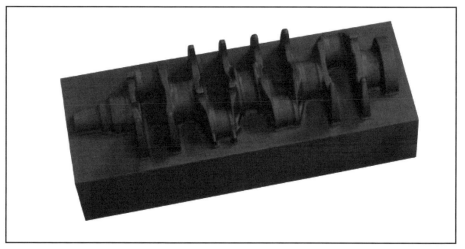

Figure 3-19:
This large, complex graphite electrode is used to produce forging dies for the manufacture of crank shafts.

the number of passes made over the part; this increased the size of the part program from 10 MB to 40 MB. Hand finishing of the electrode was eliminated.

While this part was not particularly demanding from a tolerance standpoint, the ability to create an even stock-on condition, and to maximize axis feed rates, led to a significantly better part. When the same stepover was employed on the high performance VMC as on the original (conventional) VMC, machining time was reduced from 8 hours to 2.5 hours with better part quality than the original. Contour optimization was an important element in this overall time reduction.

A common misapplication of contour optimization software is the use of overly tight contour tolerances. If the sides of a square must be produced to a dimension of 3" ±0.0002", for example, it is not necessary to set contour optimization to 0.0002". This is more a function of the geometry of the machine rather than the machine's contouring ability. But, if the corner of the square must be maintained to within ±0.0002" of the true geometry, a contour optimization setting of 0.0002" is used. It is only in the corners of the square, where the machine axes must accelerate and decelerate, that contouring is taking place.

Setting the correct tolerance for contour optimization systems is also important. In the previous example, contour optimization was set to one half of the total tolerance band. Contouring error caused by servo lag always occurs on a known side of the tool path. Therefore, the tolerance band applicable to contour optimization is not 0.0004". When the tolerance band on a contour is not symmetric (e.g., +0.0003" – 0.0002"), the lesser of the two values should be used. This is necessary because the effect of servo lag may cause the tool path to move toward or away from the final part geometry depending upon the curvature of the part and the tool's position.

A final caveat regarding look ahead and contour optimization systems: neither system will ensure that a part is produced to a tolerance equal to the contour tolerance set. While the tool path will be maintained to the contour tolerance, other effects such as tool runout, thermal growth, fixture misalignment, cutter deflection, etc., will increase the total amount of error. Therefore, it is sometimes a good idea to set contour optimization systems to a level tighter than the desired tolerance. The benefits of even tighter contour tolerances in reducing overall part error must be balanced against a reduction in feed rate and an increase in cycle time.

Gain Switching

Imagine driving an automobile with a one-speed transmission. As impractical as that would be, remember that most CNCs are built with only one gear — a single set of servo algorithms which must accommodate a wide range of machining conditions. Just as a single speed car would not be well suited to a wide range of terrain, a single-speed CNC is suboptimal for the wide range of part geometries that a machine shop must produce.

When machining intricate details with many axis reversals, high accelerations are more important than high feed rates. The importance of high servo gains was made apparent in Figure 3-13 and Table 3-4, particularly when working with intricate contouring. In other situations, such as roughing, high feed rates are desired over high servo gains and their accompanying high accelerations.

High performance CNCs provide the power to shift gears: to choose between a number of preset servo algorithms, and their corresponding servo gains, depending upon the part. The BostoMatic® BDC3200X CNC (Figure 3-20), for example, provides users with a four speed transmission, encompassing "roughing," "semi-finish," "precision," and "ultra-precision" modes. Each mode corresponds to a different servo gain. Applied to a mid-sized VMC, feed rates of 450 IPM are achieved in roughing mode with moderate accelerations. In ultra-precision mode, accelerations up to 0.9 g are achieved, while top end feed is limited to 100 IPM. Roughing mode allows very high stock removal rates when

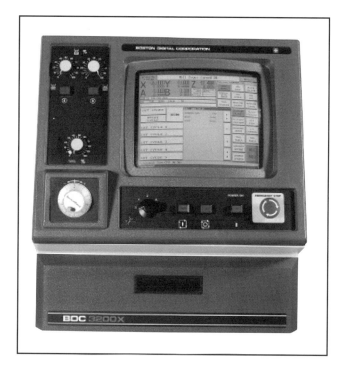

Figure 3-20:
The BDC3200X CNC is one of a few high performance CNCs that provide multiple servo gain settings along with advanced contour optimization features.

contouring accuracy is not critical. As part geometry becomes more intricate, and accelerations become more important than feed rates, precision or ultra-precision mode can be selected to provide better accuracy and shorter cycle times. Table 3-6 summarizes the motion characteristics for a range of machine work volumes using different gain switching modes.

Mode	Gain	Maximum Feed Rate by Machine Work Volume				
		18"×12"×18"	22"×16"×20"	32"×16" ×20"	40"×22"×22"	50"×22"×22"
Roughing	1	450 IPM	450 IPM	450 IPM	400 IPM	400 IPM
Semi-finish	2	350	275	275	200	200
Precision	4	200	150	150	100	100
Ultra-Precision	6	100	75	75	60	60
Maximum Acceleration		0.9g	0.75g	0.75g	0.55g	0.55g

Table 3-6:
Maximum feed rates and maximum accelerations for a range of VMCs using gain switching.

Feed rates are restricted as the servo gains and accelerations increase to prevent excessive dynamic loads from being placed upon the machine, and to prevent excessive vibration which would detract from surface finish and lead to instability in the control loop. But most applications requiring high accelerations involve intricate contouring and relatively small tools. The ability of these tools to withstand the forces associated with high feed rates is limited. So, in most applications, the lower feed rates mandated by the higher acceleration modes (e.g., precision and ultra-precision) do not limit the usefulness of gain switching.

When used with contour optimization, gain switching becomes a valuable tool for high performance machining. Consider a bottle mold with gentle curvature, machined from a block of aluminum 12"×6"×6", with tolerances of ±0.0005". The CNC is first set to roughing mode using a G-code, and a contour tolerance of 0.004" is set to ensure an even stock-on condition. The feed rate is programmed at 350 IPM, and the cavity is quickly opened up using shallow depths of cut at these high feed rates so as to work within the available spindle horsepower (15 HP). Actual feed rates during this high speed roughing operation vary between 75 and 350 IPM depending upon the local part geometry. During roughing, accelerations are limited to about 0.4 g. The cavity is finished using precision mode with its maximum feed rate of 200 IPM and higher accelerations (approaching 1 g) than roughing mode. Contour optimization is set to 0.0003, providing room for error due to cutter runout and deflection. In parts such as these, gain switching provides significant time savings (anywhere from 10% to 30%) by matching CNC performance to the requirements of the machining process.

Gain switching optimizes machine performance by providing the best of both worlds: high feed rates for roughing and noncritical machining, and high accelerations (with lower maximum feed rates) for semi-finish and finishing of complex surfaces. Gain switching helps to overcome the problem of cost-effectively providing high accelerations and high feed rates in the same machine. By recognizing that high feed rates and high accelerations are often required in different circumstances, both can be provided. In addition, users of "4-speed" machines with gain switching are not giving up anything relative to those purchasing "1-speed" machines with similar top end feed rates (450 IPM, for example). To achieve the high feed rates, manufacturers of machines with "1-speed" drop the servo gains. So, while these machines may exhibit similar material removal rates when roughing, the high performance machining center with gain switching will provide tighter tolerances and faster cycle times during semi-finish or finishing operations, which are much more time consuming than roughing to begin with.

NURBS

Today, the implementation of non-uniform rational B-splines (NURBS) within CAM systems and CNCs is a hot topic, but does NURBS miss the point? The benefits attributed to NURBS are numerous — shorter cycle times, smaller programs, more accurate parts, and better surface finishes, to name a few. Industry pundits assert that the widespread adoption of NURBS, and by extension the total annihilation of point-to-point CAM and CNC systems, is imminent. But before this new technology is embraced as a necessity, a more critical evaluation of the benefits and drawbacks of NURBS is required. In the following, a number of the more popular claims made by proponents of NURBS are explored.

NURBS allows parts to be machined with files that would otherwise be too large for controllers. This statement is an "old truth." It applies only to earlier CNCs, and current "hard wired" CNCs which have not adopted hard disk drives for program storage nor ethernet for program transfer. Surprisingly, many of today's more popular CNCs still have minimal on-board storage and require that large programs be drip fed to the CNC. A true high performance CNC possesses a hard disk drive of 100 MB or more (500 MB – 2 GB are not uncommon) and ethernet, which allows programs to be transferred to the CNC at very high speeds (10 MB/minute). Controls with these features can handle any program that could reasonably be generated for even the most complex and accurate parts.

Unfortunately, many CNCs that claim large hard disk drives still require drip feeding. Many hard wired CNC manufacturers have adopted the practice of bundling a PC with their CNC. So, while the PC has a large hard disk, and a program can be transferred quickly to it with ethernet, the link between the CNC still does not possess much memory. As a result, programs are still drip fed between the local PC and the host CNC. Careful evaluation of CNC manufacturer's claims by the consumer is required.

Linear interpolation requires a larger volume of interpolated points to define a curve to a given accuracy level than NURBS. True, NURBS compresses the amount of data required to define a surface. But simpler compression methodologies, such as PKZIP™, exist and these can be used with many open CNCs. Today's large hard disk drives, ethernet, and the widespread availability of compression software make program size a nonissue for any high performance CNC manufactured today.

NURBS interpolation defines part geometries more efficiently and accurately than point-to-point data so the definition of the curves isn't lost. More efficiently, yes; more accurately, no. A point-to-point program can define a machining contour as accurately as any NURBS curve, although it will require more data to do so. But with large hard disk drives, and ethernet connections between CNCs and CAM stations, program size is much less important than it was five years ago. NURBS tool paths, like point-to-point data, are not exact representations of the surfaces. When a plane is intersected with a NURBS *surface* to create a tool path, a NURBS *curve* does not result. The NURBS tool path must be calculated by the CAM system. This process involves approximation, so a tolerance band similar to the "chordal deviation" parameter used in most CAM systems is employed. A point-to-point tool path can be made as accurate as a NURBS tool path in every case given enough points. And, in some cases NURBS requires more data to accurately represent part geometries than a point-to-point representation.

NURBS allows points to be defined by the control and its interpolation rates instead of the block processing time. This is true for controls that were not designed with well balanced algorithms. Many popular controls require up to 4 ms to process a block of standard G-code into a form which can be utilized by the servo algorithms, and another 1.5 – 2 ms to perform the servo algorithm calculations. As a result, the amount of data these controls can handle, and the performance of the CNC as a whole, is limited by the 4 ms block processing time. By using NURBS, these CNCs reduce the block processing rate from 4 ms to 1 ms. But this only boosts the effective throughput of the NURBS CNC from 250 (1 divided by 4ms) to 700 – 1,000 blocks of G-code per second as dictated by the time required to perform the servo calculations. In this regard, NURBS is a "patch" for a weakness in the design of the CNCs block processing functions. Selling this as a benefit is akin to charging a customer for a bug fix to software (which incredibly some large software firms get away with); except in this case, a new CNC, rather than more software, must be purchased.

A well designed high performance CNC performs the block processing and interpolation processes each in 1 ms or less. These CNCs can process 5-axis point-to-point data at over 1,000 blocks per second without NURBS, while simultaneously performing several other tasks including program downloading and editing. Continued advances in DSP and RISC chip design, as well as more efficient software, promise to bring continued improvement for years to come.

Using point-to-point data generates free-form curves with a tolerance of about 10 microns (0.0004") compared to 0.25 microns (0.00001") with NURBS. The implicit assumption behind this statement is that when a tighter tolerance is employed, a non-NURBS CNC cannot process data fast enough, and data starvation occurs; thus the 10 micron limit. Parts have been routinely machined on BostoMatic High Speed Machining Centers with BDC3200X CNCs where the curves were toleranced to 0.00001" (0.25 microns). The 10 micron value prevails only in CNCs which are inadequate for high speed machining. As the performance of the BDC3200X (a non-NURBS CNC) demonstrates, NURBS is not necessary for achieving high performance, except when working with CNCs that are deficient in their basic ability to store and "crunch" data. In these cases, NURBS improves performance at the expense of added complexity in the CNC software, and added expense to the machine tool buyer in terms of both CNCs and CAM.

As an aside, these curve tolerance numbers should be taken with a grain of salt. Most machining centers are incapable of machining a 12" diameter circle at 20 IPM to better than 0.0005" TIR due to inaccuracies in machine geometry. A high performance machining center will achieve values of 0.0003" or better. Given these values, the relevance of a 0.25 micron contour tolerance must be questioned.

NURBS reduced machining time from 4 hours and 39 minutes to 3 hours and 46 minutes on a specific mold cavity. This example is typical of the claims made by proponents of NURBS because background information necessary to judge the veracity if the claim is not provided. In principle, NURBS-based CNCs will not reduce machining time compared to today's high performance CNCs because they do not perform servo algorithm calculations — the bottleneck in a well designed CNC — any faster. The claims of faster machining times made by NURBS CNC suppliers are often relative to older machines with antiquated controls, or new machines and controls which are inadequate with respect to the processing and data storage needed for high speed machining. To significantly reduce machining time, not only are higher data processing rates required, but the ability to support significantly higher accelerations and decelerations is necessary, along with superior machine geometry, the ability to correct for thermal effects, and the use of new spindle and drive train technology. To claim that the exact same machine tool and control can cut a part significantly faster when NURBS is "ON" should lead the buyer to call into question the design of the machine tool system, as the potential of the machine is being hampered by the CNC's inability to crunch data. A system which is truly optimized for high speed machining will be limited by the machine's dynamics. In other words, feed rates and (more importantly) accel/decel will be limited not by the CNC's data processing rate, but by the frequency response of the electro-mechanical system, including the servo algorithms themselves. Many of the machines to which NURBS based CNCs are fitted can only support accelerations of $0.2 - 0.3$ g. A true high speed machining center should be capable of supporting accelerations anywhere from $0.5 - 0.9$ g when using ball screw-based drive systems.

NURBS, when used to define blade geometry in CAD, and when used in the CNC for interpolation, enables high speed machining and eliminates hand-finishing. CAD and CNC systems that work with point-to-point data don't introduce additional distortions relative to NURBS, and a handful of manufacturers have been capable of producing blades which require no hand finishing for several years. NURBS is not required to achieve highly accurate components with superior surface finishes. The key elements are a CNC which can quickly process part programs, optimized motion control algorithms, *a well designed milling process*, and CNC+machine systems which are geometrically accurate, thermally stable, and which support high accelerations. NURBS is not a requirement for high speed machining because it principally addresses the up-front interpolation within a CNC, an area that has been successfully addressed by numerous CNC manufacturers without NURBS.

There are a number of other significant drawbacks to NURBS that often go unmentioned. First, the NURBS representation of a surface is difficult to interpret. The NURBS language of control points, knots, and weights cannot be directly related to machine motion by the machinist. This makes it impossible to edit programs at the machine, and makes it more difficult to interrupt and then resume a program, as is done to adjust the machining process, or to perform an inspection process. Second, there is not a universal NURBS standard. This means that each CNC and CAM manufacturer can implement NURBS differently, and the output of a CAM system may be interpreted differently by various CNCs. Until a universal NURBS standard is employed, purchasers of CAM and CNC systems must consider the possibility that the NURBS implementation on their system could become obsolete.

To summarize, NURBS has been positioned in the marketplace as a necessity to achieve high accuracies and to pursue high speed machining. To back this claim, NURBS is said to eliminate data starvation and "the inaccuracies of non-NURBS CNCs." The reality is that NURBS is of secondary importance when it comes to achieving high accuracies and pursuing high speed machining. It is a technology that was developed to solve three problems that no longer exist: a lack of internal memory for storing programs, the inability to transfer programs to the CNC at high speed, and a lack of processing power to convert small line segments to motor motion with high efficiency. Today, large hard disk drives and inexpensive memory, ethernet, high speed computer chips, and efficient motion control algorithms are eliminating these problems.

A focus on NURBS distracts machine tool builders and buyers alike from the central issues surrounding high speed and high accuracy machining. Today, the bottleneck in a true high performance machine tool is not block processing in the CNC, but rather the ability of the machine to accelerate and decelerate fast enough to provide high accuracy and high material removal rates. The focus of machine tool and CNC builders should be to develop systems that can support higher feed rates <u>and</u> higher accelerations while correcting for thermal and geometric errors on the fly. Focusing engineering talent on these areas, and capitalizing on the enhancements in processing power and data storage generated by the PC industry, will provide machine tool consumers with better, more cost-effective products.

Ball Bar Testing

The ball bar test is a dynamic test used to evaluate machine accuracy. To perform a ball bar test on a VMC, a linear transducer is attached to the spindle and the machine table using kinematic ball joints. The machine then moves in a circle with radius equal to the nominal value of the transducer. As the machine moves through 360°, a computer measures the change in length of the transducer as a function of angular position. The result is a measure of how accurately the machine moved through the circle geometry. The test can be performed in the X-Y, Y-Z, or X-Z planes on a VMC. The test can also be applied to lathes (Figure 3-21), grinders, and other contouring machine tools. Figure 3-22 illustrates the results of a 12"-diameter ball bar test performed at 20 IPM in the X-Y plane of a high performance VMC. The total error band between the ideal circle and the actual motion of the machine is plotted. In this case, the machine is capable of achieving circularity of 0.000152".

The ball bar test is an important test because it evaluates a number of aspects of machine quality including squareness, straightness, backlash, compliance in the way systems, and the quality of the motion control algorithms (including the amount of servo lag) in the CNC. The ball bar test can also measure the impact of servo mismatch between axes, which is the error caused when an identical move is commanded to each axis but they move in slightly different amounts. This can be caused by errors in the CNC or by errors in the lead and backlash compensation within the CNC. Because the ball bar test takes mea-

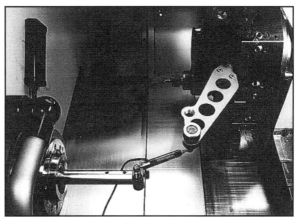

Figure 3-21:
Ball bar test set up to run a test on a CNC lathe.

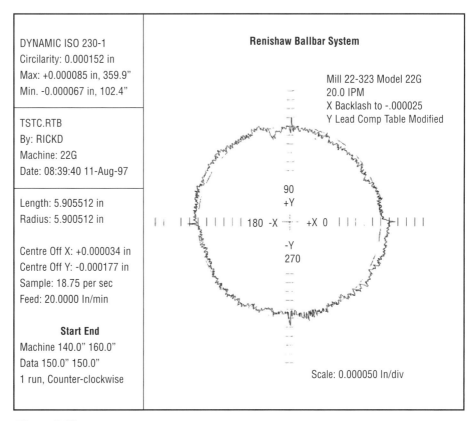

DYNAMIC ISO 230-1
Circilarity: 0.000152 in
Max: +0.000085 in, 359.9"
Min. -0.000067 in, 102.4"

TSTC.RTB
By: RICKD
Machine: 22G
Date: 08:39:40 11-Aug-97

Length: 5.905512 in
Radius: 5.900512 in

Centre Off X: +0.000034 in
Centre Off Y: -0.000177 in
Sample: 18.75 per sec
Feed: 20.0000 In/min

Start End
Machine 140.0" 160.0"
Data 150.0" 150.0"
1 run, Counter-clockwise

Renishaw Ballbar System

Mill 22-323 Model 22G
20.0 IPM
X Backlash to -.000025
Y Lead Comp Table Modified

90
+Y
180 -X   +X 0
-Y
270

Scale: 0.000050 In/div

Figure 3-22:
Ball bar result for a BostoMatic® high performance VMC at 20 IPM on a 12" diameter circle. Overall circularity is 0.00015". The test incorporates both clockwise and counterclockwise motion.

surements during machine motion, rather than while the machine is at rest, it is a good indicator of overall dynamic performance of the machine tool and is more relevant to high performance machining than simple positioning accuracy tests. By running ball bar tests at varying feed rates, it is possible to get a sense of a machine's dynamic accuracy across a wide range of operating conditions.

In addition to providing an overarching performance metric for dynamic accuracy, the ball bar test is an excellent diagnostic tool for machine tool builders and high performance machine shops alike. Cost-effective ball bar systems from companies like Renishaw, for example, can deconstruct the results of a ball bar test into various error sources. Performing ball bar tests periodically on a machine can identify maintenance requirements (such as loose gibs in hydrodynamic ways or excessive backlash in ball screws), and help validate the machine's process capabilities. Figures 3-23 and 3-24 illustrate typical ball bar test plots caused by various error sources including reversal spikes, backlash, cyclic error in the drive train, straightness, vibration, stick-slip, and lateral play.

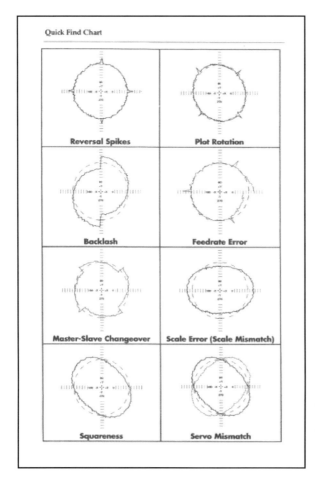

Figure 3-23:
Ball bar results can be used to identify a range of error sources in machine tools. (Courtesy of Renishaw Inc.)

General purpose machine tools will typically provide ball bar test results of no better than 0.0007", and often worse than 0.001" circularity at 20 IPM on

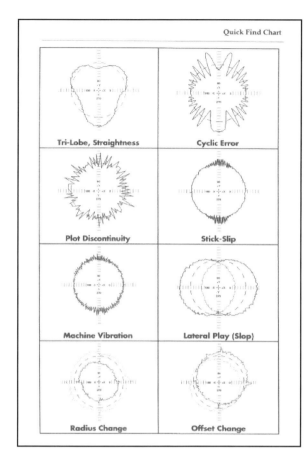

Quick Find Chart

Tri-Lobe, Straightness

Cyclic Error

Plot Discontinuity

Stick-Slip

Machine Vibration

Lateral Play (Slop)

Radius Change

Offset Change

Figure 3-24:
Additional manifestations of
error in ball bar test results.
(Courtesy of Renishaw Inc.)

a 12" diameter. For high performance machining, ISO standard ball bar results of better than 0.0003" should be sought. Some high performance machine tool builders can achieve values of less than 0.0002" ISO upon specific customer request by optimizing machine geometry, by hand selecting ball screws and other hardware, and by fine tuning the CNC.

When attempting to machine parts to tolerances of ±0.0005" to ±0.0002", the relevance of ball bar test results is readily apparent. If a general-purpose VMC is only capable of providing ball bar results of 0.0007", then as little as 70% and as much as 175% of the available tolerance band may already have

Feed Rate [IPM]	Circularity Error [in]
0.1	0.00031
1	0.00023
10	0.00019
20	0.00016
40	0.00032
160	0.00065

Table 3-7:
Circularity error on a 12"⌀ ball bar
test in the X-Y plane on a high
performance VMC. Courtesy of
Boston Digital Corporation.

been consumed just in terms of the machine's ability to move (at relatively slow speeds) through simple curvature.

Ball bar test results typically deteriorate with higher feed rates due to the effect of servo lag. A high performance VMC which achieved a 12" diameter ISO ball bar result of 0.00016" at 20 IPM generated an error in circularity of 0.00032" when the feed rate was increased to 40 IPM. At 160 IPM, the error increased to 0.00065". Similarly, as feed rates drop significantly, circularity errors will increase, primarily due to friction and reversal errors. Table 3-7 illustrates the change in ball bar test results for a high performance VMC when tested at different feed rates on a 12" diameter ISO ball bar test in the X-Y plane.

Ball bar test results for a high performance machine tool should be evaluated before purchase. The test is an important supplement to positioning accuracy data, and better relates to the expected operating conditions of high performance machining centers, specifically contouring. Keep in mind that while the ball bar test data are more meaningful than simple positioning accuracy data, the text does not measure performance in three dimensions, nor does it reflect errors experienced when actually cutting a part, such as cutter runout, deflection, and thermal growth. Further, because it is a composite measure of so many different error sources, the net ball bar results can differ significantly between individual machine units within a given model type. Nonetheless, the ball bar test is the best commercially available test method for evaluating machine tool performance.

4- and 5-Axis Considerations

Considerations for rotary axes used in high performance machining applications with respect to accuracy, the drive train, and motion control requirements are discussed below.

Positioning Accuracy and Repeatability

As with linear axes, the measurement of accuracy and repeatability for rotary axes can be affected by the measurement method employed. Careful consideration should be given to whether the ISO, JIS, or an unspecified measurement method has been used to determine the accuracy and repeatability of a rotary axis. Unfortunately, as with linear axes, many builders do not explicitly specify the accuracy of their rotary axes.

Accuracy of a rotary axis is usually measured in terms of arc-seconds. An arc-second is 1/3600 of a degree. Most general purpose rotary axes are accurate to ±15 arc-seconds, or in some cases ±10 arc-seconds. As discussed in Chapter 2, the accuracy of rotary axes is in many ways more critical than that of linear axes due to the multiplicative effect of angular errors. Therefore, for high performance machining applications, whether they be contouring or indexing, accuracies of better than ±10 arc-seconds should be sought. The larger the diameter of the part to be machined, the more accurate the rotary should be. For the production of large-diameter rotary dies (such as that in Figure 2-33), A-axis accuracies of ± 3 arc-second were required to support tolerances of ± 0.0005" in the width of the cutting lands machined onto the part. For sharpening smaller rotary dies, where land-width tolerances of up to ± 0.0002" are sought, A-axis accuracies of better than ± 5 arc-seconds are required. The same logic applies to 5-axis machines. The greater the distance between the tool tip and the center of rotary axis rotation, the more accurate the rotary must be. When utilizing a 5-axis machine which rotates the B-axis around the tool tip, accuracy of the rotary is less critical than when the tool extends as much as 12" or more from the axis of rotation, as with 2-axis spindle head or double-tilt rotary configurations.

Drive Train

Table mounted rotary axes (Figure 3-25) are typically driven by a worm gear arrangement, whereby a precision ground worm screw and mating wheel are used to provide mechanical advantage and increased accuracy. Typical reduction ratios are 50:1 or more, allowing higher speed servo motors to drive the rotaries at typical maximum speeds of 12 to 50 RPM, depending upon the design.

Three basic types of drive trains are used in rotary axes. The most popular of these for general purpose rotaries uses a worm and worm wheel, where the servo motor is belted to the worm shaft (Figure 3-26). Feedback to the CNC is provided by an encoder mounted to the rear of the servo motor. Such an assembly provides low

Figure 3-25:
Rotary axis mounted in A-axis configuration on a VMC. Note that while the X-axis travel on the machine is 32", the table extends over 50" to accommodate the rotary axis and a tailstock without a loss of working volume. (Courtesy Boston Digital Corporation.)

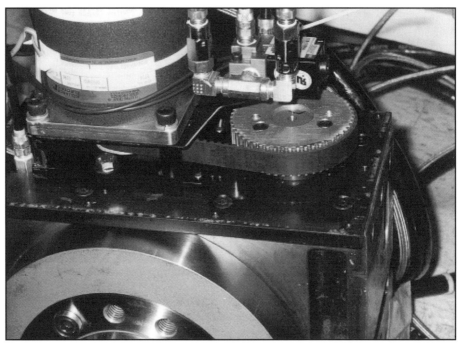

Figure 3-26:
Close-up of the belt drive used on a general purpose rotary A-axis. The belt reduces the overall stiffness, accuracy, and controllability of the unit.

accuracies, and is significantly less stiff than other designs. Over time, belt tension is likely to change, leading to a further decrease in stiffness and a loss of accuracy. General-purpose rotaries such as these provide minimal accommodation for backlash between the shaft and wheel. The components are typically manufactured of various types of bronze which wear relatively quickly. Over time, as the gear set wears, backlash increases significantly, causing inaccurate parts to be produced and requiring constant adjustment by the user.

A significant improvement upon this general-purpose design couples the servo motor directly to the worm screw. This increases stiffness and improves motion control. Further performance improvements are achieved using carbide worm screws in an eccentric carrier to provide backlash adjustment, and ion-nitrided worm wheels which are significantly harder than bronze-based wheels. A well-designed gear system, such as that made by Nikken Kosakusho, experiences relatively little wear over many years, due to the high hardness and wear resistance of the components, and a gear design which creates an oil film between the screw and wheel at high speeds, thus minimizing metal-to-metal contact. This firm's design can achieve speeds up to 44 RPM for extended periods, with minimal wear and backlash, while providing accuracies to ±7.5 arc-seconds. Because of the low backlash and wear in the system, improvements to these values can be achieved through the use of gear compensation within the CNC. This compensation is developed much the same way as for ball screws. Error in the gear set is mapped on a test stand, and a table of compensating values is stored within the CNC. During motion of the axis, the CNC looks up the compensating values in real time and adjusts the position commands accordingly.

The most accurate and expensive rotary construction, typically used when very high load capacities are required, utilizes two independent drive screws, interfaced to the worm wheel 180° apart. One screw is driven by the servo motor and CNC in a positioning mode. The second shaft is driven in a "torque mode," using a second servo motor, and maintains a constant preload against the wheel. This arrangement provides exceptionally high stiffness, low backlash, and stable operating conditions over a long operating life. (Rotary axes of this construction are used in the Campbell superabrasive grinder pictured in Figure 2-4.) Variations of this design utilize two drive shafts coupled mechanically, with only a single servo motor.

When seeking a high performance rotary axis, the role of the feedback device is also critical. Most rotary axes utilize an encoder on the servo motor to provide feedback to the CNC. This presents the same problems as servo mounted encoders coupled to ball screws. The data provided to the CNC by the encoder are only as accurate as the rotary's gear set. This problem is made worse when the servo motor is linked to the worm gear set by a belt or spur gears. To combat this problem, high resolution encoders can be mounted to the output shaft of the rotary, which is itself rigidly coupled to the face plate. Just as when using linear scales, these encoders provide direct feedback about the rotary's true position to the CNC. For high performance machining, encoders with 3, 4, or 5 arc-second resolution should be utilized on the output shaft. These encoders must be mounted to the rotary axes with care to prevent shaft misalignment, which leads to inaccuracy and possibly encoder failure. As with linear axes, the benefits of dual feedback to the CNC, from the servo encoder and the shaft encoder, apply.

Motion Control

When machining 4- or 5-axis components, a faster CNC is required. The amount of data that must be processed increases substantially because there are additional axes to be controlled. In the case of 5-axis machines, the amount of data to be processed can also increase because long linear strokes are required to maintain tool – work contact. This is particularly true for those designs where the centers of rotation are located far from the tool – work interface (e.g., double-tilt tables, 2-axis spindle heads). When evaluating the fitness of a CNC for 4- and 5-axis machine tools, it is important to determine if the block processing rate advertised relates only to 3-axis machining, as is often the case. Block processing rates can drop by 33 – 66% when CNCs must control 4- or 5-axes. A well designed high performance CNC will still run near or at 1,000 blocks per second when performing 5-axis machining.

If purchasing a 3-axis machine with an eye toward adding 4th or 5th axis capability later, determine what upgrades will be required from the CNC manufacturer to support these additional axes. Unfortunately, many CNCs are not equipped to handle the additional axes, and expensive hardware upgrades are required.

Chapter 4

Spindle Technology

Overview

The spindle plays a critical role in high performance machining because it is the interface between the machine tool and workpiece. Selecting the right spindle is necessary to optimize the performance and longevity of a machine tool. Until recently, most machine tools were offered with a limited number of spindle options. Now, as cutting tools are increasingly designed for specific machining processes (e.g., hard die milling versus graphite versus aerospace materials), there is no single spindle that can be used for all applications. As a result, high performance machine tools are offered with an increasingly wide array of spindle options. For example, BostoMatic® machining centers are offered with over 15 diffcrent spindles; and when multiple spindle configurations are accounted for, the total number of possible spindle combinations across the 3- and 4-axis product line increases to over 30. Although this level of choice seems overwhelming at first, a broad range is needed to address the increasingly unique requirements of different market segments.

It is very important for the high performance machining practitioner to properly define his machining requirements and understand spindle technology, so that the correct spindle (or spindles) can be chosen. In this chapter, some of the more important characteristics of spindles relative to high performance machining are discussed.

Desirable Characteristics of a High Performance Spindle

Speed and Power Requirements

Conventional machining spindles typically provide low speeds (10,000 RPM or less) with moderate amounts of power (15 HP). Larger machines, intended for heavy roughing, often employ spindles with lower maximum speeds of 4,000 or 6,000 RPM and 30 to 35 HP or more. Conventional machining processes utilize relatively low spindle speeds, and high torque, to remove material. Feed rates in these processes are also lower. This approach to machining has been driven largely by the limits of tooling. High speed steel or uncoated carbides, for example, are specified for use at relatively low surface speeds (see Table 4-1). Simpler part geometries also facilitate the use of low RPM spindles with high torque. When part geometries contain few complex contours, larger tool diameters can be used. As part surfaces become increasingly intricate, smaller tool diameters, accompanied by higher speeds and feeds, are necessary to access the geometry.

The feed rate for a given tool – workpiece combination is represented in terms of "feed-per-tooth." Feed-per-tooth generally increases with tool diameter, and is a good measure of the aggressiveness with which cutting can be carried out. Feed-per-tooth is also represented in Table 4-1.

The values below dictate spindle speed according to the following rela-

Workpiece Material	Uncoated Carbide End Mill, 1"⌀	
	SFM (ft/min)	*f* (inch-per-tooth)
Aluminum (2024)	500 - 1200	0.005 - 0.020
Cast Iron (32Rc)	40 - 500	0.004 - 0.008
Titanium	40 - 325	0.002 - 0.006
Austenitic Stainless Steel	90 - 320	0.003 - 0.008
Carbon Steel (30Rc)	65 - 440	0.003 - 0.007
H13 Hardened Steel (55Rc)	40 - 110	0.002 - 0.003
Inconel	10 - 100	0.002 - 0.006
Carbon Graphite	1500 - 1800	0.003 - 0.020
Copper	350 - 900	0.003 - 0.010

Table 4-1:
Surface speed and feed-per-tooth estimates for milling with uncoated carbide end mills in a variety of materials. The range of values reflects the inexact nature of the data, as well as the influence of exact material composition, tool geometry, and machine tool and process characteristics. *f* is provided for a 1"⌀ end mill. (Data are, in part, from the *Machining Data Handbook*, Third Ed., © 1980, by permission of the Institute of Advanced Manufacturing Sciences, Inc., Cincinnati, OH.)

tionship, where S is the spindle speed in RPM, D is tool diameter in inches, and SFM is the specified surface speed in feet/minute:

$$S = (\text{SFM} \cdot 12) \div (\pi \cdot D) \qquad [\text{RPM}].$$

Feed rate (IPM) in milling is calculated from the feed-per-tooth values using the following equation, where T is the number of flutes, S is the spindle speed (RPM), and f is the feed-per-tooth (in) for the workpiece – tool combination of interest:[1]

$$F = T \cdot S \cdot f \ [\text{IPM}].$$

To remove material quickly in conventional milling, large depths of cut and high power at low speeds (manifested as torque) are required.[2] While the

---

[1] This formula assumes a slotting cut with full engagement of the cutter. When side milling, higher feed rates are required. Modifications must be made to the calculations for both S and F when using ball end mills, depending upon the depth of cut.

spindle speed is dictated by the interaction of the cutting tool and workpiece, the amount of power required to remove a given volume of material is principally guided by the workpiece material properties, cutter geometry, and feed rate. Table 4-2 estimates the amount of power required to remove one cubic inch of material in one minute via milling.

Using the information in Tables 4-1 and 4-2, the spindle requirements for

Material	Power Constant (HP/[in³/min])
Aluminum (2024)	0.32
Cast Iron (32Rc)	0.9
Titanium	1.1
Austenitic Stainless Steel	1.4
Carbon Steel (30Rc)	1.1
H13 Hardened Steel (55Rc)	1.5
Inconel	2.0
Carbon Graphite	0.2
Copper	1.0

Table 4-2: Estimated power constants for milling various materials. (Data are from the *Machining Data Handbook*, Third Ed., © 1980, by permission of the Institute of Advanced Manufacturing Sciences, Inc., Cincinnati, OH.)

a specific milling cut can be estimated.[3] For specific tools and workpieces, information similar to that in Table 4-1 can be found in a machinist's handbook, shareware software programs, or the catalogs of cutting tool manufacturers. Power constants for various materials can also be obtained from the manufacturers of the material or from a range of engineering handbooks.

An iterative process is used to estimate the spindle requirements for milling a specific material. First, the type of tool (material, diameter, flutes) and the characteristics of the workpiece are determined. The theoretical spindle speed and feed rate are then calculated, and a desired depth of cut is identified. Next, the horsepower required for the cut is calculated. If the machine can provide the calculated speed, feed, and horsepower, the estimate is put into practice and refined based on actual results. Often, the calculation will have to be revised to accommodate machine limitations in power, speed, or feed. A similar iterative process is used to calculate cutting parameters for turning, drilling, and grinding.

The advent of coated carbide and ceramic tooling has altered the ideal

---

[2] While this discussion is framed in terms of "power" and "speed" throughout this chapter, it should be remembered that HP = Speed·Torque/5250. When identifying a specific power requirement at a given speed, the amount of torque necessary to remove the material at that speed is known.

[3] A number of other factors, such as tool wear, cutting fluid, machine stiffness, cutter geometry, and the type of cut, also come into play when attempting to characterize a cut. Experimentation is usually required to optimize cutting parameters for a given work – tool – machine combination.

operating point for many machining operations to higher surface speeds and feed-per-tooth values. These higher values can be attained because the coatings provide much higher hardness and heat resistance than uncoated carbide. These properties prevent the cutting edge from breaking down as quickly. The higher wear resistance of TiAlN, TiN, TiCN, and diamond coated tools is critical when attempting to machine tightly toleranced contours into parts with long tool path lengths. Table 4-3 estimates the surface speeds and feed-per-tooth for TiAlN coated carbide tooling. Contrast these values to those in Table 4-1. Note that the SFM values increase much more than the feed-per-tooth parameters.

Workpiece Material	TiAlN coated carbide	
	SFM (ft./min)	f (inch-per-tooth)
Aluminum (2024)	2500 - 5000	0.005 - 0.020
Cast Iron (32Rc)	500 - 1000	0.004 - 0.012
Titanium	175 - 350	0.005 - 0.008
Austenitic Stainless Steel	800 - 1600	0.003 - 0.010
Carbon Steel (30Rc)	900 - 1800	0.003 - 0.008
H13 Hardened Steel(55Rc) [4]	25 - 125	0.002 - 0.004
Inconel	150 - 325	0.002 - 0.006
Carbon Graphite	1800+	0.004 - 0.020
Copper	600+	0.006 - 0.010

Table 4-3:
Recommended surface speeds and feed rates for TiAlN coated carbide tools in a range of workpiece materials. (Data are, in part, from the Lovejoy Tool Company, Inc., Springfield, VT.)

The power required to remove a given volume of material per unit time (HP per cubic inch of material per minute) does not decrease dramatically with the use of new coatings. But the amount of horsepower will decrease somewhat with higher axis feed rates because more material is removed each time the cutter shears through the workpiece material. Power constants might drop by 20% in some cases as feed-per-tooth values double. Even though less power is required to remove the material, it is usually impractical to maintain conventional depths of cut when working at the elevated speeds and feeds dictated by Table 4-3. This would require extremely high power spindles that cannot be cost-effectively manufactured for broad use. It is the difficulty of simultaneously providing high spindle speeds and high spindle power that shapes high speed machining.

For example, consider machining a slot in aluminum using a 1"-diameter

---

[4] Although SFM values may not increase significantly when using TiAlN coated tools relative to carbide, tool wear drops precipitously, and surface finish improves. Data provided relate to finishing cuts.

2-flute uncoated carbide cutter versus a TiAlN coated carbide end mill. Assuming that P, the horsepower constant for aluminum, is 0.32 HP/(in³/min), and that we are taking a 0.5" depth of cut, the characteristics of the cut are as in Table 4-4.[5] Clearly, the machine required to make this cut using TiAlN tooling would be extraordinarily expensive, and is out of reach for the vast majority of machining operations. Even if the actual horsepower required dropped from 98 HP to 50 HP due to a high f value, the spindle would be very expensive. A motorized spindle capable of supporting a 50-HP cut would cost approximately $40,000 excluding the spindle drive and support equipment, such as the refrigeration system and drawbar hydraulic power unit.

Cutter Information			Estimated Cut Parameters		
Tool	Assumed SFM	Assumed f	Spindle RPM	Feed Rate (IPM)	HP Required
Uncoated Carbide	1200	0.02	4,580	184	29
TiAlN Coated Carbide	4000	0.02	15,280	611	98

Table 4-4:
Estimated cutting parameters to perform a slotting cut in aluminum with 0.5" depth of cut, using a 1"∅ 2-flute solid end mill, uncoated carbide versus TiAlN coated.

High speed machining often requires reduced depths of cut and tool diameters relative to conventional machining processes to keep power requirements (and spindle cost) within reasonable limits. Nonetheless, high speed machining maintains or increases material removal rates relative to conventional machining processes because higher spindle speeds and axis feed rates offset the reduction in depth of cut necessary to keep power requirements within manageable limits. As previously noted, the horsepower required to remove a given volume of material decreases somewhat with high speed machining processes. This is a result of the higher feed rates used, improved tool geometries, and coatings which reduce the amount of friction between tool and workpiece.

If horsepower requirements drop 10% when using TiAlN to machine aluminum, for example, it is possible to remove material more quickly with high speed machining techniques than conventional methods, even if spindle power is limited. The conventional machining process in Table 4-4 using uncoated carbide removes material at 92 in³/min with 29 HP at 4,580 RPM. Consider a high speed machining center limited to 29 HP at 16,000 RPM, with axis feed rates of 611 IPM. Assume it requires 0.29 HP/(in³/min) to mill aluminum when working with TiAlN coated cutters (a 10% reduction in unit power required). This machine could remove aluminum at about 100 in³/min. Depth of cut would be reduced to approximately 0.16" from 0.5" due to HP limits. But because of the

---

[5] For simplicity, the effects of cutter geometry, cut type, and feed rate upon horsepower requirements have been neglected. The selection of feeds and speeds is unfortunately not an exact science. Experimentation is required to achieve optimal results.

higher feed rates (611 versus 184 IPM) and lower unit power requirements, it would still remove material faster than the conventional machining process.

One of the greatest challenges posed by the high speed machining of contoured surfaces arises because tools of widely varying diameter may be required to machine a single part. When both small and large tools are required, a wide range of spindle speeds and power becomes necessary to complete the job. Figures 4-1, 4-2, and 4-3 approximate the maximum power and speed requirements to machine a range of materials using 2-fluted TiAlN end mills of varying diameter. In each case, the cutters are performing a milling operation with axial depth of cut equal to 50% of the cutter diameter, and full engagement of the tool diameter.[6] While it is likely that most machining time would be spent performing operations other than slotting, similar comparisons can be drawn for different types of cuts. Note also that exceptionally high feed rates are theoretically required to perform many of these cuts.

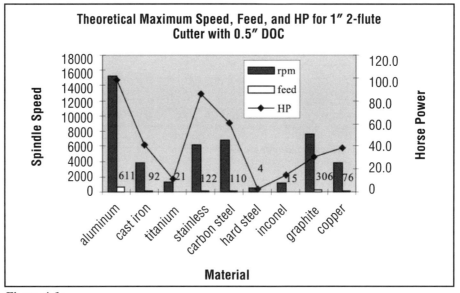

Figure 4-1:
Theoretical maximum speeds, feeds, and horsepower requirements for 1"∅ TiAlN coated cutters in a variety of workpiece materials. Feed rates are labeled for each material.

These figures illustrate the wide disparity in speed, power, and feed rate required when working with small versus large cutters. These disparities are greatest when the surface speeds and chip load requirements of advanced tool coatings come into play. Consider a cast iron mold for producing a glass wine jug like that in Figure 4-4. It is desirable to produce the mold for this part on one machine to eliminate multiple setups and reduce the time spent by the part in

---

[6] Because the optimal cutting conditions vary with tool geometry, and the exact composition of each tool manufacturer's coatings, the data presented here are meant to serve as a guide rather than a rule book. High end estimates are used for SFM, feed-per-tooth, and unit power requirements. Consult specific cutting tool manufacturer's literature for pertinent data.

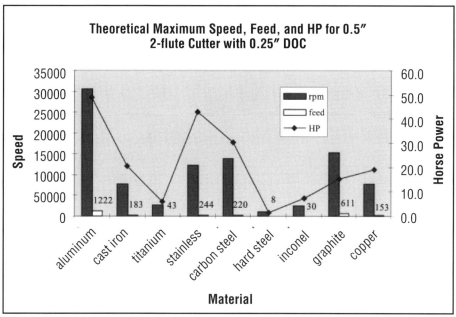

Figure 4-2:
Theoretical maximum speeds, feeds, and horsepower requirements for 0.5"∅ TiAlN coated cutters in a variety of workpiece materials. Feed rates are labeled for each material.

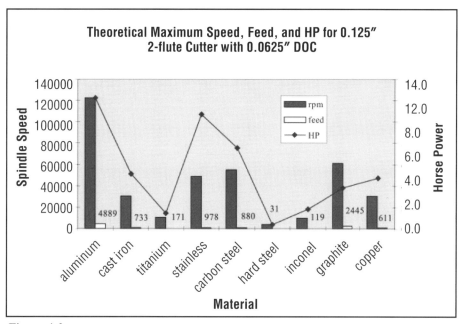

Figure 4-3:
Theoretical maximum speeds, feeds, and horsepower requirements for 0.125"∅ TiAlN coated cutters in a variety of workpiece materials. Feed rates are labeled for each material.

Figure 4-4:
To machine a cast iron mold cavity for production of this wine jug, a wide range of tool sizes is required.

queues. Ideally, the first tool for rough machining this part would be a 1"-diameter flat bottom end mill. In some areas, the part must be finished with a 0.125" ball nose end mill to generate small corner radii, for example, as in the handle. Other tools would be used between the two to complete the roughing operation, and for semi-finishing and finishing. Using information from Tables 4-2 and 4-3, the desired spindle would provide about 50 HP at 3,800 RPM for the 1"∅ roughing, and less than 0.1 HP at 30,500 RPM for finishing with the 0.125"∅ ball end mill.[7]

Providing such a combination of high end speed (30,000 RPM) and low end power (50 HP) in a single spindle is very expensive. To achieve the high speeds, a motorized spindle must be used. But cost effectively providing the necessary low-end power without a belt or gear mechanism is difficult. The necessary motorized spindle for this application would cost almost $60,000. Clearly, this is not a viable choice for most entry-level high performance practitioners, particularly as they migrate from sub-$100,000 machines. To adopt high performance machining successfully, technologies which keep machine prices below $200,000 are necessary. Such a spindle does not fit this profile.

Figure 4-5 illustrates the tradeoff between speed and power in spindles. It plots the range of spindles available from a number of leading manufacturers in terms of maximum power and maximum speed.[8] Note that there are a large

---

[7] Cutting parameters for the 1" cutter: TiAlN, 4-flute, 0.01" chip-per-tooth, 0.5" depth of cut, 1000 SFM. Cutting parameters for the 0.125" cutter: TiAlN, 4-flute, 0.005" chip-per-tooth, 0.01" depth of cut, 1000 SFM.

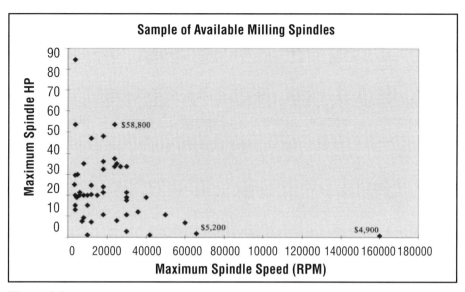

Figure 4-5:
Maximum speed and power is plotted for a range of commercially available spindles. Note that few spindles combine very high RPM and power. Those that do are very expensive.

number of spindles with moderate speed and power, but very few with both high power *and* high speed. Those units providing high power and high speed do not typically provide high torque at low RPM. This reduces their effectiveness for high stock removal roughing operations. For example, an 18,000 RPM, 48 HP motorized spindle provides only 557 in·lb of torque at the low end of the speed range compared to 1,100 in·lb of torque from an 8,000 RPM, 13 HP belted spindle. But, unlike the belted spindle, which only provides 1,100 in·lb of torque through 560 RPM before it begins to drop off, the motorized spindle provides maximum torque through 6,000 RPM.

High power spindles are very expensive, particularly when capable of achieving high speeds. For example, the spindle at point (24,000 RPM, 54 HP) in Figure 4-5 costs $58,800, excluding the spindle drive, refrigeration unit, and drawbar hydraulic unit. By the time the spindle is integrated into a machine tool, the cost to the end user will exceed $100,000. In contrast, the 160,000 RPM, 0.7 HP spindle costs $4,900. Generally speaking, spindle prices increase more rapidly with power than with speed. Figure 4-5 illustrates that commercially viable spindle technology can readily provide high speed or high power, but usually not both.

The best way to approach the tradeoff between power and speed is to recognize that in most high performance machining, semi-finishing and finishing operations require more time than roughing, and are more critical to the final part quality. Any tradeoff with respect to spindle performance should therefore

---

[8] Maximum power is usually achieved at less than maximum speed. Power will often drop off at the top end of the speed range.

be made in favor of the requirements of smaller tool diameters, as will be used in semi-finishing and finishing. This leads to a more dramatic reduction in overall part cycle time. A lower power, higher speed spindle should be favored over one that provides more power but less top-end speed. A low power/high speed spindle can still be used for roughing, it will just use smaller cutters and take longer to complete the task. On the other hand, it can significantly reduce the time required to semi-finish and finish machine the part. A low speed/high power spindle, on the other hand, will be inadequate for finishing, and can lead to significantly longer program run times and lower quality surface finishes. A way out of this quandry is to utilize a machine with more than one spindle. The benefits of such an approach will be discussed in greater depth below.

To summarize, modern tool materials and coatings are characterized by higher surface speeds and moderately increased feed-per-tooth values compared to uncoated carbide. Proper utilization of these cutters requires higher spindle speeds and feed rates. These requirements cause a dilemma with respect to spindle construction because it is difficult to cost-effectively provide high speed and high power in one spindle. When selecting spindles for high performance machining, choose higher spindle speeds with lower power over lower RPM/high power units. High speed/low power units are typically more reliable and cost-effective than high power/high speed units, and are better suited to semi-finishing and finishing operations, which make up the majority of part processing time and have a greater impact upon part quality. Selecting higher speed/lower power spindles will increase the long-term effectiveness of the machine tool by ensuring that it can support future tooling technology, which will require even higher spindle speeds.

Spindle Power Characteristics

Having discussed speed and power requirements generally, it is useful to note that spindles can possess one of a number of characteristic HP-speed/torque-speed curves. Figures 4-6 and 4-7 illustrate typical HP-speed curves for spindles. The different curves are a function of the way in which the motor is wound by the manufacturer.

The curve in Figure 4-6 depicts the performance of a spindle with a "knee" in the power curve. Such a spindle provides relatively constant torque through a portion of the speed range, and then the amount of torque drops off as speed increases. Spindles with these power characteristics mesh well with the contrasting requirements of small versus large tools. Small diameter tools will operate at the high end of the speed range, but require relatively little torque. Larger tools require more torque, but much lower RPM.

Figure 4-7 illustrates the HP-speed and torque-speed curves for a constant torque spindle. Horsepower increases linearly throughout the entire speed range. A full range of cuts can be pursued in easy to machine materials such as graphite, plastic, etc. Roughing cuts can be made with constant torque spindles in metals with lower machinability, but the maximum amount of torque available is typically much lower than with the knee-type characteristic.

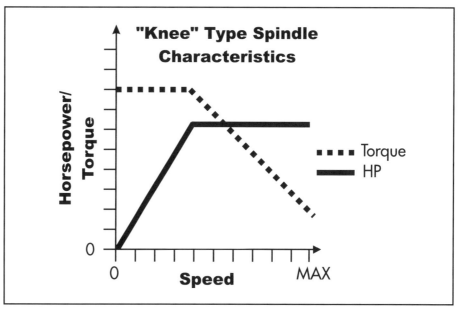

Figure 4-6:
Most spindles provide constant torque through a portion of the speed range, followed by decreasing torque at the upper end. Horsepower increases, and then at the "knee" becomes constant.

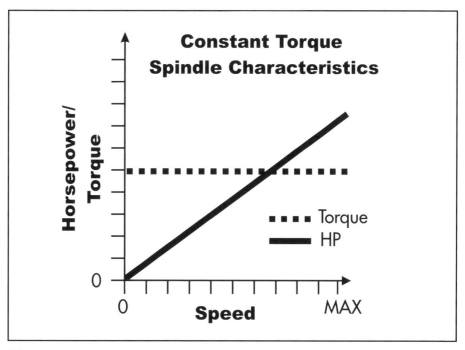

Figure 4-7:
An alternate motor winding provides constant (but lower) torque throughout the entire speed range. Horsepower increases linearly with speed.

It is important to note that the curves in Figures 4-6 and 4-7 are "ideal." With both types of spindles there is typically a drop in power as the speed range reaches its upper limits. When considering a spindle it is important to know the actual spindle performance over the complete speed range for continuous and intermittent duty.

Another important distinction between spindles is whether they are open loop or closed loop (sometimes called vector control). Closed loop spindles are outfitted with an encoder, which provides feedback to the spindle drive about speed. If the spindle begins to "bog down" and lose speed, the drive can sense this and apply more current (torque) to rectify the situation. The presence of an encoder also supports the use of a servo mode, which enables orientation and rigid tapping functions. Closed loop spindles enable a higher ratio between minimum and maximum spindle speed. For example, an open loop spindle might provide a speed range between 10,000 and 40,000 RPM. Below 10,000 RPM, the spindle does not develop adequate torque, and can't be used for cutting. Closed loop control of the same spindle motor could reduce the minimum spindle speed from 10,000 RPM to 4,000 RPM, extending the constant torque range significantly. Available torque is also increased, in some cases by 10 to 15%. Unfortunately, the benefits of closed loop spindle control cost money. A vector drive can cost two to three times more than an open loop drive.

Open loop spindles are less expensive than closed loop units, but have a number of drawbacks. Because there is no encoder feedback, rigid tapping and orientation are not supported. Speed variation under load is also higher: 2 to 3% as compared to 0.2% for a closed loop vector drive. Open loop spindles should be used principally when cutting loads are relatively low, as when semi-finishing or finishing. When heavy cuts are required, closed loop spindles provide substantial benefits over open loop designs.

Stiffness

For high performance machining, a stiff milling spindle is a necessity. A stiff spindle reduces the likelihood of chatter during cutting, and provides better surface finishes and higher accuracy.

When evaluating spindles, both radial and axial stiffness are important. While radial stiffness typically exceeds axial stiffness, the importance of one relative to the other is a function of the type of work being performed. If a machine is used principally for drilling and tapping, axial stiffness is most critical. If a machine is milling 3D contoured surfaces, radial stiffness becomes more important due to the side loads that will be placed upon the cutting tool. The importance of high radial stiffness increases with the aggressiveness of the cut, and the length of cutting tool employed. As discussed in Chapter 2, stiffness of a structure (in this case a cutting tool) is inversely proportional to its length cubed (L^{-3}). Therefore, long tools will tend to deflect significantly. If these deflections are compounded by the presence of a low-stiffness spindle, overall deflection can quickly reach unacceptable levels.

Stiffness of a spindle tends to increase with spindle diameter (by virtue of larger diameter spindle shafts and spindle bearings). Stiffness is inversely proportional to a spindle's maximum speed because faster spindles use smaller shafts and bearings to accommodate the higher speeds. Table 4-5 tabulates the stiffness for a number of motorized spindles from different manufacturers. Figure 4-8 illustrates a 30,000 RPM motorized spindle from the Pope Corporation.

Spindle #	Spindle Speed (RPM)	Spindle Diameter (in)	Axial Stiffness (lb·f/in)	Radial Stiffness (lb·f/in)
1	60,000	4.75"	171,000	468,000
2	60,000	4"	114,000	257,000
3	40,000	6"	514,000	942,000
4	40,000	4.75"	171,000	468,000
5	40,000	4.75"	156,000	936,000
6	40,000	3"	199,850	68,520[9]
7	12,000	9"	800,000	2,000,000
8	12,000	9"	1,313,000	2,000,000

Table 4-5:
Axial and radial static stiffness values at the nose for a range of motorized spindles with ball bearings. Stiffness values are rounded to the nearest thousand.

Figure 4-8:
This 30,000 RPM, 17.5 HP motorized high performance spindle utilizes 45 mm ceramic bearings with air-oil lubrication. It is supplied with 30 taper tooling and has a DN_{Rating} of 1.35×10^6. (Courtesy of Pope Corporation.)

---

[9] Stiffness of this spindle was measured at the collett, rather than on the taper, and therefore takes into account compliance between the spindle taper and the tool holder. This accounts for the dramatically lower stiffness value.

Table 4-5 illustrates that spindle stiffness varies significantly between different manufacturers, even when the spindle diameter is similar. Spindle #5, for example, provides twice the radial stiffness of spindle #4, even though they have roughly the same overall package size and the same speed range. Such differences are a result of many factors, including the number and type of bearings used, design of the spindle shaft, and the method and amount of bearing preload. It is also interesting to note that spindle stiffness typically exceeds overall machine stiffness (see Chapter 2). This is to be expected because overall machine stiffness reflects the summation of all subsystem compliances, including the spindle. If a machine tool builder cites static stiffness values for the machine tool that are approximately the same as the spindle stiffness, the veracity of the information provided, or at least the test method used, should be called into question.

The static stiffness values in Table 4-5 do not fully define the stiffness of the spindle subsystem. As the spindle rotates, the preload on the spindle bearings changes, and stiffness values will typically drop. The tool holder – spindle interface is a source of compliance as well (look at the stiffness of spindle #6). During cutting, the tool holder pulls away from the spindle due to cutting forces. To resist separation of the holder and spindle, a power drawbar with high retention force is necessary. The amount of retention force required is strongly a function of the amount of torque that the spindle can develop, and the cutting loads expected during use. Spindles designed for lower speeds and higher torque use larger tooling (e.g., HSK63, 40 taper, 50 taper) and will have the highest retention forces. Spindles designed for use with higher speeds and low torque use smaller tools (e.g., ISO20 taper, ISO25 taper) and need not provide as high a retention force. Table 4-6 surveys the retention forces provided by motorized spindles from a number of manufacturers.

Spindle Speed (RPM)	Max. Power (HP)	Tool Holder Type	Retention Force (lb-f)
50,000	6.5	HSK25 or ISO20	630
42,000	18.0	HSK40E or ISO30	1,200
30,000	9.0	ISO30	2,000
18,000	31.0	HSK63A or ISO40	4,000
8,000	24.0	HSK80A or ISO40	6,300

Table 4-6:
Drawbar retention force for a sampling of motorized spindles, as listed in a manufacturer's catalogs.

Table 4-6 illustrates that as maximum speed decreases, and power increases (thereby increasing low-end torque), the amount of retention force required rises. Nonetheless, there will be variations between spindles from different manufacturers. The 42,000 RPM spindle, for example, provides a lower retention force than the 30,000 RPM spindle, despite providing significantly more low-end torque. The relative merits of steep tapered tools versus HSK will be discussed in more depth below.

A final consideration when evaluating spindle stiffness is the quality of the spindle taper. If the taper is not ground to a high degree of accuracy, the fit between the tool holder and spindle will be compromised, reducing stiffness and geometric accuracy. A high quality spindle taper will provide at least 75% (and optimally 90%) "bearing." This is measured by bluing a master taper (male), and inserting it into the spindle (female) taper. The contact between the tapers is evaluated by observing the transfer of the blue pigment from the male to female taper. A 100% match between the male and female tapers is not desired. When the match becomes too good, it is difficult to eject the tool holder, and tools stick in the spindle. Achieving a 100% taper is also very costly.

It is not practical to define specific spindle stiffness requirements for high performance machining. Depending upon the application, requirements will vary. When working in graphite with short, small diameter tools, stiffness requirements will be lower than when working in hardened steel with larger tools and heavier cuts. That said, there is no such thing as "too much stiffness" (at least until one considers the cost). When evaluating the spindle(s) provided with high performance machining centers, seek to maximize overall stiffness in the speed/power range required. Seek high radial and axial stiffness values, and high tool retention forces. If one vendor's offering provides stiffness values significantly above or below those from other manufacturers, seek additional details. There may be a difference in the measuring method used, or one spindle may truly be superior. Keep in mind that larger spindle shafts and bearing diameters are required to increase stiffness, and that these mandate larger overall spindle diameters. This necessitates a number of tradeoffs in terms of spindle life (discussed below) and part access. As spindle diameters grow, a spindle's ability to enter cavities is compromised, requiring the use of longer tool extensions which in turn significantly reduce overall stiffness during machining.

Bearings

As with many topics covered in this book, an exhaustive discussion of bearings and bearing lubrication would fill many volumes. Here we will touch upon a number of topics critical to high performance spindles: bearing quality, the trade-off between speed and stiffness, grease versus air-oil lubrication, steel versus hybrid ceramic bearings, and the effect of belt tension upon bearings in belted spindles.

The heart of the spindle is its bearings. Typically, these consist of one or more pairs of angular contact bearings at the nose, and angular contact, deep groove, or roller bearings at the rear of the spindle. Figure 4-9 illustrates the cross section of a belted spindle used on BostoMatic Machining Centers. The front bearing pair is rigidly fixed in place as close to the nose as possible. These bearings are spaced apart to provide increased stiffness. The bearings are also preloaded to increase stiffness, and to reduce skidding between the balls and races during acceleration of the spindle. Skidding must be minimized because it

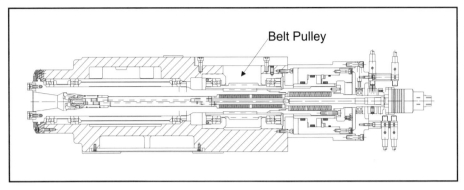

Figure 4-9:
This 15,000 RPM belted spindle is manufactured to support either HSK63A or CAT40 tooling. A unique bearing arrangement reduces the adverse affects of belt tension, while providing 1,100,000 lb•f/in radial stiffness.

contributes to wear, heat generation, and eventually failure of the bearing. The rear bearings support the back end of the spindle shaft. The floating isolated belt assembly accommodates thermal expansion of the spindle shaft, and prevents excessive loads due to these thermal effects. Unlike most belted spindles, the one in Figure 4-9 has complete bearing support above and below the belt pulley. This allows higher belt tension to be used, enables higher torque to be applied through the spindle, and reduces one of the primary causes of failure in belted spindles — overtensioning of the belt. The pulley bearings are also angular contact bearings. The spindle is rated for up to 15,000 RPM and 20 HP.

Bearing Accuracy

The ability of a spindle to provide smooth rotary motion with minimal runout and long life is closely related to the class of bearing utilized. Bearing quality is represented by an ABEC number of either 1, 3, 5, 7, or 9. ABEC 1 bearings are typically used in appliances, and are the lowest grade. ABEC 5 bearings are used in lower grade machine tools. High performance spindles should utilize ABEC 7 or ABEC 9 bearings. The ABEC class dictates the tolerances held on the various dimensions of the bearing. The higher the bearing class, the smaller the accepted deviation. ABEC 9 bearings, for example, limit total radial error motion of the inner race to 3 microns (0.00012") in a 70 mm bearing. ABEC 7 bearings limit this error to 4 microns (0.00016"). In contrast, an ABEC 1 bearing allows radial error motion of 20 microns (0.0008") in the inner race.

Speed versus Stiffness Tradeoffs in Rolling Element Bearings

Beyond the class of bearing, its DN_{Rating} value is an important factor to consider. DN_{Rating} identifies the speed limit for a bearing. The DN speed value in a specific application, DN_{Atual}, is calculated as follows:

$$DN_{Actual} = \text{Bearing Bore} \cdot \text{RPM}$$

where the bearing bore is in millimeters. DN_{Rating} is established for a bearing in terms of the type of bearing (angular contact, radial contact, etc.), the type of cage used to space the balls (nylon, welded steel, bronze, etc.), the lubrication method (grease, oil, air-oil), bearing seal type, bearing ABEC class, and ball material (steel, silicon nitride).

For a bearing to survive, DN_{Actual} must be less than DN_{Rating}. For example, the properties of a Holo-Rol™ brand hollow cylindrical roller bearing are shown in Table 4-7.

Model	DN$_{Rating}$		
	Grease Lubrication	**Oil Bath**	**Air-oil Lubrication**
HH3000	350,000	400,000	440,000
H-100	500,000	550,000	600,000
HC-100	1,000,000	1,100,000	1,300,000

Table 4-7:
Selected values of DN_{Rating} for Holo-Rol™ cylindrical roller bearings. (Courtesy ZRB Bearings, Harwinton, CT.)

Consider the use of Holo-Rol 65 mm ID bearings in the rear end of a 12,000 RPM motorized spindle. In this application, $DN_{Actual} = 12,000 \cdot 65 = 780,000$. If grease lubrication was desired, the HC-100 bearing is suitable for this application. If the maximum speed of the spindle was 18,000 RPM, DN_{Actual} increases to 1,170,000 and air-oil lubrication would be required.

DN_{Actual} increases with rotational speed (RPM) and bearing diameter. This explains, in large part, why it is difficult to build spindles that provide both high speed and high power. As bearing diameters increase, stiffness and load ratings go up. But, at the same time, the maximum speed that the bearing can support decreases. To maintain a given RPM, the rolling elements in a ball bearing move at higher speeds around the race as the bearing diameter increases. This faster motion increases the amount of heat generated. DN_{Actual} increases rapidly with large bearing diameters. Consider a spindle specification seeking high power (110 HP) and stiffness (3,300,000 lb•f/in radial stiffness) with high speed (20,000 RPM). To achieve the stiffness, a pair of 150 mm diameter angular contact bearings are required at the spindle nose. At 20,000 RPM, DN_{Actual} for this bearing is 3,000,000. In reality, it is difficult to find a roller element bearing that can provide a DN_{Rating} of over 1,600,000 using air-oil or grease lubrication.[10] Typical spindles providing this level of stiffness and power for heavy cuts are limited to speeds of less than 10,000 RPM to keep DN_{Actual} to a reasonable level (<1,600,000).

---

[10] Oil jet lubrication can support DN values over 1,600,000. But the cost of the system and its high power losses limit applicability to specialized applications, often in the aerospace industry.

Lubrication

As expressed in Table 4-7, the type of lubrication plays a central role in determining the speed limit for bearings. Grease lubrication typically provides the lowest DN_{Rating}, while air-oil lubrication can significantly increase the maximum operating speed of a bearing. Although air-oil lubrication is necessary to increase spindle speed and stiffness, and provides the benefit of continuously flushing the bearings of contaminants, it also has a number of drawbacks. First, it is more expensive due to the requirement for a metering unit, which must be controlled by a CNC or PLC, and monitored closely for failure. Cost must be added to the spindle to scavenge the oil after it has passed through the bearing, otherwise it will drip from the spindle nose. In many applications, such as graphite electrode machining, oil drip is unacceptable. Finally, air-oil lubricated spindles are sensitive to changes in the composition of the air/oil mixture, and the timing of its delivery. Because air-oil lubricated spindles are running at high DN_{Actual} values, if the proportion of oil decreases or increases relative to desired norms, the bearings can quickly overheat and fail.

Grease lubrication does not support the combination of high speed and power possible using air-oil lubrication. But grease lubrication is permanent in nature and less expensive. Further, with the advent of hybrid-ceramic bearings, the DN_{Rating} values attainable with grease are significantly higher than the limits imposed by steel bearings. For example, a 15,000 RPM belted spindle using 70 mm $\varnothing$ steel bearings required air-oil lubrication. When using hybrid ceramic bearings, a similar design, also using 70 mm $\varnothing$ bearings was able to attain 15,000 RPM with grease lubrication. This cut the cost of the spindle by $4,000, increased reliability such that the bearing life increased to over 8,000 hours, and eliminated oil drip from the spindle nose.

Generally speaking, grease lubrication is simpler and costs less. But to provide higher speeds and greater stiffness with rolling element bearings, air-oil lubrication is necessary. But beware: with the increased performance of air-oil lubrication may come higher maintenance costs.

Steel versus Hybrid-Ceramic Bearings

Steel ball bearings have been the standard in the machine tool industry for decades. In recent years, hybrid-ceramic ball bearings have been integrated into a larger proportion of high performance spindles. Hybrid-ceramic bearings use steel bearing races and silicon nitride balls to provide a number of performance benefits including higher rigidity, lower operating temperatures, reduced wear, better heat resistance, higher accuracy, and longer life.

Silicon nitride has a modulus of elasticity approximately 50% higher than steel. As a result, higher axial and radial stiffnesses can be achieved in spindles using hybrid-ceramic bearings. Because the silicon nitride balls are also harder than steel, they tend to wear less than steel balls. Unlike steel balls, wear particles won't become embedded in the silicon nitride balls. This helps to prevent the races from being damaged, and increases bearing life. Also, silicon nitride balls won't gall due to contact with the metal race. This helps prevent wear particles from spoiling the grease, which would otherwise significantly reduce bearing life.

One of the most beneficial aspects of hybrid-ceramic bearings is their increased robustness relative to steel balls. Hybrid-ceramic balls are more crash resistant than steel balls because it is harder to plastically deform them. The silicon nitride balls also have a lower coefficient of thermal expansion than steel balls. This limits their expansion under extreme heat, and can prevent catastrophic and/or premature bearing failure. For example, a 15,000 RPM spindle with hybrid-ceramic bearings was still rotating with minimal vibration during a power-up test after temperatures at the spindle nose rose to over 200° F. The extreme heat caused the seals of the rotary union (for coolant-through-spindle) to melt, and the bearing grease began to liquefy and run out of the spindle. Nonetheless, the spindle continued to run smoothly for over 30 minutes at these elevated temperatures before the problem was discovered and the spindle was shut down. With a steel ball bearing spindle, the bearings would have seized long before the temperature reached such a high level.

Silicon nitride balls weigh less than steel balls, and this reduces the centrifugal forces on the balls. Centrifugal forces cause the balls to move radially in relation to the angular contact bearing races. These movements in turn cause axial displacement of the spindle shaft, which is highly undesirable. The amount of displacement due to this effect varies with spindle speed, and can exceed 0.0005" in spindles using steel balls.

Although hybrid-ceramic bearings are more expensive than their steel counterparts, the performance benefits are significant. A stiffer, more robust spindle, with longer life, and a better speed/power profile can be constructed when using this technology.

Runout and Vibration

To provide high quality surface finishes and part accuracies, axial and radial runout of the spindle nose must be minimized. Likewise, spindle vibration must be low to support good surface finishes and to prolong spindle life.

Spindle runout is measured in a variety of ways. Some manufacturers specify the axial and radial runout at the spindle nose (method A), while others specify the axial runout at the nose and the radial runout at a specific gauging distance from the nose (method B). Figure 4-10 illustrates the different measuring methods. Of the two methods, method A is more directly comparable across various manufacturers' products. With method B, the gauging distance used varies between manufacturers. This makes it difficult to compare values across spindles. But it is important to note that method B can be a better indicator of actual performance, particularly if the gauging distance is similar to the actual tool length used in machining. For example, if the spindle is to be used for machining cavities 4" deep, it is likely that the tool tip would extend 6" from gauge line. If the radial runout of the spindle were measured 6" from gauge line, excellent information about runout in this application would be gleaned from the manufacturer's specification. Ideally, radial runout values for a spindle should

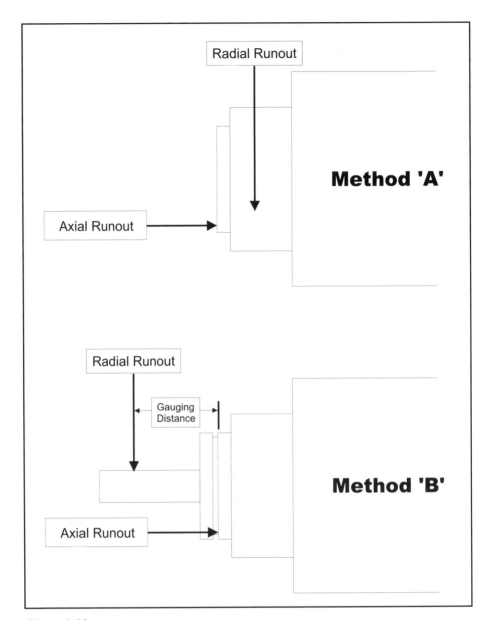

Figure 4-10:
Radial runout can be measured either inside the taper (Method A) or using a test arbor at a specified distance from the gauge line (Method B). Method B better represents actual use of the spindle, but can make comparison across spindles more difficult. Axial runout is almost always measured at the spindle nose.

be provided both at the spindle nose and at a gauging distance between 6" and 12" from the nose. The user will then have a lower and upper bound on the amount of runout that can be expected during actual use of the spindle.

Table 4-8 suggests runout specifications (TIR) for high performance spindles. Measurements made away from the spindle nose require a precision test arbor.

Runout Measurement	Maximum Acceptable Value (TIR)
Axial Runout – measured at spindle nose	0.0001"
Radial Runout – measured inside spindle taper	0.0001"
Radial Runout – measured 6" from spindle nose	0.0004"
Radial Runout - measured 12" from spindle nose[11]	0.001"

Table 4-8:
Runout measurements should be equal to or better than these values for high performance machining of 3D contoured surfaces.

When trying to produce parts to tolerances of ±0.0002" to ±0.0005", radial runout of 0.0001" or 0.0002" consumes a significant portion of the error budget by causing the tool to cut oversize. Axial runout tends to have less impact upon overall process accuracy because the effect is small relative to other errors such as thermal growth along the spindle axis.

A number of manufacturers are capable of producing spindle units with improved runout values. The belted high performance spindle in Figure 4-11, for example, provides axial and radial runouts at the spindle nose of less than 0.00006" with HSK63A or CAT40 tapers. Even better results can be achieved with optimal manufacturing processes. Pope spindles, for example, are produced with axial and radial runouts down to 0.00004" at gauge line when the spindle is ground off its own roller element bearings.

Figure 4-11:
This belted spindle is manufactured with axial and radial runouts at the nose of less than 0.00006".

---

[11] This measurement is not applicable to high performance spindles using smaller tools and tool holders (e.g., ISO30/HSK40 and smaller).

While runout measures the geometric quality of the spindle, vibration specifications are used to characterize the dynamic performance of the spindle. Spindle manufacturers present vibration specifications in at least one of three forms: displacement, velocity, or acceleration. The most popular formats for vibration data seem to be velocity and displacement. For high performance spindles operating at high speeds, vibration displacement should be less than 50-millionths of an inch (0.00005") peak to peak, and velocity should remain below 0.04 inches per second.[12] To achieve these values, the spindle must be intensively balanced, first as individual components, and then as a complete assembly at the spindle's maximum operating speed. To maintain these low vibration levels, relatively well-balanced tooling must be used, particularly as spindle speeds exceed 10,000 RPM. The subject of balanced tooling will be discussed in greater depth in Chapter 6.

Tool Holder Technology

Steep tapered tool holders such as BT40, CAT50, and ISO30 are used in the vast majority of milling spindles today. HSK tool holders, on the other hand, are rapidly being adopted for high speed and/or high power machining applications. When adopting high performance machining practices, the type of tool interface selected requires careful consideration.

Tapered tool holders establish their axial location in the spindle through the mating of two tapers. As spindle speeds increase, the spindle shaft tends to expand due to centrifugal force and thermal effects. As this occurs, the tapered tool holder is drawn further into the spindle due to the retention force applied by the drawbar. When the spindle stops rotating it attempts to return to its original size, but the presence of the tool prevents this. Thus, a much higher ejection force is required to overcome what is effectively a shrink fit between the tool and spindle.

Machines using steep tapered spindles are more susceptible to chatter than HSK because the interface between the tool and spindle is not as stiff. The lower stiffness of the interface drops the machine's natural frequency, and limits the use of aggressive cutting parameters. Reduced stiffness also makes steep tapered tool holders more prone to fretting when working with long tools, as when flank milling 5-axis turbo-machinery components with tapered end mills, or working with long ball-nose cutters in mold cavities.

HSK tooling (Figure 4-12) offers a number of benefits over steep tapered tooling that are important for high performance machining. HSK tooling is retained in the spindle by the use of grippers that sit inside a hollow cup behind the gauge line of the tooling. As spindle speeds increase, metal-to-metal contact between the spindle and tool holder is maintained because centrifugal forces

---

[12] These values can vary somewhat depending upon maximum spindle speed. The values provided are for motorized spindles with top speeds of 20,000 RPM or more. For slower running spindles, higher vibration amplitudes can be accommodated without causing undue wear and tear on the spindle or adversely affecting surface finish.

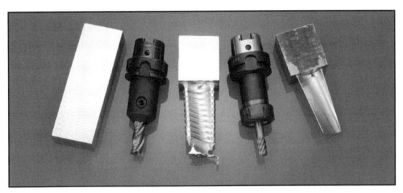

Figure 4-12:
HSK63A tool holders enabled aggressive milling cuts to be made in this stainless steel bar. The two tools shown roughed and finished the blade from raw stock on a 5-axis machining center. (Courtesy of Boston Digital Corp.)

cause the grippers to expand within the tool holder, pressing it tightly up against the inside of the spindle shaft. This increases stiffness of the interface and enables more aggressive cutting.

The HSK tooling system provides a higher degree of accuracy than steep tapered tooling. GMN motorized spindles, for example, are specified with radial runout of 0.0002" at a gauging distance of 6" when outfitted with HSK63A tooling. When 40 taper tooling is utilized, the radial runout specification degrades to 0.0004". When drawn into the spindle, HSK tooling provides simultaneous fit on both the spindle nose (via a flange) and the spindle taper. Locating against the spindle nose, rather than just the taper, ensures high repeatability when inserted and removed from the spindle and prevents the tool from being drawn into the spindle. As a result, the tool ejection force is more repeatable, and accuracy is maintained.

A number of different HSK tooling sizes and types are available. Each model is designated using a two- or three-digit number followed by a letter. The number corresponds to the OD of the flange used to locate against the spindle nose. HSK63A tooling, for example, has a 63 mm OD flange. The letter designation for high performance machining will typically be either A, B, E, or F. Type A tooling is recommended for general service, and is the most popular. Type B utilizes a larger flange than A to support heavier duty work. The larger flange is created by reducing the size of the taper. HSK80A and HSK80B tooling are not, therefore, interchangeable. Types E and F eliminate all drive keys and markings that would adversely affect tool balance. These HSK types are intended for use in the highest speed operations. Types C and D are similar to A and B, with the addition of wrench access holes for manual clamping mechanisms as used in lathe turrets, for example.

Many spindles are manufactured in both HSK and steep tapered versions. Table 4-9 indicates which HSK and ISO tapered tool holders are likely to be offered as options in the same spindle. The largest taper size for a spindle is dictated by the size of the spindle shaft and bearings utilized in the spindle.

A spindle built to accept this steep taper . . .	. . . will often be available with this HSK taper
ISO 20	HSK25
ISO 30	HSK32 or HSK40
ISO 40	HSK50 or HSK63
ISO 50	HSK80 or HSK100

Table 4-9:
Complementary ISO and HSK tapers with respect to packaging within a spindle. Stiffness values are not equivalent, even though a given spindle can be manufactured to support either tool holder type.

In most high performance spindles, HSK tooling is the ideal choice. It is stiffer, more repeatable, and will be better retained in the spindle at high speeds. Many shops resist adopting HSK spindles because the tooling costs more, and because they own large stocks of steep tapered (usually 40 or 50 taper) tooling. Ironically, this is one of the best reasons to adopt HSK spindles for high performance machining. Because new machines with HSK spindles will not be able to share tooling with the rest of the shop, the tooling can be better monitored and controlled for quality, reducing the likelihood of poorly balanced or damaged tools entering the spindle. Also, the HSK tool holders are less likely to drift throughout the shop because none of the other machines can use them!

Although HSK has many benefits, testing indicates that while larger HSK sizes (HSK40+) provide significant benefits in terms of stiffness and repeatability, the smaller tool sizes (HSK32 and smaller) are more susceptible to chatter than steep tapered tooling (e.g., ISO20 or $25\varnothing \times 16°$ cone). It is hypothesized that this is due to the greater extension from gauge line required to support a given tool length (gripped shank + exposed flute) when using HSK. The longer extension is necessary with HSK tooling because the hollow cup behind the gauge line leaves no room for collets or other tool clamping mechanisms. Instead, collets must reside entirely in front of the gauge line. With steep tapered tooling the collet can be located partially behind the gauge line in the body of the taper itself, reducing the effective length of the tool assembly. Stiffness of a tool in bending decreases as the cube of its length, and increases with the diameter to the fourth power.

$$\text{Stiffness} \approx D^4, L^{-3}$$

When working with small HSK tool holders, the length of the tool holder + tool measured from the gauge line can be higher than when using steep tapered tooling. As a result, the stiffness of the HSK system is lower, and vibration is more easily induced during cutting. As larger HSK tool holders are considered, the diameter of the holder body grows so that its stiffness (increasing as D^4) overcomes the adverse effects of a longer overall length.

At Boston Digital Corporation, HSK tooling was first introduced on its 5-axis product line in 1995, replacing CAT40 spindles. The change to HSK63A spindles was pursued because the life of CAT40 spindles in demanding 5-axis applications was inadequate. The use of tapered end mills up to 7" long, in difficult to machine materials such as titanium, stainless steel, and high nickel content alloys, quickly degraded the spindle tapers. Since the change from CAT40 to HSK63A tooling, spindle life has increased dramatically, significantly higher material removal rates are being pursued, and improved surface finishes are achieved. HSK63A tool holders are now available on the firm's entire line of 3-, 4-, and 5-axis machine tools. The principal drawback encountered during the adoption of HSK tooling is the sensitivity of the HSK system to the presence of chips or other contaminants. If not properly cleaned during the tool change cycle, the spindle nose might get chips on it. This prevents the HSK tool holder from seating properly in the spindle, leading to a system fault. Also, the hollow cup on the HSK tool holder has the potential to fill up with chips, coolant, or other contaminants. As such, it is very important to properly seal the tool changer mechanism, and to blow off the tool holder before it is placed into the spindle.

HSK tooling is recommended for use in spindles operating at over 12,000 RPM in place of ISO40 or ISO50 steep tapered tooling for high performance 3D machining. HSK tooling should also be considered for lower speed applications where hard materials and difficult machining conditions are expected, such as in hard die milling and the machining of aerospace alloys. When working with spindle speeds at or below 12,000 RPM, steep tapered tooling is adequate, particularly if cutting forces are relatively low. When working with smaller tool holders, steep tapered tool holders (e.g., ISO25) have been found to match or exceed their HSK counterparts with respect to part surface finish. But, responding to widespread demand in Europe, spindle builders are transitioning exclusively to HSK tooling, even in these smaller sizes.

Drawbar Technology

The spindle drawbar assembly typically utilizes a gripper and a series of springs to retain the tool in the spindle during cutting, and hydraulic or pneumatic pressure to eject it during a tool change. The drawbar also serves as a conduit to provide air blast to the spindle taper and/or coolant through spindle (CTS). There is a wide variety of different drawbar constructions available, and machine tool builders must concern themselves with the details of their characteristics. But from the standpoint of the high performance machine tool user, only a few elements of drawbar performance are of concern.

First, the retention force provided by the drawbar must be high enough to retain the tool during high speed rotation. Second, the drawbar must be capable of providing support for CTS or air blast as desired. Third, the spindle should be equipped with adequate proximity sensors to determine whether or not a tool is in the spindle by monitoring the drawbar position. Not all spindles are outfitted with these sensors, and without them the dangerous condition of a spindle rotating with a partially gripped tool can occur.

Another important distinction between various drawbar types is whether the actuating unit is rotating or nonrotating. Nonrotating actuators are better suited to high speeds because the spindle assembly can be more easily balanced. Finally, the drawbar unit should be constructed so that when ejecting the tool, no load is applied to the spindle bearings. Because ejection forces are high, applying these loads to the bearings while they are not rotating can cause premature bearing failure over an extended number of drawbar actuation cycles.

Drive Method (Belts versus Direct versus Gear Driven)

Spindles are manufactured in one of three general types: belted, direct drive (motorized), and gear driven. All three types have been widely used in conventional machining. The applicability of each spindle type to high performance machining is now discussed.

For high performance machining, gear driven spindles are not recommended. Although they provide the benefit of multiple speed ranges and very high torque at low RPM, the gears create vibration that can adversely affect surface finish. Gear driven spindles are also less efficient at converting motor power into usable power at the spindle nose. While motorized direct drive spindles are 100% efficient in this regard, and belted spindles are up to 90% efficient, geared transmissions are only between 70% and 80% efficient. This leads to higher heat generation in the spindle, which can cause excessive thermal growth. Finally, gear driven spindle systems are not capable of the speeds necessary to facilitate high speed machining. If the machining process to be pursued will require top-end speeds below 8,000 RPM, geared spindles should be considered. Otherwise, look to belted or motorized spindles instead.

Belted spindles provide an important middle ground between the high torque/low speed characteristics of geared units and the low torque/high speed nature of motorized spindles. The use of a belt allows power to be smoothly and efficiently transferred to the spindle from the spindle motor. Like the geared spindle, the separation of the motor from the spindle also simplifies maintenance, and reduces the cost to replace the spindle in the event of a crash. Belted spindles are capable of low vibrations (< 60-millionths of an inch depending upon RPM), high stiffness (over 1,000,000 lb•f/in), and relatively high speeds. Speeds of up to 15,000 RPM can be achieved with belted spindles while providing high bearing life. Another significant benefit of belted spindles is that they are relatively cost-effective compared to motorized spindles, particularly with speeds of 15,000 RPM or less.

The principal drawbacks of belted spindles are that they require more room for installation than motorized units, and cannot be balanced to the same degree of accuracy. They also tend to have higher thermal growth, and are louder due to belt noise.

Motorized spindles provide the highest speed range possible, but have lower torque. This is because motorized spindles do not possess a transmission to convert high motor speeds into lower spindle speeds with more torque. For speeds over 15,000 RPM, motorized spindles are a necessity. Unfortunately, motorized spindles are relatively expensive, not only because of the spindle construction itself, but because of the support equipment required to operate them. Because the motor is often located between the spindle bearings, high capacity cooling systems are required to evacuate motor heat from the spindle cartridge. As speeds increase, more sophisticated lubrication systems are required, and bearing life generally decreases very rapidly. The decrease in bearing life is not intrinsically a function of motorized spindles, but is related to the use of larger diameter bearings (for stiffness) at high RPM. While a limited number of high performance machine tool manufacturers will warranty their motorized spindle offerings for 2 years or 4,000 hours, many motorized spindles are warranted for only 6 months or 1,000 hours. This amounts to less than ½ shift of operation each working day for one year. If a high power/high speed motorized spindle is intended for continuous duty, ensure that a suitable warranty period is provided.

Main + Auxiliary Benefits

There are significant tradeoffs between belted and motorized spindles. Belted spindles can more cost-effectively provide power at lower RPM (< 15,000) than motorized spindles. But at higher speeds, motorized spindles are without peer. Unfortunately, many high performance machining jobs require lower speeds for roughing and semi-finishing with moderately sized tools (< 1"∅), and high spindle speeds for finishing with smaller tools. Both sets of characteristics can be provided in a single motorized spindle. Unfortunately, the cost of such a spindle, as discussed previously, is extremely high.

A solution to this dilemma is the use of a main + auxiliary spindle pair (Figure 4-13). A belted main spindle up to 20 HP and 15,000 RPM can be used

Figure 4-13:
A main + auxiliary spindle combination. The motorized auxiliary spindle provides 2.5 HP and speeds up to 40,000 RPM and supports tools up to ³/₈"∅. The main spindle provides 12,000 RPM and 15 HP. (Courtesy of Boston Digital Corp.)

for roughing and semi-finishing operations in a range of materials, including hardened steel, aluminum, copper, and graphite. The main spindle pictured in Figure 4-13 provides 12,000 RPM and 15 HP. A 20-tool ATC services the spindle, and an integrated air seal prevents contamination (e.g. coolant, mist, graphite dust) from entering the spindle. A relatively low power motorized spindle is mounted to the main spindle. Affixed to a hand scraped pad on the side of the spindle, the motorized spindle will typically provide maximum spindle speeds between 25,000 and 60,000 RPM. Spindle power can range anywhere from 1.5 HP for a 60,000 RPM spindle to 8 HP for a 25,000 RPM unit. The auxiliary spindle is fully integrated into the machine tool. Through the CNC, the user switches between spindles on the fly, and the auxiliary spindle can be serviced by its own 20-tool ATC. A separate spindle drive and refrigeration system support the motorized unit. Figure 4-14 illustrates an alternate main + auxiliary spindle arrangement.

Figure 4-14:
A front mounted auxiliary spindle arrangement. The motorized auxiliary spindle provides 8 HP and speeds up to 25,000 RPM and supports tools up to ½"∅. This geometry is often used when maintaining the full X-axis travel is critical. (Courtesy of Boston Digital Corp.)

There are a number of benefits to a main + auxiliary spindle arrangement. Most significantly, both high RPM (up to 60,000 or more) and high power can be cost-effectively embodied in a single machine tool. The composite HP-speed curve for such a machine is better suited to a wide range of work and working conditions than a machine using a single motorized spindle. Main + auxiliary spindle combinations are particularly useful in the mold and die industry, where a wide range of dissimilar materials (e.g., steel, graphite, copper, and hardened steel) need to be machined. With a main + auxiliary spindle arrangement, one machine can effectively address a wider range of machining requirements. This is important for shops migrating to high performance machining but unable to afford a dedicated machine for graphite or copper, and another for steel.

A machine with a main + auxiliary spindle setup also has the potential for greater uptime than a VMC using a single high power motorized spindle. If one of the two spindles goes down, the machine can still be used until the faulty unit is repaired. With a single spindle machine, the machine is idle once the spindle fails. This is particularly important when using machine tools with very high axis feed rates, which increase the probability of a crash considerably. The author was once told, in response to his question about bearing life in a 100 HP 16,000 RPM motorized spindle, "Don't worry about bearing failure, the mean time between crashes with most customers using these spindles is less than six months." This can make for a lot of downtime, not to mention expensive repair bills.

An interesting development in motorized spindles that could reduce the cost of crashing a motorized spindle is the concept of a detachable spindle nose. Available on spindles from Step-Tec AG, the spindle nose, which contains the front bearings and a portion of the spindle shaft, can be removed from the motor section by loosening a number of bolts. In the event of a crash, the nose can be quickly replaced without removing the entire spindle from the machine. Although the impact of this concept upon overall cost, reliability, runout, and stiffness was not immediately available, it warrants close scrutiny by high performance machine tool builders.

Single Spindle versus Twin Spindle

For many years, multispindle machines have been used to produce two or more identical components at the same time on a single machine. By using two, three, or even four spindles in parallel, a single VMC can significantly boost output. The use of twin spindle (or triples, etc.) machining centers in high performance machining applications requires careful consideration.

Twin spindle machines (Figure 4-15) are incapable of holding tolerances as tight as single spindle or main + auxiliary spindle machines. First, it is difficult to ensure that tool lengths and diameters will be identical for each spindle. Second, the X-axis center distances between the two spindles will change as the spindles heat up. Even when spindle temperature is tightly controlled and CNC thermal growth compensation is employed, the center distance can change by at least 0.0005" over the course of several hours. Without sophisticated thermal control systems, the center distance can vary by over 0.001". Variation in the relative Z-axis positions of the spindles should also be expected. Finally, when machining two parts at the same time, it is very important that "part zero" be accurately located relative to the true position of each spindle.

As a result of these drawbacks, tolerances better than ±0.0005" are very difficult to achieve when using twin spindle high performance machine tools. The tolerance band opens up further when three or more spindles are employed. To mitigate the weaknesses of multispindle machine tools, some builders will pro-

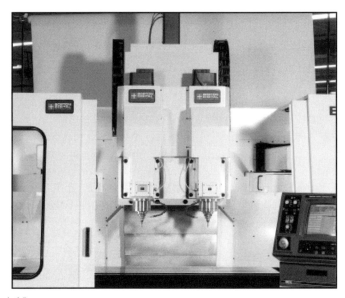

Figure 4-15:
The BostoMatic 50TS provides two 15 HP, 10,000 RPM spindles along with 50" of X-axis travel and an 85"×22" worktable. Holding tight tolerances is more difficult with a twin spindle machine than with a single spindle or main + auxiliary VMC. (Courtesy of Boston Digital Corp.)

vide Z-axis adjustments for each spindle. This is useful to correct for variations in tool length, but does not address variations in tool diameter, runout, or thermal and fixturing errors. When tolerances better than ±0.0005" are required, single spindle or main + auxiliary arrangements are required. It becomes necessary, when seeking tight tolerances in 3D contouring, to only machine one component at a time.

Nonetheless, multispindle machines play an important role in high performance machining, given adequate attention to detail. For example, when producing large quantities of identical electrodes for automotive forging dies, twin spindle machines prove highly efficacious. Figure 4-16 illustrates such a machine with twin 25,000 RPM motorized spindles. When manufacturing scroll compressors, twin spindle machines are often used to rough and semi-finish the male and female scrolls. Single spindle machines subsequently finish the scroll forms, the walls of which must be machined to tolerances of ±0.0002" (Figure 4-17).

Thermal Properties

All spindles, whether motorized, belted, or geared, change temperature during operation. The generation of heat in the spindle, due to the bearings and/or motor, causes thermal expansion. Thermal growth in spindles is a significant contributor to inaccuracy in high performance machining. The effects of spindle thermal growth, and methods of combating it, are detailed in Chapter 5.

Figure 4-16:
Twin spindle graphite machine employs two 25,000 RPM motorized spindles with automatic tool changers to produce graphite electrodes for automotive die casting. (Courtesy of Service Tool & Die.)

Figure 4-17:
Cast iron scroll prototype being finished machined using a 15,000 RPM belted spindle. For production, the components are roughed and semi-finished using twin spindle machines. For finishing, the single spindle and rotary C-axis help ensure that tolerances of ±0.0002" are achieved. The auxiliary spindle is not used in this application. (Courtesy of Boston Digital Corp.)

Hydrostatic Spindle Technology

The presence of rolling element bearings in high performance spindles gives rise to a number of performance restrictions. Rolling element bearings have limited lives and are a source of compliance, runout, and vibration; and they do not provide much damping, which is necessary when seeking high quality surface finishes (the need for damping is further accentuated when working in hardened materials).

Hydrostatic spindles use fluid film bearings in lieu of rolling element bearings. Figure 4-18 illustrates the cross section of a Plasel hydrostatic spindle, available in the United States from Precise Corporation. The front and rear bearings consist of ceramic pads on the spindle shaft surrounded by narrow gaps in the radial and axial direction. High pressure oil, forced into the gaps through several orifices, keeps the spindle shaft centered by maintaining a constant gap between the shaft and the housing. The oil is scavenged, and returned to a pump, where it is cooled and recirculated back to the spindle.

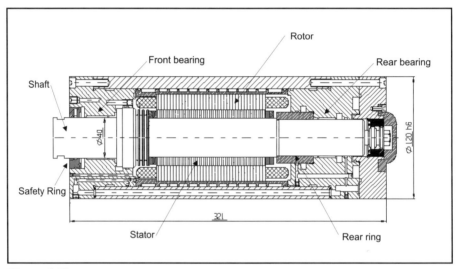

Figure 4-18:
Cross section of Plasel hydrostatic spindle identifies the key elements of the design, including the bearing surfaces. (Courtesy of Precise Corporation.)

The bearings in the spindle are self-compensating. As forces are applied to the spindle, the gap on one side of the spindle will narrow. This in turn increases flow resistance to the pad, generating a force in the direction of the load. At the same time, resistance decreases at the pad resisting the cutting load. The changes in resistance lead to an alteration in oil flow to each pad. The response of the system is extremely fast, and provides very high stiffness. A 5.5" diameter, 16,000 RPM, 12.7 HP Plasel hydrostatic spindle provides radial and axial stiffness of 1,430,000 lb•f/in and 3,400,000 lb•f/in, respectively. A 6.7"diameter 20,000 RPM, 20 HP hydrostatic spindle provides radial stiffness of 1,700,000 lb/in and axial stiffness of 3,400,000 lb/in. Compare these values to those in Table 4-5.

The high pressure (1,100+ psi) oil used as a bearing material is pumped through the spindle at 2 to 4 gallons per minute. The oil based bearings provide superior damping, estimated at twice that for ball bearing spindles, and 1,000 times an air bearing spindle.[13],[14] The high amount of damping significantly improves surface finishes. In cutting tests performed in aluminum to compare the hydrostatic spindle's performance to comparable ball bearing spindles, the hydrostatic unit typically improved the R_a surface finish by 50% compared to ball bearing spindles.

The self-compensating nature of the hydrostatic bearings, and the absence of rolling elements, enables exceptional shaft runout to be achieved. Plasel reports rotational shaft accuracies of 0.000008" (0.2 μm) or better.

The drawbacks of hydrostatic spindles should be considered before adopting this technology. First, the oil film bearings generate a lot of heat due to the shearing of the oil film. This makes thermal control of the spindle more difficult; and although specific tests have not been performed on the units in question, quite a bit more thermal growth is expected than when using rolling element bearings. Second, there is some concern regarding the crash resistance of these units. If the pads are scuffed or damaged, the spindle bearings will not operate properly. To address this problem, Plasel has integrated a safety ring that will make contact with the spindle before the bearing surfaces themselves, inducing a shutdown. The safety ring can be easily replaced in the field. Also, if the spindle is crashed or overloaded beyond the safety ring, the ceramic coating on the shaft will help reduce the likelihood of damage. Finally, the cost of the spindles is higher than similar speed/power ball bearing units. The spindle itself can cost 1.5 to 2.5 times that of a ball bearing spindle. The hydraulic unit, hoses, and oil can add another $12,000 to the price tag. In addition, a larger refrigeration unit will be needed to cool the oil and spindle motor than with a ball bearing spindle.

Despite the cost, hydrostatic spindles will be adopted in high performance machining applications where high stiffness, low runout, and exceptional damping are required. The machining of hardened steel and difficult aerospace materials are applications where these units are likely to be most widely adopted to improve surface finishes and increase tool life.

5-Axis Considerations

This chapter has focused on spindle technology that is applicable to a wide range of milling machines, including 3-, 4-, and 5-axis versions. For 5-axis applications, a number of additional considerations must be kept in mind.

Many 5-axis machine tools embody one or two rotational axes in the spindle

---

[13] Cohen G., and U. Rondé. *Use of Spindles with Hydrostatic Bearings in the Field of High Speed Cutting*. (Plasel, LTD. Tefen, Israel), 1997.

[14] An alternative hydrostatic spindle concept uses water rather than oil. Developed by Aesop and MIT, this technology has been successfully applied to a number of high power milling spindles.

unit. If the spindle rotates (as in Figures 2-26 and 2-27), it must be sealed against coolant entry in a range of orientations. Typically, spindles in VMCs are designed for "nose down" operation. They depend upon gravity to drain coolant or other contaminants from a labyrinth seal protecting the bearings. In 5-axis machine tools, the spindle nose can operate in a "nose up" configuration for significant periods of time. In such cases, it is very important that the spindle be constructed to prevent gravity from pulling contaminants into the front bearings. This can be achieved through a number of mechanisms, including "sling discs" that propel coolant away from the spindle nose via centrifugal force, pressurized air seals, or specialized labyrinth seals.

5-axis machining processes often require the use of very long tools. For example, when machining the hubs of blisks or impellers, high aspect ratio (length:diameter) tools must be used to fit between the individual vanes (Figure 4-19). Also, when porting racing heads, for example, very long, slender tools are required to access the interior of the port. High lateral loads are applied to the spindle when machining 5-axis components due to the low machinability of aerospace materials and the use of flank milling, which is often desired when

Figure 4-19:
The machining of components such as this 26" diameter stainless steel impeller stresses the tool – spindle interface through heavy variable loads. (Courtesy of Turbocam.)

machining ruled (rather than arbitrary) surfaces.

These two factors — long tools and high lateral loads — stress the interface between the tool holder and spindle. These time varying stresses cause vibration, degradation of the spindle taper, and consequentially poor surface finishes and low accuracy. To combat these effects, HSK63A or larger tool holders should be used in demanding 5-axis applications. High drawbar retention forces must also be employed to maximize rigidity of the spindle/tool holder assembly.

One of the more interesting aspects of 5-axis machining is that the spindle power requirements are often lower than in 3- and 4-axis machining applications with similar size workpieces. Because 5-axis component geometries are often convoluted, there are relatively few "wide open spaces" upon which large diameter tools can be effectively used. And, because the tools required to access the part are often long and slender, the amount of power they can transmit to the cutting zone without breaking is limited. In effect, a large proportion of 5-axis processes are limited by tooling, rather than spindle power. While it is possible to purchase 5-axis machines with very high power spindles, they often do not process parts any faster than more cost-effective machines with low to moderate power (5 to 15 HP) spindles.

For example, consider an 18"∅ aluminum impeller with a total of 22 vanes and splitters, machined from solid. The part was produced on two similar machines — one with a 10,000 RPM, 5 HP spindle, and the second with an 8,000 RPM, 13 HP spindle. Despite the significant increase in available HP and low end torque when using the 13 HP spindle, production time was only reduced by 10%. A significant cycle time reduction was not realized because the part geometry did not lend itself to high stock removal rates given the limited clearance for tooling between the vanes. Further, the majority of machining time was in finishing, rather than roughing. The higher power and torque available in the 13 HP spindle does not facilitate reduced cycle times during the finishing process relative to the 5 HP unit.

Chapter 5

Thermal Growth and Control

Overview

Most machinists recognize that variations in temperature affect the physical dimensions of machine tools and workpieces. But although there is a general understanding that temperature changes adversely affect precision, few machine shops fully appreciate the significance of thermal effects. This chapter explores the impact of temperature changes, manifested as thermal growth, upon high performance machining.

Methods of Heat Transfer — The Nature of Thermal Expansion

The temperature of a body is a function of its energy state and will change with the transfer of heat into or out of the body due to conduction, convection, or radiation. Conduction is the process by which heat is exchanged between two bodies in direct physical contact without relative motion between them. Conduction occurs, for example, when a hot workpiece is placed on a cold machine table. Convection is the transfer of heat due to the movement of a fluid (a gas or a liquid) over the surface of a body. When coolant flows over a cutting tool, it is removing heat through convection. The third type of heat transfer occurs through electromagnetic radiation. When a bright light shines on a workpiece and heats it, radiation-based heating is taking place. Radiant energy is also responsible for browning toast in an electric toaster. Radiation is typically much less important than conduction and convection with respect to high performance machining.

All three methods of heat transfer — conduction, convection, and radiation — must be guarded against to prevent changes in a machine tool's temperature. Very small changes in temperature can lead to significant errors in machine accuracy. Table 5-1 quantifies the impact of several temperature changes within a vertical machining center. Identifying the cause of, and means to combat, temperature changes like these is the subject of this chapter.

The size of most objects is a function of temperature, and the vast majority of materials will expand or contract with changes in temperature (graphite, with a coefficient of thermal expansion of zero, is an exception). The change in length of an object (ΔL) is related to its change in temperature (ΔT) by the following relationship,

$$\Delta L = \Delta T \cdot L \cdot \alpha$$

where L is the initial length of the object in inches, ΔT is measured in degrees Fahrenheit, and α is the coefficient of thermal expansion for the material. This relationship assumes a uniform temperature distribution throughout the object,

Description of Temperature Change	Impact of Temperature Change
36" cast iron column of VMC changes temperature by 5° F.	Column grows by 0.0012".
40" X-axis ball screw temperature increases by 10° F.	X-axis mispositions by 0.0026" on a 40" move.
A cast iron bolster, measuring 20" in Y, heats up by 15° F.	The bolster grows by 0.002" along the Y-axis.
Flood coolant at 60° F flows over a 24" aluminum component at 70° F.	The aluminum component is now 23.997" long.
8" titanium parts, machined at 80°F are inspected at 68° F.	The parts are found to be 0.0005" undersize.

Table 5-1:
Impact of temperature changes within a vertical machining center.

as well as uniform material properties. Although these assumptions are often incorrect, the equation is useful for "back of the envelope" estimates of thermal growth. The change in the length of an object not only varies with temperature, but is directly proportional to the object's initial length. An object twice as long will experience twice the thermal growth if it is made of the same material and experiences the same change in temperature. This fact strengthens the argument, first made in Chapter 2, for making a machine tool structure as small as possible. Table 5-2 lists thermal expansion coefficients for some common engineering materials.

Material	Coefficient of Thermal Expansion, $\alpha \times 10^{-6}$ [in/(°F·in)]
Cast Iron	6.7
Steel	6.5
Stainless Steel	6.3
Aluminum	13
Glass	0.4
Titanium	5.3
Polymer Concrete	6.8
Nickel	9.0
Copper	11
Graphite	≈ 0
Polycarbonate	32

Table 5-2:
Thermal expansion coefficients for materials commonly found in machine tools and/or workpieces. Values will vary depending upon the exact composition of the material.

Using the information in Table 5-2, and the above equation, it is relatively straightforward to calculate the change in size of a component given a specific temperature change. For example, consider a block of aluminum, measuring 12" in X, 10" in Y, and 8" in Z at 68° F (the temperature at which standards of measurement are defined). If the temperature of the aluminum increases to 75° F, the change in length along each axis is calculated as follows:

$$\Delta L_X = \Delta T \cdot L_X \cdot \alpha, \; \Delta L_Y = \Delta T \cdot L_Y \cdot \alpha, \; \Delta L_Z = \Delta T \cdot L_Z \cdot \alpha$$

$$\Delta L_X = 7° \cdot 12" \cdot 0.000013" = 0.0011"$$

$$\Delta L_Y = 7° \cdot 10" \cdot 0.000013" = 0.0009"$$

$$\Delta L_Z = 7° \cdot 8" \cdot 0.000013" = 0.0007".$$

The size of the block at 75° F is 12.0011"×10.0009"×8.0007". In the context of high performance machining this represents a significant change. When seeking tolerances of ±0.0002" to ±0.0005", thermal growth of this order of magnitude is certainly unacceptable.

Effects of Ambient Temperature Changes

One of the most overlooked detriments to high performance machining is a change in the ambient temperature. Many machine shops are not temperature controlled. As a result, severe temperature swings can be experienced during the time required to machine one or more high precision parts. In warmer climates, it is common for a machine shop to undergo a temperature swing of over 15° F in a 24-hour period. Returning to the example of growth in a 36" column, a 15° F temperature change in the machine casting would cause it to elongate by over 0.003"!

Many machine shops advertise their ability to machine to "tenths." Walking through some of these shops one finds machines exposed to significant temperature variations. Some machines are located near exterior walls, or windows through which the sun shines. Others are placed near loading docks or employee entrances which are propped open in the summer to provide a cool breeze, and in the winter so employees can "catch a quick smoke." Still other machines are located directly under central heating or cooling vents. Each of these situations represents a serious problem for high performance machining because the machine is exposed to temperature variations. Sunlight shining through a window on a machine can heat the back of a machine through radiation. A cooling vent might expel air 15° cooler than the ambient air onto the top of a machine, chilling it through convection. Tight control of the ambient temperature in a machine shop is a prerequisite for high performance machining. If temperature is not closely regulated, investments made in precision machine tools, fixturing, tooling, and gauging will be wasted. How tightly temperature must be controlled is a function of part tolerance, part size, and the length of time over which a part, or a batch of parts, is machined.

Consider production of a steel part for use in a mechanical assembly. The part (Figure 5-1) contains two 1" ∅ bores with a positional tolerance of

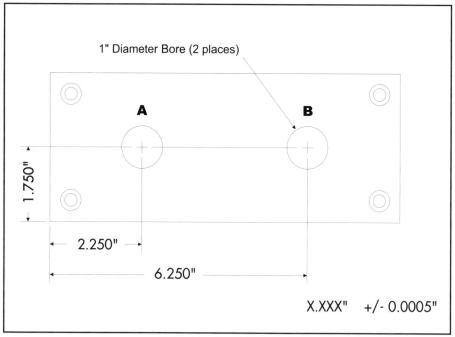

1" Diameter Bore (2 places)

A   B

1.750"

2.250"

6.250"

X.XXX"   +/- 0.0005"

Figure 5-1:
This simple steel part demonstrates the impact of temperature change upon the ability to hold tight tolerances. The position of bore B is more strongly influenced by a change in temperature than bore A.

±0.0005". The most difficult of these to maintain from a thermal standpoint will be that with the longest overall dimension. In Figure 5-1 this is the distance between the reference edge and the bore marked "B," nominally 6.250" at 68° F (20° C).[1] To determine how much of the tolerance band for this dimension can be allocated to thermal error, other error sources must first be quantified. In this case, machine positioning error is of principal concern because the feature does not require contouring. Assuming a high performance machine which can position to ±0.0001" ISO and negligible other errors, ±0.0004" is left to accommodate thermal expansion or contraction. If thermal behavior of the machine is ignored, the temperature of any part in the batch must not vary by more than ±9.8° F from 68° F.[2] When the part is placed in the machine's vice against a positive stop, the hole will be bored 6.250" ±0.0001" from the reference edge regardless of the part's temperature. But when the part is later inspected at 68° F, the distance between the bore and the reference edge will increase or decrease as the part contracts or expands. If the part were machined at a temperature of 82° F, the final dimension would be 6.4994" at 68° F, which is out of tolerance.

---

[1] 68° F (or 20° C) is the internationally recognized temperature for making measurements. Without a specified temperature, it becomes impossible to compare measurements made in different locations or at different times.

[2] $\Delta T = \Delta L / (\alpha \cdot L)$

Importance of Maintaining a Fixed Shop Temperature

A common misperception regarding thermal growth is that temperature variations in machines, parts, gauging, and fixturing are acceptable, as long as the variations are the same for everything. In other words, it is okay if the machines and parts are 60° F in the morning and 70° F in the afternoon, as long as their temperatures change at the same rate. Unfortunately, this is not true. Because materials have different coefficients of thermal expansion, they expand or contract by varying amounts depending upon the absolute temperature. An aluminum part measuring 10" long at 68° F will measure 10.0013" at 78° F. A steel measuring gage 10" long at 68° F will be 10.00065" long at 78° F. Only if every part, machine, and measuring gage in a shop is made of the same material is the absolute temperature unimportant. Given that this is impractical, it is critical that machine shops maintain a fixed temperature year round.

Another important factor that must be considered is the time dependency of temperature changes. If identical size blocks of cast iron and aluminum, both at 60° F, are brought into a room at 70° F, they will not approach room temperature at the same rate. The rate at which each changes temperature is guided by the following equation:

$$T = T_{room} + (T_{part\text{-}initial} - T_{room}) \cdot e^{-t/\tau}$$
$$\text{where } \tau = \rho \cdot c_p \cdot V/(h \cdot A).$$

T_{room} is the room temperature, $T_{part\text{-}initial}$ is the temperature of the part when it enters the room, t is the elapsed time in hours, ρ is the part density, c_p is the specific heat of the part, V is the volume, A is the area, and h is the convective heat transfer coefficient.[3] For still air, the value of h is approximately 1.7 [Btu/hr·ft²·°F]. This relationship applies while a measure called the Biot number is much less than 1, which is the case for most metals.[4] When considering materi-

Property	Aluminum Block	Cast Iron Block
$T_{part\text{-}initial}$ [°F]	60°	60°
T_{room} [°F]	70°	70°
ρ, density [lbm/ft³]	169	449
c_p, specific heat [Btu/lbm·°F]	0.2	0.1
V, part volume [ft³]	1	1
A, part surface area [ft²]	6	6
h [Btu/(hr·ft²·°F)]	1.7	1.7

Table 5-3:
Relevant material properties for determining block temperature as a function of time.

---

[3] The value for e is approximately 2.718282.
[4] The Biot number equals the quantity $h \cdot k/L$, where k is the thermal conductivity and L is the characteristic length (approximates the distance from surface to center of body). If the Biot number is close to or greater than 1, these relationships do not apply.

als such as concrete, glass, and graphite, this is not true, and the above relationship does not describe the cooling or heating of such parts when exposed to a change in air temperature.

Returning to the example of cast iron and aluminum blocks, Table 5-3 outlines the relevant material properties needed to determine the temperature over time of 12"×12"×12" cast iron and aluminum blocks brought from an ambient temperature of 60° F into a room at 70° F.

Using this information we solve the above equations for cast iron and aluminum.

$$T_{aluminum} = 70 - 10 \cdot e^{-t/3.31} \qquad [°F]$$

$$T_{cast\ iron} = 70 - 10 \cdot e^{-t/4.4} \qquad [°F].$$

Figure 5-2 illustrates the temperature of the two blocks as a function of time. Note that the temperature of the cast iron block lags that of the aluminum, and both require many hours to change temperature by 10° F.

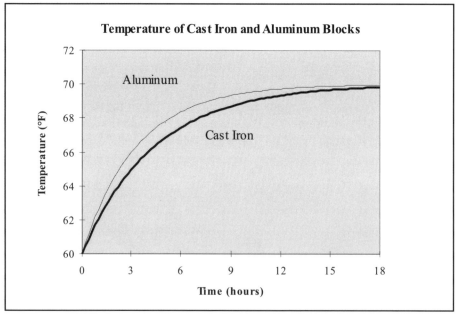

Temperature of Cast Iron and Aluminum Blocks

Figure 5-2:
Temperature of steel and aluminum blocks, originally at 60° F, after being moved into a room at 70° F.

The value τ, called the time constant, represents the time required for a body to change 63% of the initial temperature difference (6.3° F, in this case). The time for a body to change 95% of the temperature difference is $3 \cdot \tau$. The time to steady state can be written as

$$t_{steady\ state} \approx t_{95\%} = 3 \cdot \tau_{estimate} = 1.76 \cdot \rho \cdot c_p \cdot V/A \qquad [hours]$$

for materials cooling or warming in still air. $t_{steady\ state}$ can be used to perform a "back of the envelope" calculation for how long it takes different machine components or parts to reach a new steady state temperature.[5] Table 5-4 quantifies the time required for a number of different components to approach a steady thermal state. How close a component must be to its final steady state temperature before it is machined or measured depends upon the allowable temperature variation in the part (see above). If a piece of raw material is brought into a warm shop from an outdoor shed in the middle of the winter, one should probably wait the entire time as dictated by the equation for $t_{\text{steady state}}$. If, instead, a part is moved from a room at 68° F to another at 72° F, it may be adequate to wait only $t_{\text{steady state}}/2$ hours or less because the initial difference in temperature was small.

Material	Dimensions [in × in × in]	$T_{\text{part-initial}}$ [°F]	T_{room} [°F]	$t_{\text{steady state}}/3$ [hours]	T [°F] at $t_{\text{steady state}}/3$	$t_{\text{steady state}}$ [hours]	T [°F] at $t_{\text{steady state}}$
Aluminum	12×12×12	75°	68°	3.3	70.6°	9.9	68.35°
Cast Iron	12×6×6	85°	68°	3.2	74.3°	9.6	68.85°
Steel	6×6×6	50°	68°	2.4	61°	7.2	67.1°
Titanium	3×4×1	60°	68°	0.8	65°	2.4	67.6°
Copper	3×3×3	65°	68°	1.2	66.9°	3.5	67.85°

Table 5-4:
Examples of time for a solid part to change by 63% ($t_{\text{steady state}}/3$) and 95% ($t_{\text{steady state}}$) of the initial difference between the part's temperature and room temperature.

Maintaining a constant temperature throughout the shop requires more than setting the thermostat and throwing away the key. Within a shop there will undoubtedly arise temperature gradients. The discussion to this point has focused on homogenous temperature changes. The entire machine or part has been assumed to *uniformly* change temperature. Temperature gradients cause parts and machines to change temperature in a nonuniform manner. When this occurs, not only do components change size, but their geometry is distorted as well. Machines placed near doors, windows, or heating ducts are often exposed to significant temperature gradients. For example, a machine shop in Minnesota installed a small VMC near an exterior wall of a poorly insulated cinder block building. During the winter, the shop lowered the heat significantly at night to save money. Each morning, when the machine was turned on, a geometry check found the column leaning back by over 0.001", creating a Y-Z squareness error. Over the course of the day, the column would again become square with the work table. After many misdiagnoses, the shop determined that the exterior wall became so cold at night that the column experienced a significant difference in temperature between the rear, which was up against the wall,

---

[5] In reality, determining the time to steady state is much more complex, as the part in question is also in contact with a table or other surface through which substantial heat transfer takes place. Nonetheless, this is a good way to gain insight into the time dependent nature of temperature change.

and the front, which faced the interior of the shop. This temperature difference caused the rear of the column to contract more than the front, creating an error in machine geometry. Although this example is extreme, smaller effects will create geometric errors that are significant when machining precision components.

Another potential source of temperature gradients is the stratification of air in a shop. Warm air tends to rise, while colder air sinks. As a result, the temperature in a shop can vary significantly from floor to ceiling. In machine tools, subsystems which extend over significant vertical distances are adversely affected by stratification. A large horizontal machining center, for example, may be exposed to a temperature difference of over 10° F between the bottom of the base and the top of the column. The variation in temperature can cause thermal growth and distortion in the machine geometry. To avoid thermal gradients, it is important that the air in a shop be "well mixed," and that local sources of heat be isolated from machine tools, parts, fixtures, and gauging.

To provide a thermal environment conducive to high performance machining, it is very important to maintain a fixed room temperature. Maintaining 68° F within the shop is the ideal choice because it is the universally accepted temperature at which to make dimensional measurements. Machines should also be located away from potential sources of temperature gradients, such as heating and cooling vents, exterior doors and walls, sunlight, and heat generating equipment. How tight the temperature must be controlled is largely a function of the size of the part and machine in question. The better the temperature control, the more of the tolerance band will be available to accommodate other error sources besides thermal growth.

Ball Screw Growth

Within the machine tool itself, thermal effects are also an important factor when producing high precision parts. One of the components most susceptible to changes in temperature are the ball screws. Ball screws convert rotary motion into linear motion very efficiently; about 90% of the energy put into the screw is available to move the machine slides. The remainder is consumed deflecting components in the ball screw, or is transformed into heat. In addition to heat generated at the ball screw nut, heat is also produced at the ball screw support bearings. If these bearings are not well aligned with the ball screw, or are subjected to high loads, excessive heat can be released into the ball screw, causing further growth.

Because ball screws can be quite long, slight changes in temperature cause significant changes in the overall length of the screw, even if both ends of the ball screw are fully supported.[6] Changes in ball screw length are of great concern to the high performance machine shop because in many machines the ball screw is the standard of length. When motor encoder feedback is used, the CNC only counts the number of screw rotations. If the linear distance traversed for

---

[6] See Chapter 3.

each rotation of the screw changes, the CNC is not aware of this change, and a positioning error results.

For example, consider a mid-sized vertical machining center with motor encoder feedback (and no linear encoders). As part of a test of the machine's thermal stability, an 8" diameter circle was continuously run "in air" at 100 IPM for 8 hours with the spindle off. Ambient temperature was controlled to within ±2° F. Measurements were made every hour by picking up the location of a reference pin. Even at these moderate feed rates, the X-axis grew by 0.0007" and the Y-axis by 0.0013".[7] Y-axis growth exceeded X-axis growth because the Y-axis moves the weight of the X-axis assembly in addition to the Y-axis slide. Figure 5-3 charts the error in each axis, throughout the 8-hour test. Most of the error accumulates during the first few hours of testing, and eventually the machine achieved thermal equilibrium. In many 3D contour machining applications, machine activity will vary enough so that thermal equilibrium of the ball screws is not achieved, either because the feed rates vary and/or the location of machining within the work volume changes with time.

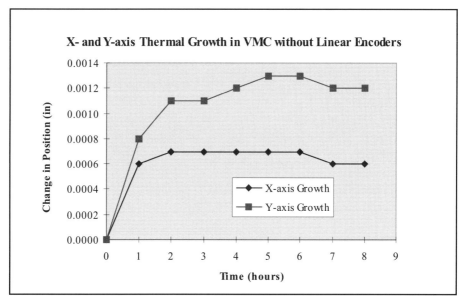

Figure 5-3:
Significant positioning errors are caused when ball screws change temperature during operation. The growth in each axis of this machine was a result of cutting an 8" Ø at 100 IPM. The Y-axis growth, illustrated as a positive quantity in the graph, is actually experienced as a negative shift in the Y-position on VMCs. The use of linear encoders significantly reduces these errors.

If axis growth of this magnitude is possible at low axis feed rates, the amount of growth experienced at higher feed rates can certainly become

---

[7] These measurements were made with a 50-millionths indicator, introducing measuring error that is significant relative to the values measured.

problematic. Many shops underestimate the impact of thermal growth in ball screws because they are used to working at lower feed rates, which generate much less heat in the ball screws.

There are a number of methods employed to combat thermal growth in ball screws, and some are significantly more effective than others. One method that has gained popularity in recent years is to run cool liquid through the ball screws. The ball screws are hollowed out, and rotary unions are attached to one or both ends. Liquid is then circulated through the screws to remove heat. While this method is better than nothing, it has a number of serious drawbacks. First, when machining, most axis motion is confined to a relatively small portion of axis travel for significant periods of time, as when 3D contouring a mold cavity. A machine with X-Y travels of 32"×16" might be used to machine a hardened 12"×8" mold cavity. During the machining process, the mill might spend several hours within a 4"×4" portion of the mold to create the necessary detail. As a result, the 32" X-axis ball screw will not undergo a uniform temperature change. There will be hot spots in the area of intense motion, and the screw will be cooler further away from this area. When cooled liquid is circulated through the screw, it will help to reduce overall growth of the screw. But in the localized part of the screw, where heat is being generated, the temperature will still increase and the lead of the ball screw will change. Therefore, in the area of greatest interest (i.e., where machining is taking place), the ball screw still expands, and this change can quickly exceed the tolerances required for high performance machining.

Another weakness of many ball screw cooling systems is that they maintain the ball screw temperature relative to ambient. This means that as the room temperature changes, the temperature of the coolant changes too. If the coolant temperature varies, the temperature of the ball screw will change, as will its length. This is exactly what must be avoided. If a machine shop experiences a temperature swing of 10° F, and the coolant is controlled to within ±2° F of ambient, the ball screw temperature will change by as much as 14° F over the course of the day. Ball screw coolant systems also reduce the torsional and axial stiffness of the ball screw by hollowing out its center. Vibration can be induced in such screws because the bore through the screw is rarely straight. As a result, when the screw rotates at high speeds, an imbalance condition is created. Such oscillations may adversely affect surface finish, reduce ball screw life, and limit how aggressively the servo system can be tuned.

Of all the methods available for compensating for ball screw growth, the best is the use of linear scales. Because the linear scale measures actual position of each machine slide, the thermal growth of the screw becomes a nonissue. Linear scales eliminate all of the positioning error due to thermal growth in ball screws. No other solution provides as comprehensive a defense against ball screw growth. And, priced at or about $10,000 for a mid-sized VMC, linear scales are a cost-effective solution as well. When the aforementioned test was run on a high performance VMC with linear encoders, the variation in X-Y positioning was reduced to 0.0001" in X and 0.0002" in

Y.[8] This represents an 85% reduction in both X- and Y-axis ball screw growth.

Spindle Growth

The spindle is the most problematic source of thermal growth in a machine tool. On a typical general-purpose VMC, Z-axis growth in a belted 10,000 RPM CAT40 spindle can exceed 0.003". Less capable machines will exhibit growth of 0.005" or more. In addition to Z-axis growth, heat generated by the spindle can cause growth in other axes. On a VMC, Y-axis growth is most common, and can approach 0.001" for a belted 10,000 RPM spindle, depending upon the countermeasures employed. X-axis growth can also be experienced, but because VMCs are typically symmetric in the X-axis with respect to spindle center line, this effect is usually less significant.

Causes of Thermal Growth in Spindles

Spindle growth occurs because of inefficiencies within the spindle system. As the bearings rotate, heat is generated due to slipping between the balls and the races, and due to shearing of the grease or oil used to lubricate the bearings. Inefficiencies in the spindle motor, and in any transmission between the motor and spindle shaft, also generate heat. In belted spindles, heat is generated at the spindle bearings, the pulleys connecting the motor and spindle, and at the spindle motor itself (Figure 5-4). In geared spindles, heat is similarly generated at the bearings, spindle motor, and in the gearbox. The lower the effi-

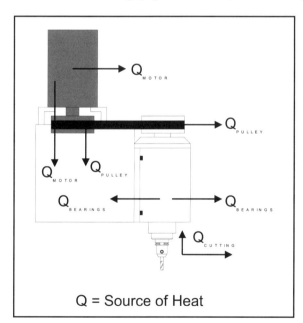

Figure 5-4:
Heat sources in a belted spindle assembly on a vertical machining center. Heat is transferred into the bolster casting and other machine subsystems, as well as the surrounding air.

---

[8] These measurements were made with a 50-millionths indicator, introducing a noteworthy component of measuring error.

ciency of converting motor power to power at the spindle, the higher the potential for thermal growth. In geared spindles, the transmission efficiency is typically about 70 to 80%, while belted spindles are approximately 90% efficient. Direct drive motorized spindles are totally efficient in this regard, as there are no power losses through transmission. Hydrostatic spindles, and spindles employing oil-jet lubrication, for example, are characterized by significantly higher losses in the bearings than in spindles using roller element bearings with grease or oil mist lubrication. This lost power is manifested as heat, and must be removed to prevent excessive thermal growth.

To understand the relationship between heat generation and thermal growth in a spindle, consider a belted spindle system, for which the transmission is 90% efficient. Assume also that the motor is 95% efficient and that the spindle bearings are 99% efficient.[9] The total amount of power generated as heat by this system is

$$q_{Heat} = [1 - (E_{motor} \cdot E_{belt} \cdot E_{spindle})] \cdot (\text{Input Power}) \ [HP]$$

$$q_{Heat} = 0.15 \cdot (\text{Input Power}).$$

If 20 HP is input to the system by the spindle drive, heat is generated at the rate of 3 HP [2.2 kW]. This rate of heat generation, if not removed from the machine tool, will cause significant amounts of thermal growth. For example, if the bolster casting of a VMC measures 20" along the Y-axis, and weighs 500 lb, the impact of dumping heat into the casting is approximated using the equations

$$\Delta T = r \cdot (q_{heat} \cdot B \cdot t)/(m \cdot c_p)$$

$$\Delta L_Y = \Delta T \cdot L_Y \cdot \alpha$$

where r is the percentage of heat which enters the casting rather than entering the air or being carried off by a cooling system, t is the time during which the heat is generated [hours], B is a conversion factor for HP·hours to Btu, m is the mass of the casting [lb], and c_p is the specific heat of cast iron.[10] Assuming that only 10% of the heat enters the bolster casting from the motor and spindle, and that this occurs for one hour, we calculate

$$\Delta T = r \cdot (q_{heat} \cdot t)/(m \cdot c_p)$$

$$\Delta T = 0.1 \cdot (3 \cdot 2545 \cdot 1)/(500 \cdot 0.1)$$

$$\Delta T = 15°F$$

$$\Delta L_Y = \Delta T \cdot L_Y \cdot \alpha$$

$$\Delta L_Y = 15° \text{ F} \cdot 20 \cdot 6.7E\text{-}6$$

$$\Delta L_Y = 0.002".$$

---

[9] Rolling element bearings exhibit very high efficiencies. However, depending upon the type of lubrication used, power losses can increase by several percentage points or more.
[10] One horsepower-hour equals 2545 Btu.

This simplified example illustrates the importance of removing as much of the heat generated in the spindle system as possible. Even when removing 90% of the heat created, significant thermal errors (0.002") resulted.

Characterizing Thermal Growth in Spindles

The amount of thermal growth in spindles varies significantly, depending upon the countermeasures employed to combat it. But, in all cases, spindle thermal growth shares a number of important characteristics.

Spindle growth varies directly with spindle speed. In most spindles, the amount of thermal growth increases proportionally with spindle speed. In other models, there will be significant growth at low speeds, followed by growth increases that are less than linear with increased spindle speed. Table 5-5 tabulates maximum Z-axis spindle growth for a range of refrigerated belted spindles at different speed ranges. Each of the spindles utilizes CAT40 tooling, and similar bearing diameters. Otherwise, spindle construction varies between each unit.

Spindle Characteristics				Z-axis Thermal Growth at Percentage of Maximum Speed [in]			
Spindle #	Max. Speed	Max. Power	Bearing Type	Lubrication	25%	50%	75%	100%
1	10,000	5 HP	Steel	Grease	0.001	0.0015	0.002	0.0023
2	10,000	15 HP	Steel	Grease	0.0003	0.0006	0.001	0.0015
3	12,000	15 HP	Hybrid Ceramic	Grease	0.0005	0.001	0.0014	0.0018
4	15,000	15 HP	Steel	Oil-mist	0.002	0.0016	0.0024	0.0038
5	15,000	15 HP	Hybrid Ceramic	Grease	0.0006	0.0014	0.002	0.0031

Table 5-5:
Maximum Z-axis spindle growth at various speed levels for a range of refrigerated high performance belted spindles.

The thermal growth curve for a specific spindle speed is exponential in nature. Regardless of the amount of growth, each curve for a particular spindle will have the same time constant. Figure 5-5 illustrates a family of exponential growth curves for spindle #1. Each pair of exponential growth and decay corresponds to 25%, 50%, 75%, and 100% of rated speed with the spindle being turned on and then off. These curves are very similar in form to those in Figure 5-2, and are guided by similar formulas. The curves in Figure 5-5 have a time constant of about 36 minutes. Therefore, to reach 95% of the final Z-axis growth value, 108 minutes (3τ) must elapse. This is a significant period of time, but is not unusual for a belted spindle. If this spindle is used for high precision work at 10,000 RPM, and tolerances of better than ±0.0005" are required in the Z-axis,

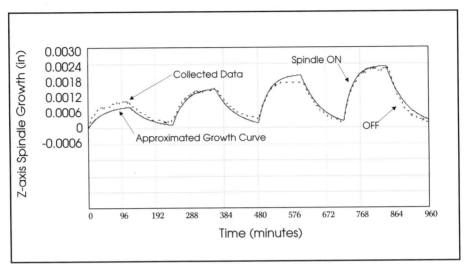

Figure 5-5:
Thermal growth data and the calculated growth curve for a 10,000 RPM, 5 HP belted milling spindle with refrigerated cooling. The data were collected for 25%, 50%, 75%, and 100% of maximum speed, and are displayed for each speed reading from left to right on the graph. The exponential nature of the growth can be seen when the spindle is turned on and off at each speed.

the user will have to warm the spindle up for about 70 minutes before machining commences.

The time constants, τ, for each spindle listed in Table 5-5 are identified in Table 5-6. For any change in the spindle speed, the spindle will grow 63% of the difference between its current growth state and the final state in time τ. It will grow 86% of the difference in 2τ, and 95% of the difference in 3τ. For example, consider spindle #5, running at 3,750 RPM (25% of max. speed) with a measured steady state Z-axis growth of 0.0006". If the speed is increased to 7,500 RPM, in 40 minutes spindle #5 will grow an additional 0.63·(0.0014" – 0.0006") more. Total Z-axis growth is now 0.0011". Similar effects govern the behavior of spindles when speed is reduced, or brought to zero RPM. It is important not only to consider the spindle's current speed when thinking about thermal growth, but also to consider the range of speeds used when producing precision parts. Variation in speed, whether up or down, will cause the spindle position to change.

Spindle #	Time Constant, τ [minutes]
1	36
2	27
3	41
4	44
5	40

Table 5-6:
Z-axis thermal growth time constants for spindles in Table 5-5.

Growth time constants can differ for each axis (X, Y, Z) because the structural geometry varies along each axis. The design of the cooling system also affects the spindle growth time constant. Each of these spindles used the same refrigeration unit and flow rate of cooling liquid, but the construction of the cooling jacket differed significantly between each spindle. Finally, each spindle was mounted to a different model machine. The machine structure acts as a heat sink, and its characteristics will affect the time constant of the spindle.

Motorized spindles also exhibit exponential growth curves. Table 5-7 identifies the thermal properties of two motorized spindles. Generally speaking, motorized spindles present additional problems with respect to thermal growth because the spindle motor is so close to the spindle shaft. Motor heat enters the shaft directly, despite the use of high power refrigeration units, because the spindle cooling jackets are located on the outside of the motor. This arrangement does not guard against heat moving radially inwards to the shaft. This effect is not as much of a problem with low HP units, such as those in Table 5-7. Both units provide very high speeds, but limited horsepower. Therefore, the amount of thermal growth is fairly limited. In larger motorized spindles, the integration of high power motors can lead to significant thermal growth — often beyond the acceptable limits for high performance machining. This is another reason to consider the use of main+auxiliary spindle pairs, as they can have better thermal properties.

Spindle Characteristics				Z-Axis Thermal Growth at Percentage of Maximum Speed [in]			
Spindle #	Max. Speed	Max. Power	Lubrication	τ, time constant [minutes]	25%	50%	75%	100%
6	25,000	8 HP	Grease	5.5	0.0001	0.00022	0.00038	0.0005
7	40,000	2.5 HP	Grease	2.5	0.0003	0.0007	0.001	0.0013

Table 5-7:
Z-axis spindle growth properties of a low- and moderate-power motorized spindle. Each spindle is outfitted with an absolute temperature refrigeration system to remove heat.

The spindles in Table 5-7 exhibit very short time constants relative to the heavier duty spindles in Table 5-5. Within 16.5 minutes, the 25,000 RPM spindle will have reached 95% of its final growth state at a given speed. The 40,000 RPM spindle only requires 7.5 minutes to approach 95% of its steady state Z-axis position. The benefits of small time constants such as these are that less time is required to "warmup" the spindle before use, and once the spindle is in the cut, variations in Z-axis position due to spindle thermal growth are less.[11]

In addition to Z-axis spindle growth, Y-axis spindle growth can also be an important error source. X-axis spindle growth, on the other hand, is usually mini-

---

[11] The thermal growth state of the spindle can change dramatically if the cutting loads change during a cut.

mal, as long as the machine structure and spindle housing is symmetrical. Table 5-8 compares Y-axis and Z-axis spindle growth at maximum operating speed for the spindles in Tables 5-5 and 5-7.

Spindle #	Max. Speed [RPM]	Z-Axis growth at Max. Speed [in]	Y-Axis growth at Max. Speed [in]	Y Growth as % of Z Growth
1	10,000	0.0032	0.0004	13%
2	10,000	0.0015	0.0006	40%
3	12,000	0.0018	0.0008	61%
4	15,000	0.0038	0.0013	34%
5	15,000	0.0031	0.0014	45%
6	25,000	0.0005	0.0003	60%
7	40,000	0.0013	0.0004	31%

Table 5-8:
Y-axis and Z-axis thermal growth compared at maximum spindle speed.

Combating Spindle Growth

To achieve tolerances of ±0.0005" to ±0.0002", very little thermal growth in the spindle can be tolerated. To prevent spindle growth from consuming the entire error budget of a machining process, active countermeasures are required. Simply warming up a spindle is insufficient to bring spindle growth within reasonable levels. As illustrated above, spindle growth varies significantly with speed. Therefore, when a machining process employs multiple speeds, warming up a spindle to a steady state condition will not prevent spindle growth from introducing significant inaccuracies. Warming up a spindle before use is still a good idea but, in and of itself, is insufficient to combat thermal growth.

Spindle Cooling

The most common method for reducing thermal growth in belted or geared spindles is to cool the spindle. A cooled liquid circulates around the spindle, and in some cases the spindle motor is within a sealed "water jacket." The water jacket can take on a number of forms — from a simple cavity at the rear of the spindle, to a series of channels which provide 360° coverage. The more comprehensive the water jacket, the better. Jackets which totally surround the spindle remove heat more effectively, and reduce the possibility of distorting the spindle housing due to thermal gradients.

The fluid running through the jacket is usually water based, with a rust-inhibiting additive. The simplest cooling systems route the fluid through a water-to-air heat exchanger after it exits the spindle jacket. The heat exchanger does not contain a secondary refrigeration circuit. The liquid is cooled to near room temperature as it flows through the heat exchanger, and then returns to a reservoir. A pump forces water out of the reservoir and back to the spindle. Figure 5-6 illustrates the elements of a heat exchanger based system.

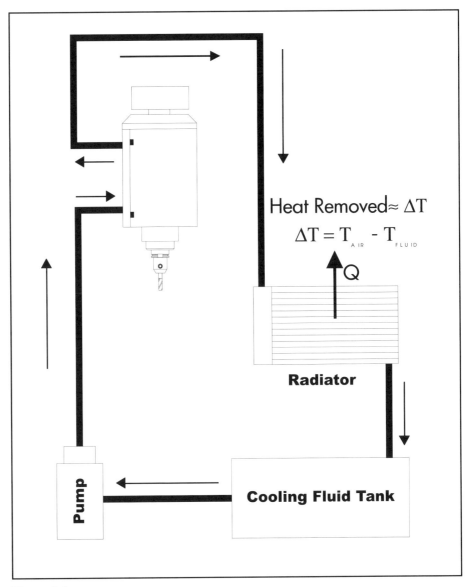

Heat Removed $\approx \Delta T$

$\Delta T = T_{AIR} - T_{FLUID}$

Q

Radiator

Pump

Cooling Fluid Tank

Figure 5-6:
Elements of a heat exchanger based spindle cooling system. Because the radiator uses room temperature air as a heat sink, the cooling capacity of the system, and therefore the spindle temperature, varies with changes in ambient temperature.

Heat exchanger based cooling systems possess a number of drawbacks. These systems exchange heat between the spindle and room temperature air. This is a problem because the amount of heat that can be removed per unit time, q, is a function of the temperature difference between the source (e.g., recirculating fluid) and sink (e.g., room temperature air). K is a constant that depends upon the properties of the fluid in the heat exchanger, and the air surrounding it.

$$q \approx K \cdot \Delta T \quad [\text{Btu/hr}]$$

$$q \approx K \cdot (T_{fluid} - T_{room}) \quad [\text{Btu/hr}]$$

The greater the temperature difference between the source and sink, the more heat can be removed. In warm shops, heat exchangers may be unable to remove all (or even most of) the heat generated by a hard-working spindle. Therefore, after the water passes through the heat exchanger and returns to the tank, it remains above room temperature. A second problem is that the temperature of the room varies with time. As a result, the amount of heat removed from the spindle varies, as does the steady state operating temperature of the spindle. Even if the spindle maintains a constant running speed, the amount of thermal growth in the spindle will change with variations in room temperature. Heat exchanger based cooling systems are inadequate for high performance machining for this reason, and also because the rate at which they remove heat from the spindle system is relatively low.

A significantly better type of cooling system replaces the water-to-air heat exchanger with a refrigeration unit. Heat is transferred from the fluid running through the spindle to liquid running in a separate refrigeration circuit. These systems work better than water-to-air heat exchangers for several reasons. First, refrigeration based systems have a higher capacity to remove heat. Rather than exchanging heat between fluid at 100° F and air at 68° F (a difference of 32° F), the temperature difference between the cooling water from the spindle and that in the refrigeration circuit can be much greater. This enables more heat to be removed in less time. Refrigeration systems respond more quickly to sudden changes in heat output by the spindle, and reduce the overall level of thermal growth. Second, a thermostat controls the coolant circulating through the spindle to a fixed *absolute* temperature. This is important because it eliminates changes in spindle growth due to variations in ambient temperature. The thermal state of the spindle becomes independent of room temperature.

Refrigeration-based cooling systems are found on almost all motorized spindles, particularly those where the motor is mounted inboard of the spindle bearings. High performance belted spindles also utilize these systems. Chiller systems should provide high flow rates and the ability to remove large quantities of heat quickly. This is often measured in terms of Watts or Btu/hour. To remove heat from the 15,000 RPM belted spindle (#5) in Table 5-5, and restrict its thermal growth to the values indicated, a 2.1 kW (7,160 Btu/hr) refrigeration system with a flow rate of one gallon per minute at 60 psi was used. For multiple spindle configurations, or higher power spindles, a higher power refrigeration system is often employed, and flow rates of up to four gallons per minute may be necessary.

The heat removal requirement for a chiller [Btu/hour] can be determined through experimentation by pumping fluid through the spindle and measuring the flow [gallons per hour] and temperature difference [°F] of the inlet and outlet fluid.

$$\text{Heat Removal Requirement} = \text{Flow} \cdot \text{Fluid Weight} \cdot c_p \cdot \Delta T \quad [\text{Btu/hour}]$$

$$\text{Fluid Weight} = 8.33 \text{ lb/gallon (for water)}$$

Tight control of spindle cooling fluid temperature is critical to minimize thermal variation and, therefore, growth. A fixed temperature should be maintained within ±2° F or better over the full operating range of the spindle. The aforementioned chiller maintained the output temperature within ±1° F as long as the amount of heat to be removed was within the rating of the chiller. A good way to evaluate the effectiveness of a chiller system is to measure the temperature of the fluid being pumped to the spindle as spindle RPM is brought from zero to full RPM. An under powered chiller will not be able to remove heat quickly enough as spindle speed increases, and will take longer to stabilize the temperature of the fluid.

Both of the chilling systems described above — water-to-air heat exchangers and refrigeration systems — are closed-loop systems. The cooling liquid runs from the spindle to a heat exchanger and tank, then back to the spindle. This is a must for high performance machining. Some machine tool builders, in an attempt to economize, combine the flood coolant and spindle chilling functions. Tool coolant is pumped from the flood tank into the water jacket surrounding the spindle, where it increases in temperature. From there it is sprayed onto the workpiece through coolant nozzles. The coolant then flows through the machine enclosure and back to the flood tank. These systems are inexpensive, but very ineffective. In addition to picking up heat from the spindle and dumping it onto the workpiece (causing thermal growth), they pick up additional heat as the coolant flows over the tool – work interface. This warm coolant is then pumped back through the spindle without running through a chiller. Systems of this nature have been reported to result in Z-axis spindle growth of over 0.005". When using a machine with such a system, it is highly recommended to decouple the flood coolant from the spindle chilling system. Purchase a refrigeration unit and modify the machine to create an independent spindle cooling system.

Spindle Preheat

An alternate means of controlling spindle temperature is to heat, rather than cool, the spindle. A thermostat controlled preheat unit pumps warm liquid through the spindle's water jacket, and through the surrounding machine elements, such as the bolster casting. Although these heating systems are not applicable to motorized spindles, they have been found to provide better stability than refrigeration systems for belted spindles.

Figure 5-7 illustrates elements of a preheat system used to control the temperature of the bolster casting and spindle. The recirculating fluid is heated to within a few degrees of the spindle's expected operating temperature. The fluid runs through the spindle housing as well as the bolster casting. This ensures that

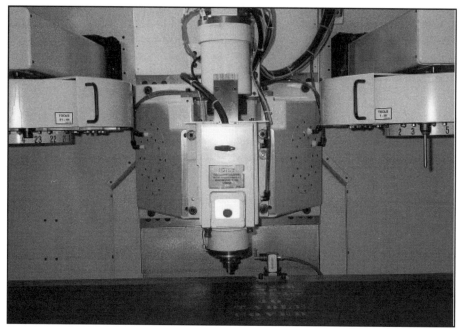

Figure 5-7:
Front view of a BostoMatic™ 40 (covers removed) illustrates the inlet and outlet lines for preheated liquid which runs through the bolster casting and spindle. Behind the round plates on the bolster are a series of channels that maximize the surface area exposed to the liquid, and thereby optimize heat transfer. The preheat system provides greater thermal stability than cooling systems for belted spindles. (Courtesy of Boston Digital Corporation.)

the bolster casting is also thermally stabilized and reduces Y-axis growth caused by heat from the spindle motor. The system is in operation 24 hours per day, 7 days per week. Table 5-9 compares the thermal growth of spindle #5 (Table 5-5), when outfitted with a refrigeration system versus a preheat system.

15,000 RPM 15 HP Belted Spindle, #5	Z-Axis Thermal Growth at Percentage of Maximum Speed [in]			
Temperature Control Method	τ, Time Constant [minutes]	25%	50%	75%	100%
Refrigeration	40	0.0006	0.0014	0.002	0.0031
Preheat	40	0.0004	0.0008	0.0012	0.002

Table 5-9:
Z-axis thermal growth of 15,000 RPM spindle (#5), temperature controlled using refrigeration versus preheat. (Courtesy of Boston Digital Corp.)

The preheat system is more effective because the spindle assembly is brought close to its thermal equilibrium before the spindle is turned on. The fact that the spindle will become warm is accepted because it is recognized that the temperature value is less important than the temperature remaining constant over time. Maintaining a temperature of 95° F, for example, is preferable to a spindle temperature that varies between 70° F and 85° F. It is better to have a hot but constant spindle temperature than a "cool" spindle with varying temperature.

CNC-Based Countermeasures

Even when using a preheat system on a belted spindle, or a refrigeration unit with a motorized spindle, thermal growth may exceed acceptable levels for high performance machining. To achieve tighter tolerances, CNC-based compensation is necessary. In some high performance machine tools, the CNC tracks the operation time of the spindle, and makes X-, Y-, and Z-axis corrections based on the initial state of the spindle, the spindle speed, and the time of operation. A well designed system predicts the spindle's growth state even if the machine is switched off and restarted. The bulk temperature of the column is also measured and a correction is made to the Z-axis position to compensate for any growth of the main structure that is not compensated by the glass scales.

On BostoMatics, the Therm-a-trol™ CNC-based compensation system combined with preheat typically reduces thermal errors to less than 0.001" TIR for the Z-axis, and 0.0005" TIR for the X- and Y-axes when employed with belted spindles running below 15,000 RPM. For motorized spindles, thermal growth is reduced to less than 0.0005" TIR in each axis. These results are maintained over a 24-hour period across the entire speed range of the spindle, including zero speed, regardless of the number of speed changes made. For most users, Therm-a-trol provides results significantly better than these specifications because: 1) part cycle times are less than 24 hours; 2) the entire speed range is not used on every part; and 3) most of the error in the system occurs during the first few seconds after the spindle is turned on or off. During this time the tool is rarely in the workpiece. With shorter cycle times, and limited speed changes, Therm-a-trol can reduce thermal growth in each axis to less than 0.0004". Figure 5-8 plots typical Z-axis error due to thermal growth in a 15,000 RPM belted preheated spindle with and without Therm-a-trol.

The Therm-a-trol system is also highly effective for main+auxiliary spindle arrangements and twin spindle machines. When employed with main+auxiliary spindles, a separate compensation algorithm is maintained for each spindle, and corrections made to each axis reflect the state of the spindle currently in use. On twin spindle machines, growth is significantly reduced compared to when only refrigeration or preheat is employed. But, because each spindle grows independently and they are both used at the same time, the thermal error correction is not as good as for single spindle or main+auxiliary spindle combinations.

In addition to reducing Z-axis thermal growth as evidenced in Figure 5-8, Therm-a-trol significantly reduces X- and Y-axis growth. A BostoMatic 32G machining center with an 8 HP, 25,000 RPM spindle, linear scales, and Therm-a-trol yielded X-axis and Y-axis drift of only 0.0002" and 0.0004", respectively, over a 24-hour period. These results were achieved while running a customer's

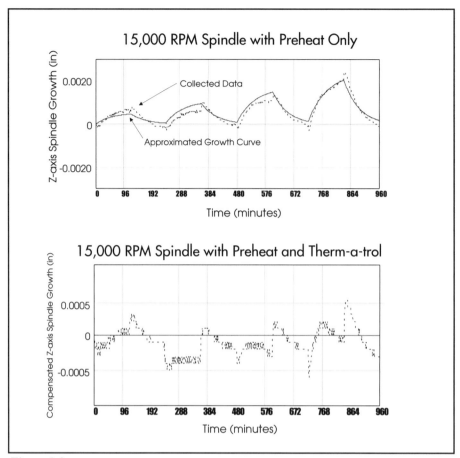

Figure 5-8:
Thermal growth in a 15,000 RPM belted spindle with preheat is compared to the same system with preheat and CNC-based thermal growth compensation (Therm-a-trol™). The use of Therm-a-trol cuts the level of growth by 50%. The "jumps" observed in the Therm-a-trol data occur immediately after the spindle is turned on or off, and occur due to imperfections in the algorithm used in the CNC. The jumps do not affect overall accuracy because the spindle is not in the part during this period, which is less than one second upon startup or shutdown of the spindle. With only refrigeration, this spindle exhibits a maximum thermal growth of 0.0031". (Courtesy of Boston Digital Corporation.)

part program, which contained significant variations in axis feed rate and spindle speed. Given the amount of axis drift encountered on a linear encoder machine with the spindle off (see above), this is an excellent result.

Even with Therm-a-trol, total thermal errors exceeding 0.0005" can accumulate in each axis, particularly when using high power spindles. To further reduce positioning errors due to spindle thermal growth, variability in the machining process must be eliminated. Spindle speeds must be constant, and cutting loads should be relatively stable. When spindle speeds vary widely throughout a part program, achieving Z-axis tolerances of ±0.0002" is nearly impossible, and ±0.0005" is very difficult. After accounting for thermal growth in the spindle, very little of the tolerance band is left to accommodate other error sources such as tool runout, servo lag, and geometric inaccuracies.

Effects of Tool Coolant

Machining without the use of flood coolant has recently become very popular. Contaminated waste liquid is eliminated, and chips don't have to be dried before disposal. But since the use of flood coolant and high pressure coolant-through-spindle (CTS) is still widely used, its impact upon thermal stability must be considered in the context of high performance machining.

Oil- or water-based coolants are used to lubricate the cutting process and to remove chips and heat from the work zone. Because the coolant washes over the part and the interior of the machine tool, it causes temperature variations. These variations are highly localized, and therefore can lead to distortion of the machine geometry. When utilizing flood coolant or CTS, a number of guidelines must be followed to ensure that tight part tolerances are achieved.

Flood coolant should not be used to cool the spindle. The flood system must be dedicated to its purpose: to remove heat and chips from the tool – work interface. If the coolant system is also used to remove heat from the spindle, its temperature will vary considerably. This in turn will introduce thermal growth in the part.

The flow of coolant across the part should be constant, both in terms of flow rate and coverage of the part. The ability of a liquid to add or remove heat when moving over a surface increases with higher flow rates. If the flow rate of the coolant varies significantly during a machining operation, or if it only flows across a section of the part, a nonuniform temperature field will arise. This leads to uneven thermal growth and distortion. When possible, use a high volume of coolant which bathes the entire part. This helps ensure that the part quickly achieves a uniform temperature, and that the temperature is maintained over time.

Ensure that the flood pump does not add significant heat to the flood coolant. Pumps heat the coolant when pumping it to the work area, and they also generate significant heat when recirculating the coolant to tank. Some machines are configured so that the flood pump runs continuously. When the flood coolant is "off," the pump circulates the coolant directly back to the flood tank. This continuous pumping to and from the tank dumps heat into the coolant, and raises its temperature significantly. Seek efficient pumps that add minimal heat to the coolant. If possible, allow the pump to shut down when the coolant is turned off.

Carefully manage the temperature of the coolant in the flood tank. Several steps can be taken to stabilize the temperature of the flood coolant. First, the tank should have a large capacity. The bigger the tank, the more time the coolant will have to equilibrate its temperature after returning from the work area. A large tank allows some of the heat picked up from the cutting process to be radiated or conducted away from the coolant. It also reduces the magnitude of changes to the coolant temperature because the thermal mass is higher. If the tank is too small, the coolant can change temperature rather quickly, leading to inaccuracy in the part. When adding liquid to the coolant tank, make sure that its temperature is close to that of the fluid already in the tank. A high performance machine shop making small medical molds was controlling the temperature of their machining area to within ±2° F to help achieve part tolerances of ±0.0002". Every few weeks they would produce a batch of parts which were out of tolerance. It was eventually discovered that the shop refilled the flood tank with cold water directly from a tap, which was 20° F colder than both the coolant in the tank and the temperature of the room. The cold coolant ran over the parts and machine table, causing significant thermal distortion. Once this problem was discovered the shop developed a procedure whereby they would run water from the tap into a 55-gallon drum. The drum would then sit next to the machine until its temperature matched that of the tightly controlled room. Only then would the water be poured into the flood tank. The periodic loss of accuracy was eliminated.

If seeking machining tolerances better than ±0.0005" while employing flood coolant or CTS, a temperature control unit for the flood system is highly recommended. Well-designed systems share many characteristics with the spindle refrigeration or preheat units described above, although separate units should be used for the spindle and flood coolant. Ensure that the system has enough cooling power to remove heat from the flood coolant, and that an absolute temperature is maintained via a thermostat. If large amounts of coolant are to be used during the machining process, it is a good idea to run the coolant system prior to machining to ensure that the liquid, and the surfaces it comes into contact with, are brought to a state of thermal equilibrium. Again, controlling the flood coolant to 68° F (20° C) is a good practice.

When using chilled air or air-oil mist systems in lieu of flood, similar precautions are required. Chilled air systems have the potential to create significant temperature changes on the surface of the workpiece and in the tool, and shops should test the effects of such units before attempting to achieve tight tolerances when using them. Fortunately, both types of systems are much more localized in their application than flood coolant. Relative to flood coolant, they are less likely to cause distortion to machine structures or workpieces, unless the parts are small and contain very thin cross sections.

Other Sources of Thermal Growth

The primary sources of thermal growth have been discussed. A number of secondary sources should also be considered when seeking to fully optimize machine performance.

Most machine tools contain a large number of heat generating devices. Each axis contains a servo motor. Tool changers also contain motors, whether they are electric or hydraulic. Hydraulic or pneumatic cylinders are sometimes used as counterbalances. Hydraulic pumps are used to activate spindle drawbars, and/or fixturing. High intensity work lights illuminate the work area. A large number of electronic devices, from servo drives to CRT's, are also contained within the machine's electric cabinet and CNC panel. Transformers are used to condition incoming power to meet machine requirements.

Each of these devices radiates or conducts heat into the machine tool. To minimize the negative effects of these heat sources, they should be isolated from the machine tool structure. Motors should not be embedded deep within the machine. Transformers and electric cabinets should be mounted to the machine structure to provide an insulating air gap which reduces heat transfer into the machine column and base. Hydraulic pumps should also be mounted on stand-offs, or packaged independently of the machine altogether. Air should be allowed to flow across heat generating devices, and the vertical space above heat sources should be open so that warm air flowing upwards doesn't distort other machine elements or become trapped in a structural cavity. If a heat generating unit must be mounted in close proximity to a thermally sensitive subassembly, insulation should be used to deflect heat away from the area of concern.

Unfortunately, these common sense measures run counter to the trend of creating highly compact machine tools. To minimize floor space requirements, most machines are packaged so that all hydraulic, pneumatic, and electric subsystems are contained within a sheet metal skin. This has the undesirable effect of trapping heat near the machine structure. This can lead to thermal growth in the machine, or at least the need to actively cool these areas with heat exchangers or refrigeration units, adding cost to the machine. Although machines which shroud everything in sheet metal are more aesthetically pleasing, such measures make good thermal control more difficult, particularly when heat sources are mounted directly to the machine structure and contained within compact sheet metal enclosures with minimal air circulation. When evaluating machines for high performance applications, resist the urge to buy the best looking machine. Instead, focus on the design which provides the best functionality. After all, "form follows function."

Importance of Machine Warm-up Cycles

Thermal effects take time to occur. Minimizing their impact requires that machines be exercised prior to use. No matter how sophisticated a machine's thermal countermeasures, warming up a machine before use further reduces the magnitude of thermal errors.

Of primary importance is the spindle. It should be warmed up at or near the expected operating speed long enough to ensure that subsequent thermal growth represents only a fraction of the total tolerance band available. Many machine tools offer "Auto On" features which allow the CNC to turn on the spindle at a set time. Before the machinist arrives at work, the machine can turn on the spindle to warm it up.[12] Although safety requirements often preclude the unattended initiation of axis motion, running a typical program "in air" prior to machining is another good way to bring the machine closer to a state of thermal equilibrium.

When warming up a machine, seek to exercise all relevant subsystems as

---

[12] Such features require full enclosures and safety interlocks to meet safety requirements.

they would be used in production. If many tool changes are going to be performed, exercise the tool changer; if flood coolant is going to be run, turn it on too; if the part and fixture can be placed in the machine during the warm-up period, do so. All tool and part setups should be finalized after the machine has warmed up. Otherwise, much of the benefit of warming up the machine is lost.

Often, shops warm up their machines at maximum speed and feed. If these are higher than the values to be used during machining, such a warm up cycle is detrimental to achieving high performance. Running a machine at speeds and feeds higher than necessary brings the machine to an elevated temperature. Once the parts are set up and machining begins, the machine tool will cool down and generate thermal errors. A machine that is cooling down during production is as problematic as one that is warming up. The key is to maintain a constant absolute temperature whenever possible.

Multispindle Considerations

Twin spindle machines present unique challenges in terms of thermal growth. Each spindle generates heat that is dumped into the bolster casting. As the bolster temperature rises, the center distance between the spindles increases. Unfortunately, no correction can be made for variations in spindle centerline on a twin (or triple, etc.) spindle machine because the spindles move in opposite directions along the X-axis (Figure 5-9). Also, slight differences in growth between the spindles in the Y- or Z-axes means that one will be compensated for better than the other.

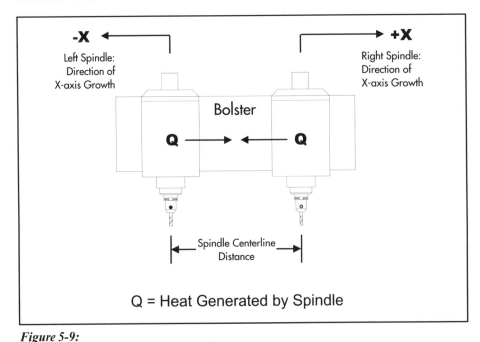

Figure 5-9:
Twin spindle machines cannot easily compensate for thermal growth. As heat is dumped into the bolster casting by each spindle, the distance between spindle centerlines will change. This cannot be automatically corrected for without an additional servo axis.

These difficulties reduce the effectiveness of CNC-based compensation systems for machines where multiple spindles are cutting simultaneously. These problems do not occur on main+auxiliary spindle machines because only one spindle is cutting at any given time. Therefore, there is only one component of growth in each axis. By contrast, a six spindle machine will have six slightly different growth patterns in the X-, Y-, and Z-axes. To compensate for each effectively, CNC-controlled 3-axis slides with a few thousandths of an inch of travel would be required for each spindle. This would be an extraordinarily expensive approach, as it would effectively create an 18-axis machine!

The inability to compensate for growth in each spindle independently, either through the CNC or via heating or cooling, reduces the accuracy achievable with multispindle machine tools. A realistic high performance tolerance band for twin spindle machines is between ±0.0005" and ±0.001". Achieving ±0.0005" tolerances requires the use of tools of practically identical length and diameter, and requires meticulous care when setting up the tools and fixtures. Tolerances of ±0.002" are more readily achieved, but even here significant attention to detail is required. To achieve tolerances better than ±0.002" with multiple belted spindles, spindle preheat is an absolute necessity. Only by preheating the bolster can the change in centerline distance be kept to reasonable levels. A 10,000 RPM twin spindle VMC utilizing spindle preheat and Therm-a-trol underwent a 0.0004" change in spindle centerline along the X-axis. Using only refrigeration, a similar machine exhibited a change of 0.001" in the X-axis distance between centerlines.

5-Axis Considerations

Thermal growth in 5-axis applications is very similar to that in 3- or 4-axis environments. The most significant difference is that with 5-axis applications, the problem of geometric distortion is more acute and harder to correct for. If angular errors in the spindle, rotaries, or other machine elements are created due to thermal growth, the impact upon accuracy can be profound. Therefore, sound structural design is even more important.

5-axis designs which utilize asymmetric geometries will tend to bend and grow when the temperature increases. For example, consider the double-rotary design illustrated in Figure 5-10. As the A- and C-axes operate, heat is being generated in each gear set. This heat migrates into the support arm, creating a nonuniform temperature field. As a result, the arm will not only change size, it will change shape. This deformation causes angular errors in the workpiece, and these errors will be magnified with increasing distance between the tool – work interface and the sources of angular error.

To provide the necessary work envelope and part access, large overhangs and structural extensions are often required in 5-axis machines. These factors exacerbate the effect of temperature variations relative to simpler 3- and 4-axis designs. To minimize the impact of temperature change upon the accuracy of 5-axis machine tools, it is again important to provide an environment controlled to a fixed temperature. Furthermore, seek 5-axis machines that minimize the dis-

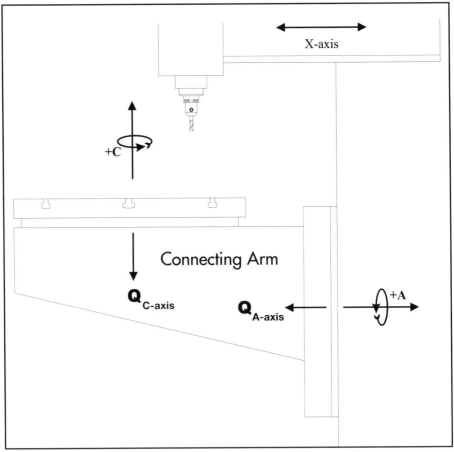

Figure 5-10:
As heat is dumped into the connecting arm between the A- and C-axes of this 5-axis VMC, the arm experiences thermal gradients. These gradients cause the arm to distort.

tance between the tool tip and centers of rotation. The greater the distance between the end of the tool and the rotating axes, the larger the errors due to temperature changes. For the same change in temperature, a 5-axis machine which locates the tool 1" from the center of rotation will experience only 10% of the thermal error of a mill where the pivot point is 10" away from the tool tip.

Chapter 6

Part Processing

Overview

"GIGO" — garbage in, garbage out — is a popular adage most often applied to computers and computer programming, but it applies equally well to machining. A high performance machine tool is only as good as the part process applied to it. This chapter discusses the factors that should be considered when developing part processes for use with high performance machine tools, as compared to general purpose machinery. Recent developments pertinent to high performance machining are also explored.

This discussion also applies to the migration of machining processes from general purpose to high performance machines. One of the greatest impediments to realizing the full benefit of high performance machine tools is an unwillingness, or inability, to design machining processes that fully utilize the capabilities of the machines. Too often, part programs, tooling, and fixturing are simply moved from existing, less capable, equipment to new machine tools. Dissatisfaction with the new machine tool's performance is the inevitable result.

To maximize profitability with today's high performance machine tools, part processing methods must be given more attention than when working with general purpose machine tools. Although this requires heightened attention to detail, highly refined process knowledge is a machine shop's most significant and defensible source of competitive advantage. Other shops can buy the same equipment, the same CAM systems, and the same tooling. But, they cannot as easily replicate specific part processing practice.

Tooling Selection & Application

Selecting the right tooling for the job is an increasingly complex process. The range of available cutter geometries and coatings is mind boggling, with new offerings constantly being introduced. Often, people respond to seemingly overwhelming choice by "sticking to what they know." Unfortunately, this usually means "sticking one's head in the sand." Constant experimentation with new cutter geometries and coatings is a must for the high performance machine shop. Although one cannot test every cutter on the market, time must be allotted for investigating the benefits of new cutter technology. Cutter manufacturers are often willing to provide free sample cutters, and high performance machine shops must take advantage of this resource.

When comparing cutters, it is important to design meaningful experiments. Don't change more than one variable at a time, and test each cutter under conditions that are as controlled as possible. Most shops test cutters by swapping them into a specific part process in lieu of an existing cutter. This does little more than prove whether the cutter works better or worse for the specific job in question. Although this is okay if the goal is only to optimize machining of a specific part, it can lead to a wide range of cutter types being used in the shop, which results in increased operating costs and inventory. The goal when testing cutters is to arrive at a more general conclusion which can be applied across a range of parts. This is necessary to keep tool inventories and costs in control, and it helps minimize change over time from one job to the next. If a machine can be loaded with a range of cutters that apply to many jobs, less operator intervention is required between jobs to change over the tools.

When first evaluating a cutter, the best tests are the simplest. Cutting straight slots through a material allows comparison of surface finish, cutter wear as a function of distance machined, and achievable surface speeds (SFM) and chip load values. Cutting 2D arcs measures the cutter's ability to withstand varying chip load. After a cutter's general characteristics are established, shops should develop a limited range of test parts that simulate the work performed in the shop. These test parts should be used repeatedly to compare the performance of different cutters under more "realistic" conditions. This approach is well suited to shops producing low quantities of parts, such as mold and die producers. In high volume machining operations it obviously makes sense to optimize cutter selection, and to perform testing, on the actual part in question.

It is important when performing cutter tests to minimize the number of variables that are changed at one time. If cutter 'A' is tested on part 'A,' with tool holder 'A,' on machine 'A,' then cutter 'B' should also be tested with the identical part, tool holder, and machine configuration. To do otherwise introduces significant uncertainty into the test process. For more comprehensive testing, orthogonal experiment design can be used to modify multiple factors at the same time while establishing causality between the experiment's variables and outputs.[1] This can significantly reduce the number of experiments required to determine the best combination of cutting parameters, resulting in savings of both time and money. Unless using an experimental design which allows multiple parameters (e.g., speed, depth of cut, feed rate, lubrication, etc.) to be varied simultaneously, *never* vary more than one parameter at a time. Varying multiple parameters simultaneously makes it almost impossible to identify the optimal cutting parameters, and often leads to significantly worse cutter performance.

Many shops maintain that they can't test cutters because they produce a wide range of parts in low quantities using many different materials. This is a good sign that a shop is not focused enough in its work. To be competitive in

---

[1] A good book on this subject is <u>Taguchi Techniques for Quality Engineering</u> by Phillip J. Ross, McGraw Hill Publishing Co., New York, 1988.

high performance machining, a shop must develop a focused skill set. A shop that machines an overly wide range of components will find itself unable to compete with shops which are more specialized, and can therefore perform the necessary testing and process development.

HSK Tooling

As discussed in Chapter 4, HSK tooling can provide significant benefits. In the larger sizes it is stiffer, provides lower runout, and is highly repeatable. Most shops do not possess large stocks of HSK tooling, which is a further incentive to use it, rather than a disincentive. The unique nature of the tooling will ensure that the high performance machine tool does not end up using well-worn or unbalanced tools from conventional machines. It also prevents the HSK tooling from drifting off into other areas of the shop.

If considering the use of HSK tooling in sizes smaller than HSK40, carefully evaluate the stiffness of the spindle and holder by performing test cuts. Tests performed at Boston Digital indicate that steep taper tooling such as 20 or 25 taper can provide better surface finishes than equivalent size HSK holders.[2]

Tool Clamping

The most common method for clamping tools in tool holders is to use a collapsible collet. Tightening a nut collapses the collet around the tool, exerting pressure that clamps the tool into place. Conventional collets are adequate for general purpose use and many roughing and semi-finishing operations in high performance machining, and they are both cost effective and flexible. A range of different collets can be used in the same tool holder to retain tool shanks of various diameters. A very high quality collapsible collet can provide runout as low as 0.0003" approximately 1" from the face of the tool holder. To achieve such results, a high quality holder must be used, and the collet must be manually adjusted relative to the tool holder to adjust for errors in the collet bore, collet taper, and tool holder taper. When selecting collets it is important to carefully evaluate the tolerances to which they are manufactured. Otherwise, significantly higher runout values will be experienced.

Unfortunately, collapsible collets are not sufficiently stiff or accurate for many high performance machining operations. In such cases, hydraulic and heat-shrink tool holding technologies are recommended. Both provide superior accuracy and stiffness relative to conventional tool holding systems. Figure 6-1 illustrates a cut-away view of a hydraulic expansion chuck. An oil chamber surrounds an expansion sleeve, and a set screw is turned to force the piston and seal against the hydraulic fluid. This forces the fluid into the chamber, compressing the expansion sleeve under extremely high pressure. The oil chamber is designed to equally distribute pressure in this enclosed system. Because the system is totally sealed-off from the environment, contamination of the clamping

---

[2] Refer to Chapter 4.

Figure 6-1:
Cut-away view of hydraulic tool holder. Hydraulic tool holders provide very high tool clamping forces and low runout. (Courtesy of Schunk Inc.)

mechanism is not susceptible to the penetration of grease, chips, or other contaminants.

Hydraulic tool clamping minimizes runout of the tool relative to the tool holder. Schunk Tendo chucks, for example, provide runout of less than 0.00012" TIR measured a distance two-and-a-half times the cutter diameter from the end of the holder. This degree of runout ensures a more uniform chip load on the cutting tool that extends tool life and improves surface finish. To accommodate tools of varying diameters, intermediary sleeves can be used between the tool holder and the tool. The sleeves will typically introduce an additional 0.00008" of runout to the system as a whole.[3] In comparison, the best conventional collets will provide runout of approximately 0.0003" TIR. Less accurate collet designs exhibit runout values of 0.0005" at the tool holder nose, and as much as 0.0025" measured 4" from the end of the tool holder.

While it is possible to obtain low runouts with conventional solid tool holders, the combination of accuracy and stiffness obtained with hydraulic tool holders cannot be matched by conventional means. Very high cutting loads are supported by hydraulic tool holders. For example, a Schunk holder with a 1" clamping diameter supports lateral forces on the tool of 2,240 lb·f at the end of the holder, and 1,450 lb·f two inches from the end of the holder. This same holder accommodates an applied cutting torque of up to 195 ft·lb.

The principal drawback of hydraulic tool holders is their cost. A CAT40 hydraulic expansion chuck can cost as much as five times more than a conventional chuck. Given this significant difference in cost, it is not practical for most

---

[3] Schunk Precision Workholding Systems catalog number 9707.

shops to exclusively use hydraulic tool holders. It is wise to employ them first in finishing operations, and then work backwards to semi-finish and finally roughing operations. A point of diminishing returns may be found such that conventional tool holders will be adequate for many roughing or semi-finish operations. In difficult machining operations such as hard die milling, where the cutters are highly susceptible to breaking due to unbalanced cutting loads, hydraulic tool holders are recommended for use in all process steps for optimal results.

An alternative technology to hydraulic tool holders is heat-shrink tooling. Unlike the hydraulic holders, there is no mechanism internal to the tool holder to provide clamping pressure. Instead, the tool holder is simply solid, with a precision bore to accept the tool. At room temperature, the holder bore is smaller than the tool shank diameter it is meant to accept. Using an induction heater, the tool holder is heated, causing it to expand. The tool is then inserted into the holder. As the holder cools, very high pressures are exerted on the tool, clamping it securely in place. Like hydraulic tool holders, heat-shrink tooling provides excellent runout and stiffness. The heat shrink holders are also simpler and less expensive to produce because there are no internal chambers for hydraulic fluid. But, an additional piece of hardware, the induction heater, is required to clamp and unclamp tools from the holder. A significant benefit of heat shrink tool holders is that they can be perfectly symmetric. No set screws are needed to actuate a hydraulic cylinder or to otherwise clamp a tool, making it possible to manufacture these tool holders (excluding imbalance due to tooling) to a very low level of imbalance.

A word of caution – the performance of both heat-shrink and hydraulic tool holders depends upon the accuracy of the tool shank and the operating temperature during machining. In the case of hydraulic holders, if the shank diameter is less than nominal by more than 0.001"× tool diameter, stiffness will be compromised. And, if the temperature during operation exceeds 120° F, the integrity of the holder may be compromised.[4] Similar effects govern the behavior of heat shrink tooling. Because thermal contraction is used to secure the tools, further sensitivity to elevated operating temperatures should be expected. As temperatures increase, the amount of clamping pressure can decrease.

Tool Balancing

It is generally accepted that for high spindle speeds, balanced tooling is necessary to achieve good surface finishes and to extend tool life. But, the speed and other conditions at which balancing becomes a necessity are less well understood.[5]

---

[4] For applications where the operating temperature is expected to exceed 100° – 120° F for extended periods, hydraulic holder manufacturers can produce special holders with less hydraulic fluid in the reservoir.

[5] This section draws upon two articles; "Should You Balance Your Tools?" by Peter Zelinski in *Modern Machine Shop* (1997), and "Balanced Toolholding for High Speed Machining" by James Zelinger in *Modern Machine Shop* (1989).

Balancing seeks to rectify the adverse effects of tool eccentricity. Eccentricity is the extent to which a tool's mass is off-center, defined as the distance between the axis of rotation of the tool and the tool's center of mass. The balance of a tool is defined in terms of the amount of mass multiplied by the eccentricity. Common units are "gram-millimeters."[6] Therefore, a tool with an unbalance rating of 5 g·mm, can be thought of as having a 5 gram [0.011 lb] mass attached to an otherwise perfectly balanced tool a distance of 1 mm [0.04"] from the center of rotation. An identical unbalance rating would be realized if a 1 gram weight was attached 5 mm from the center of rotation.

The presence of any asymmetric features on the tool holder contributes to a tool's imbalance. Keyways that are not absolutely identical will cause imbalance, as will set screws for affixing tools. Slight dimensional variations in the tool holder can also cause its center of mass to deviate from the center of rotation. This does not mean that the tool holder has been improperly manufactured. Like all mechanical parts, the features on a tool holder are produced to specific tolerances. Even if these tolerance bands are achieved, slight shifts in position due to dimensions that stray from nominal can cause imbalance.

Other sources of imbalance are the cutting tools and collets used in the tool holders. When a balanced tool holder is purchased, the balance is usually achieved without the tool or collet. When these are added, the presence of tool runout or eccentricity generates additional imbalance. The heavier and longer the tool, the greater the contribution to imbalance is likely to be. A single point boring bar, for example, can generate significant imbalance because it is intrinsically asymmetric. Without the use of specialized tools, such as Nikken's high speed balanced boring heads, imbalance is introduced (Figure 6-2).

Figure 6-2:
ZMAC boring heads from Nikken provide fine balancing, enabling operation up to 12,000 RPM. (Courtesy of Heartech Precision Inc.)

---

[6] 1 g·mm = 0.00008 lbm·in

Imbalance in and of itself does not inherently cause problems. It is the combination of imbalance and speed that applies vibratory forces to the machine, cutter, and workpiece. These forces result in decreased tool life, accelerated wear and tear on the machine tool (particularly the spindle), and degradation of part surface finish. The forces caused by imbalance in a tool holder are defined by the equation

$$F_{imbalance} = U \cdot (S/20140)^2 \text{ [lb·f]}$$

where U is the amount of imbalance [g·mm], and S is the spindle speed [RPM].[7] Figure 6-3 illustrates the amount of force experienced due to various levels of imbalance with increasing speed. The rapid increase of $F_{imbalance}$ with spindle speed in Figure 6-3 is clear. If a holder/tool combination has an imbalance of 4 g·mm or 8 g·mm, the amount of imbalance force can be significant relative to the cutting force, particularly when finishing.

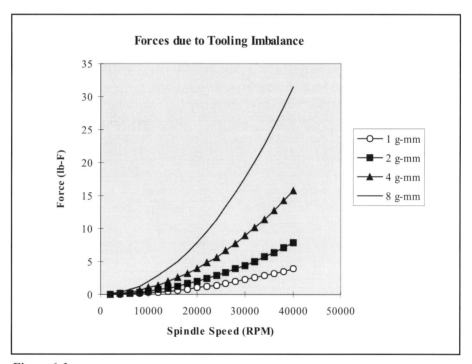

Figure 6-3:
Vibratory forces as a function of spindle speed are graphed for a variety of out-of-balance conditions. The force level increases as the square of spindle speed.

It is recommended that the force due to tool imbalance, $F_{imbalance}$, be maintained below the cutting force. If a milling operation is going to generate a periodic cutting force of 25 lb·f, a very safe rule of thumb is to restrict $F_{imbalance}$ to

---

[7] Although it is usually bad form to mix metric and English units, imbalance is usually represented in metric units, and so we make an exception here.

6 lb·f, or about 25% of the cutting force. To restrict the value of $F_{imbalance}$ to 10% or even 5% of the cutting force is to go past the point of diminishing returns.

Today, the most widely accepted standard for establishing tool balance is ISO1940-1. This standard identifies "G-class" values. The lower the G-class number, the better the balance. Many producers of balanced tooling, seeking to establish a definitive yardstick, produce tool holders to G2.5 or G1.0 class. The G-class value dictates the maximum acceptable imbalance using the formula

$$U = (4333 \cdot m \cdot G) / S \ [g \cdot mm]$$

where U is the acceptable imbalance in g·mm, m is the mass of the tool assembly, G is the G-rating from ISO1940-1, and S is the spindle speed in RPM. Unfortunately, this standard, which was developed for balancing turbine rotors, is overly stringent for many machining applications. Consider a 5 lb holder/ tool assembly rotating at 15,000 RPM. To meet the G2.5 specification, the maximum permitted imbalance is 3.6 g·mm.[8] Calculating $F_{imbalance}$, this corresponds to a force of only 2 lb·f. Given that the cutting force is likely to exceed 50 lb·f, this level of balance is probably overly aggressive. If G1 balance were specified, the maximum acceptable imbalance would decrease to 1.44 g·mm.

Another problem with the ISO1940-1 standard is that it allows increased imbalance, U, for heavier tools. Experiments carried out by Sandvik Coromant indicate that the amount of imbalance that can be accommodated *decreases* with heavier tools. This directly contradicts the requirements of ISO1940-1 and suggests that tool balance requirements will be unrealistic if G-classes are used to define them.

That G-class specifications are overly restrictive is good news for the high performance machine shop, because achieving G2.5 or G1 balance in practice is very expensive. First, expensive tool holders, balanced to these standards, must be purchased. Then the entire tool assembly (holder + collet + tool) must be balanced by the user. Otherwise, the amount of imbalance introduced by the tool, collet, and any runout in the system will quickly exceed the G-class requirements. This would require the high performance machine shop to own a dynamic balancing machine.

Given that the use of G-classes may dictate tighter balance requirements and more expensive tooling than necessary for high performance machining, what guidelines should be used? If the cutting forces can be calculated, try and ensure that $F_{imbalance}$ remains well below these levels. Experimentation is the best way to determine what level of balance is acceptable. As when evaluating different cutters, perform test cuts at various levels of imbalance. Start with 20 g·mm and reduce the imbalance until acceptable surface finish and tool wear are achieved. If such testing is impractical and the cutting forces are unknown, it is likely that below 20,000 RPM up to 20 g·mm of imbalance will be acceptable. At higher spindle speeds, or when optimal surface finish is required

---

[8] This is equivalent to taking a stick of chewing gum (2.7g) and sticking it on a tool holder only 0.052" from the center of rotation. In other words, it doesn't take much to get 3.6 g·mm of unbalance!

at lower speeds, 5 g·mm of imbalance will prove adequate for most applications. To help minimize imbalance, use these steps: minimize tool runout, use short tools whenever possible to reduce weight, and handle all tooling carefully. Dings and nicks can also contribute to an out-of-balance condition.

Minimize Tool Extensions at all Times

Although minimizing tool length may seem like an obvious thing to do, its importance nonetheless warrants mention. The overall length between spindle gauge line and the tool tip should be minimized for a number of reasons. First, stiffness drops quickly with increased tool length. The stiffness of a cylindrical beam of constant cross section in bending and torsion is

$$K_{bending} \approx D^2 / L^3$$

$$K_{torsion} \approx D^4 / L$$

where D is the diameter of the beam, and L is its length. Clearly, the longer the tool, the less stiff it will be. If the length of a tool holder/tool assembly is doubled, its stiffness in bending will drop by at least a factor of eight, while its torsional stiffness will drop by 50% or more, depending on whether the tool holder is tapered or not. The above relationships for stiffness indicate that increased tool length can be compensated for by using larger tool and tool holder diameters. While this is true, larger tool diameters create other problems such as restricting clearance to small cavities and introducing greater imbalance. Longer tool holders also introduce additional runout. Increased runout reduces the accuracy of the parts produced, and leads to accelerated tool wear by inducing vibration. Runout will generally increase linearly with extension from gauge line.

Tool Tolerances

High performance machining ideally seeks tolerances of ±0.0002" to ±0.0005" on 3D contours. It is therefore important that the tolerances on tooling be held to relatively tight figures as well.

For milling, diameter tolerances are of greatest concern. Length is set on the machine or on a measuring device, and can be adjusted for in the CNC. Diameter, on the other hand, is manufactured into the tool itself. For end mills, the diameter of the cutter must be consistent along the entire flute length so that an accurate wall is produced without taper when side milling.

The actual diameter value of the end mill is not very important. Cutter diameter compensation allows the CNC to compensate for the cutter's actual size. But, because the CNC can only adjust for a single diameter value, variation in the diameter along the length of the tool will introduce errors into the machining process. Common end mills are manufactured to diameter tolerances of no better than +0, -0.002" for larger tool diameters, and +0, -0.001" for smaller diameters. As a result, it is possible to consume the entire tolerance band for a high precision part when using such tools. To achieve high performance tolerances, specialized tools ground to a higher degree of precision must be used, particularly in finishing operations. Such tools can be purchased with diameter tolerances held to +0, -0.0002".

Of greater concern is the diameter tolerance on ball end mills. When machining 3D contours, the ball end mill will cut with various portions of its geometry, depending upon the angle between the spindle and the surface being cut. CAM systems work with a single diameter value that is assumed to apply to the entire ball end mill. In reality, a range of diameters is likely to be experienced. High performance insert ball end mills typically have diameter variations of 0.0004" to 0.0008" TIR over the included angle of the insert (typically greater than 180°) when errors in the insert radius and the radius seat are taken into account. Because of the tolerances available on these cutters and the range of interactions between the cutter and the surface (up- and down-ramping, for example), it is very difficult to achieve tolerances of better than ±0.0005" when using ball end mills. It is therefore extremely important to optimize all other aspects of the machining process, including machine accuracy, fixturing, thermal stability, runout of the tool assembly, etc., when working with ball end mills.

Role of Highly Repeatable Fixturing, and the Trouble with Pallets

To repeatably manufacture high precision parts, they must be located precisely within the machine tool. Otherwise, operator intervention is required before each part cycle to align the component and identify its reference location. A number of guidelines should be followed to prevent the introduction of inaccuracy when utilizing fixturing and/or pallets for high performance machining. For the purposes of this discussion, fixturing is defined as the hardware used to locate a part relative to a machine. Pallets are a type of fixturing element that allow parts (and often additional fixturing) to be quickly positioned relative to a machine, using pre-established reference surfaces and a clamping mechanism.

Automatic pallet changers are increasingly popular for vertical and horizontal machining centers. Pallets enable parts to be loaded and unloaded while the machine produces another set of parts at the same time. This leads to better utilization of the machine tool and workforce. Pallets can also increase machine utilization by allowing unattended operation. Unfortunately, the use of automatic pallet changers may reduce the accuracy of machined parts and the repeatability between parts. Consider a shuttle type dual pallet system for a vertical machining center. The pallet unit is mounted next to the machining center and transfers pallets in and out of the CNC using a shuttle arm. The pallets locate on a series of dowel pins in a pallet receiver, which is mounted to the machine table. Many of these pallet systems provide repeatability between the pallet and pallet receiver of no better than 0.0004". Variability in the position of the pallet causes the location of the part to vary each time a pallet is reunited with the receiver. When purchasing pallet systems, it is important to understand the meaning of the published repeatability specifications. Are they per axis or volumetric?

In addition to positioning errors, angular errors can be introduced by a pallet system. If the pallet is skewed relative to the X- and Y-axes of a VMC, for example, the alignment of features machined on the VMC will be in error with respect to those machined previously. Pallets also increase the stack-up height between the way systems and the tool-part interface. This contributes to geometric errors in the part. One way to combat positioning and angular errors introduced by pallets or fixturing is to use on-machine probing cycles to locate the part once it has been placed within the machine. By probing at least three points that are not co-linear, the true X-Y position of the part can be established. Another series of points can be probed to ensure that the part is oriented properly and to establish its Z-position. The data from the probe is utilized by G-code programs in the CNC to correct for these errors through modification of work offsets and the application of rotation commands.

While conventional pallet systems may introduce significant error into machining processes, high performance machining requires the standardization of mechanical interfaces used throughout the shop to couple parts and machine tools. A number of companies, including System 3R and EROWA, have developed highly repeatable *fixturing systems* (including pallets) suitable for high performance machining. These systems usually include precision chucks and pallet receivers which are mounted to various machine tools. A range of different pallets and part holders travel with the parts throughout the machining process, interfacing the parts to the receivers on different pieces of equipment. Repeatability of 0.00008" is achieved between the palletized workpiece and a family of receivers across a number of machines.[9]

These systems grew out of the EDM marketplace because large volumes of electrodes have to be moved from machining centers and grinders to EDM sinkers with a high degree of accuracy. Over the years, these fixturing concepts have been expanded to encompass a wide array of machining processes and part sizes. EROWA, for example, produces a range of pallets and fixtures for use on EDM machines, machining centers, lathes, and grinders. In addition to the conventional graphite or copper electrodes, these systems are being used to manipulate larger steel and aluminum parts. Components up to 20" square are accommodated by the EROWA UPC system (Figure 6-4), with a clamping force of almost 9,000 lb·f. Smaller components, such as electrodes, or small mold, die, or medical components, can be accommodated by smaller power chucks and pallets (Figure 6-5). Such systems bring the benefits usually reserved for high volume production fixturing to much lower production volumes.[10]

Some highly repeatable fixturing systems can be employed with automatic work changing systems (Figure 6-6) to facilitate around-the-clock unattended

---

[9] This does not include error due to the difference between the actual position of any given receiver and the perceived position of the receiver, as reflected in the fixture offsets within the CNC.

[10] A similar range of chucking systems is available from System 3R.

Figure 6-4:
The EROWA® UPC palletizing system accommodates large parts while providing high repeatability between machines. (Courtesy of EROWA Technology Inc.)

Figure 6-5:
The EROWA® ITS power chuck accommodates smaller parts, including metal parts and EDM electrodes. Clamping forces of 2,200 lb·f are realized. (Courtesy of EROWA Technology Inc.)

Figure 6-6:
The System 3R WorkMan® can be used to handle tools and workpieces in milling machines or grinding wheels and workpieces in grinding machines. (Courtesy of System 3R USA Inc.)

machining. While expensive ($100,000 + is typical), these work changing systems are being adopted to address manpower shortages and to reduce manufacturing lead-times by enabling 24-hour operation.

Many of the same requirements that apply to pallets also apply to fixturing. The fixturing should be highly repeatable in its method of locating and clamping the part. It should also be insensitive to the method used by the operator to clamp the part in the fixture. For example, if a fixture requires the operator to tighten down a series of bolts to restrain the part, a means of regulating the torque applied should be provided. Otherwise, overtorquing the bolts will distort the part or fixture, while undertorquing will lead to chatter during the machining process. Automatic actuators can be used to ensure that the part and fixturing experience consistent clamping loads. The power chuck in Figure 6-5, for example, utilizes a spring actuated mechanism to clamp an electrode holder or pallet and compressed air to release the clamping mechanism. The part is in turn bolted to the pallet or holder. If a series of these chucks are used across all manufacturing equipment (EDM, milling, turning, grinding, inspection), and the part remains attached to the same pallet or holder through all processing steps, errors due to refixturing are reduced to the repeatability of the fixturing system. Because all operations are undertaken without separating the part from the pallet or holder, the relative orientation of the two pieces at the time they are joined is usually immaterial. In contrast, if a part is moved from one machine to another independent of a pallet or other part carrier, its position must be re-established relative to each machine, a time-consuming and error-prone process.

The time savings resulting from using a precision shop-wide fixturing system are significant. Consider a component that will first be milled on a 3-axis machine in two orientations, then electrical discharge machined, and finally finish ground.[11] If the part is moved independently between operations, four setups are required. If each setup requires ten minutes, a total of 40 minutes of labor and lost machining capacity will result. But, if a shop-wide fixturing system is employed, it will take only 10 minutes to initially affix the part to a carrier and to establish the part's location with respect to the pallet's datum. Thereafter, it will take minimal time to interface the part carrier with each machine. Thirty minutes of productive machine time is recovered and manufacturing costs are reduced.

The benefits of a shop-wide precision fixturing system are much less dramatic when manufacturing a long run of identical parts. Once the fixturing for a long run is established, setup time for each operation is small, even if the part is moved independently from one operation to the next. The true benefit of a shop-wide fixturing system is that it enables one-piece-flow through the shop. Relatively dissimilar parts can flow through the shop in a manner once reserved for high volume production of identical components. One-piece-flow reduces production lead times and work-in-process inventory, enabling productive capacity to better match customer requirements. Most low volume/high mix machining operations resist adopting a shop-wide precision fixturing system because of the initial investment. This is a mistake because the return on investment can be very high. Additional profits will be realized through reductions in setup time, work-in-process, and lead time. Increased machine utilization and throughput also boosts profitability.

A number of tooling system manufacturers have taken the concept of palletizing workpieces one step further. System 3R, for example, offers prepped electrode blanks mounted on disposable holders. The holders are integrated into their Macro or MacroJunior fixturing system. Electrodes can be transferred from a machining center to an EDM sinker with a high degree of repeatability and little or no setup. The benefits of using a universal work fixturing system throughout a high performance machine shop cannot be overemphasized. Where practical, such a system largely eliminates errors due to fixturing by minimizing the number of times the part must be realigned with a machine tool's axes.

To conclude, it is necessary to distinguish between the isolated versus the system-wide use of pallets and fixturing. When used locally on one machine, the benefits of pallets are limited to increased utilization of the machine by enabling multiple parts to be queued and (possibly) automatically loaded and unloaded. If, on the other hand, a palletizing system is employed on all machines which will process a given part, overall setup times can be drastically

---

[11] The benefits of a shop-wide fixturing system extend to operations that do not use EDM. At present, it is most popular in mold and die shops that employ EDM, but it should be adopted for a range of high performance machining activities.

reduced, and accuracy enhanced significantly. A one-piece flow can also be developed, further reducing lead times and increasing throughput. Employing a global fixturing system represents a sizable initial investment, and may be impractical if a very broad range of component sizes and geometries must be produced. But, because many high performance machine shops specialize in a particular type of work, it is often feasible to identify an appropriate pallet system which can carry a part through all manufacturing steps.

Importance of Minimizing Stack-up

In Chapter 2, the importance of minimizing axis stack-up was discussed. By keeping the distance between the way systems and the tool-part interface to a minimum, the negative effects of angular errors are contained. When constructing fixturing, or using pallets, the same principals apply. Position the workpiece as close to the machine's axes as possible, minimizing the distance between the part and the way system farthest from it. This reduces amplification of errors in the way systems, and increases the closed loop stiffness of the machine. Figure 6-7 illustrates a poorly fixtured component on a VMC. The part is mounted to a quick change tool post. The tool post receiver has, in turn, been mounted to a vice, which is itself affixed to a sizable block of steel. This arrangement puts the part (which is less than 4" high) approximately 8" above the surface of the table.

Figure 6-7:
This part is mounted an excessive distance from the machine table, magnifying the negative effects of angular errors in the X- and Y-axes.

On a c-frame vertical machining center, placing the part close to the machine's axes translates to minimizing the distance between the table top and the part. On a gantry or fixed rail bridge, the opposite is true. Because two (fixed rail) or three (gantry) of the machine axes are located above the work zone, angular errors are minimized as the part is mounted further away from the machine table. To minimize the distance between the tool – part interface and the way system farthest from the part on a bridge machine, the part should be mounted as high above the work table as possible. It is important to consider the positioning of the workpiece in the context of the machine geometry in order to optimize accuracy.

CAM Systems and Tool Path Generation

Modern CAM systems greatly simplify the process of generating tool paths for complex parts. With relative ease, a tool path can be laid over a 3D surface and exported to a CNC machining center. Unfortunately, complications in generating a suitable tool path often arise: for example, surfaces imported into a CAM system may possess imperfections or voids. These voids between surfaces can lead to invalid tool paths.

Such difficulties not withstanding, the ease with which a (sub-optimal) tool path can be applied to a surface masks the importance of a well designed tool path. In many shops, generating tool paths, not machining, is the bottleneck process. This is particularly true when working in easy-to-machine materials such as graphite or aluminum, or when a large number of different features must be burned into a single cavity using EDM. As high performance machine tools operate at ever greater speeds, CAM programming increasingly gates machine shop throughput. Too often, shops invest heavily in high performance machine tools while neglecting to upgrade their CAM operations — either in terms of the software used or, more often, the number of well trained programmers employed.

Under-investment in CAM software and personnel places intense pressure on programmers to generate tool paths to keep up with the rate at which high performance machine tools produce parts. This generally leads to sub-optimal tool paths produced by defaulting to the CAM system's simplest mode of operation. In the vast majority of cases, even the CAM system's easiest-to-construct tool path will cut a part. But, even though that part program can be created quickly, it is often a highly inefficient tool path.

Another common problem in machine shops is that the CAM programmer is somewhat disassociated from the machining process. Often, programmers have limited machining experience, or are under such intense time pressure that they do not consider the context in which the program will be used. In either case, the result is tool paths that are not a good match for the capabilities of the machine tool on which they run. This leads to higher cycle times, lower part accuracy, and less profit for the shop.

In the remainder of this section a number of considerations relevant to programming for high performance machine tools are discussed.

Parallel Machining versus Z-Level Cutting

Typically, a 3D contoured part is machined by laying a series of parallel tracks over the surface, creating a zig-zag pattern. The cutter moves across the part in a straight line along the X- or Y-axis (or sometimes at an angle such as 45°), clears the part, steps over a fixed amount, and then moves across the part again (Figure 6-8).[12] Sometimes the part is cut in only one direction so that the tool moves through air above the part before cutting another track. This is usually done because the machine has excessive backlash, or to ensure that only conventional or climb milling occurs, but not both. Typically, the tool makes contact with the part in both directions to minimize non-cutting time.

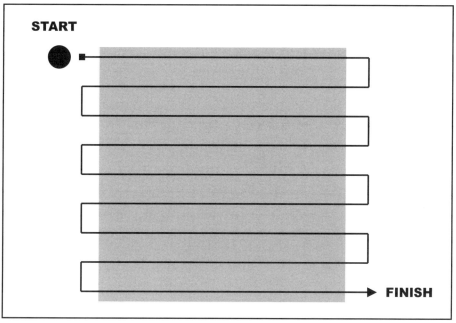

Figure 6-8:
In parallel machining, the tool moves back-and-forth across the part in the X-Y plane while the Z-axis moves up and down to follow the local part geometry. The tool must completely clear the part after each pass to ensure that the axis reversal occurs off-part.

Another method of cutting 3D parts which has been gaining in popularity is Z-level cutting, which is sometimes called water-level machining. Rather than move across the part in a straight line and reverse direction off part, Z-level cutting works as if the part is submerged in water. As the "water level" recedes, the machine cuts everything above the imaginary water line. The water "recedes" an amount equal to the step down after each pass of the cutter over the part. This process continues until the part is complete. Z-level cutting is claimed to substantially reduce machining times by keeping the tool in almost constant contact with the workpiece.

The suitability of parallel cutting versus Z-level cutting for high performance machining is highly dependent upon the specific part. Parallel cutting does offer some benefits over Z-level in terms of accuracy. Because X- and Y-

---

[12] Warning! Some CAM systems do not automatically take the tool path beyond the edge of the part. In some systems, the surfaces must be manually extended beyond the end of the part to ensure that the tool clears the work after each pass.

axis reversals take place off the part, less error is introduced to the surface. The effects of mechanical backlash are isolated from the part because the backlash is taken up during the reversal, which again occurs off-part. Z-level cutting, on the other hand, maintains almost constant contact with the workpiece, particularly if a continuous convex or concave form is being cut (Figure 6-9). This means that the X- and Y-axis reversals are occurring on the part. (Referring back to the discussion of ball bar tests in Chapter 3, axis reversals are a major contributor to contouring error in machine tools.) As a result, a Z-level cutting strategy requires a higher quality machine tool to achieve the same level of accuracy as when using a parallel machining approach. Without a capable machine tool, defects in the surface finish will be observed at the axis reversal points on the part and will increase in magnitude with higher feed rates.

Figure 6-9:
This steel bottle mold component is a candidate for Z-level cutting because it is a continuous form with generally concave curvature.

While the observations made above are generally true, it is still important to select the approach to cutting a part which best matches that part's geometry. It is not possible to state that Z-level cutting is unequivocally better than parallel cutting or vice versa. A number of specific examples make this point clear.

Consider the telephone electrode in Figure 6-10. The most straightforward approach to generating a tool path across this part is to use a parallel pattern along the length of the part. A parallel path that runs along the width of the part should not be used because it will entail many more axis reversals for a given step-over. Each reversal consumes valuable time, increasing overall cycle time. Further, axis reversals at fast feed rates place high dynamic loads on the machine and facilitate wear, and even the use of a parallel path along the length of the part is far from optimal. As the tool moves along the part it must conform to the surface. At each of the buttonhole locations the tool will have to dive into the hole, move along the floor, pull up along the far wall, and continue to proceed along the top surface of the phone. Figure 6-11 illustrates the motion required when a simple parallel tool path is laid over this part geometry.

The problem with this approach is that for each hole, the axis must change direction four times. Each change in axis direction requires a period of decel-

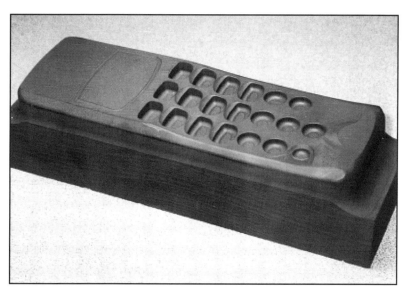

Figure 6-10:
A generic tool path can easily be applied to this cellular phone electrode. But to optimize machining performance, the tool path must be carefully constructed to match the local geometry of the phone, including the buttonholes.

eration and acceleration. As a result the programmed feed rate is not maintained for the full duration of the tool path. In fact, given the small size of the holes and the short distance between them, the machine will spend relatively little time at full feed rate. This is hard to recognize when working at the CAM station because it determines cut time simply by dividing total tool path length by programmed feed rate. It does not take into account that the machine must decelerate and accelerate every time it changes direction. As a result, the CAM system will significantly underestimate the time required to machine the part. A popular 3D CAM system estimated that the time to machine this part (Figure 6-10) would be 29 minutes. When the program was run on a high performance ma-

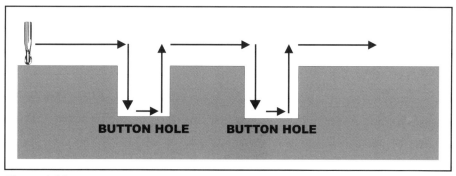

Figure 6-11:
When the entire phone is machined with a single tool path, the buttonhole features require the tool to change direction several times over a very short distance. This adversely affects machining time and accuracy.

chine tool using the parallel tool path, actual machining time was 39 minutes — an increase of 34% over the CAM estimate.

A better production method for this part uses a combination of tool path approaches. A parallel approach should be used to cut the general form of the top of the part, which has a slight radius. After the top of the part is cut, Z-level cutting should be used to spiral down each of the button holes as an independent entity. This approach has several benefits. First, it will cut machining time significantly by reducing the number of sharp turns that the machine must make, and therefore the amount of time required to decelerate and accelerate the machine. Second, it reduces machine tool wear because the motion is less "jerky" — the machine is not being asked to plunge down the wall of a "cliff" and then to climb up the other side in short order. Third, a more accurate part will be produced because the effects of servo lag will be diminished. When a machine must make a sharp turn (as when transitioning from the top of the phone to a vertical wall), the effects of servo lag are high (see Chapter 3). Fourth, a larger tool can be used when the top of the part is machined independent of the other features. This significantly reduces processing time by allowing a larger step-over to achieve the same surface finish. Finally, the tool will experience a more even chip load, thereby extending tool life and providing a more consistent surface finish throughout the part.

The part in Figure 6-12 appears at first glance to be a good candidate for Z-level cutting. It consists of a thin wall with a varying Z-height, a dome, an elliptical pillar which is to be hollowed out, and a square with a round peg on top. When a popular CAM system was instructed to apply a Z-level cutting path

Figure 6-12 through 6-15:
The application of a generic Z-level tool path to this part causes the tool to jump between the different features, rather than completely machining a single entity and then moving to the next. This results in a machining process that is longer than necessary.

to this part, the part required approximately 2 hours and 20 minutes to machine. Observing the machining process on a high performance machining center, it is readily apparent that the standard tool path created by the CAM program is far from optimal. This part contains five separate entities (wall, dome, exterior ellipse, interior ellipse, square/peg). The logic of the CAM system instructs the machine to jump from one entity to the next at each Z-height. This is illustrated in Figures 6-12 through 6-15 for the finish pass. At each given Z-axis height, the VMC first cuts along the thin wall, then jumps to the square block, followed by the outside of the ellipse, the inside, and finally the dome. This adds significant air cutting time to the program, and inaccuracy as well. Each

Figure 6-13

Figure 6-14

Figure 6-15

time the tool returns to a surface, it must do so exactly. Otherwise, a defect in the surface will result. On parts such as these, which may run for several hours, thermal effects and tool wear can lead to positioning errors. These errors will have a greater effect upon surface finish and accuracy when the tool continually jumps away from, and back to, a specific surface.

A better way to machine this part, and one that requires greater intervention on the part of the CAM user, is to create separate tool paths for each of the five entities. Using this approach, machining time was reduced to less than 1 ½ hours, and part quality was improved. This represents a 36% reduction in machining time compared to the Z-level tool path developed by the CAM system using its default method of operation, which treats the entire part as a single entity.

To conclude, the application of the tool path to the part is one of the most critical steps in high performance machining. Using the default methodologies embedded in a CAM system rarely provides optimal results in terms of accuracy or cycle time. Very often, improved results can be achieved by breaking the part down into a larger number of distinct surfaces. The tool path can then be optimized for each distinct geometry. This is a time consuming, non-trivial process. It is therefore important to provide part programmers with the best tools, and enough time to do the job properly. Unfortunately, many shops are understaffed in the CAM area or employ personnel with little practical knowledge of machining. As a result, they cannot easily determine which type of tool path is best for a specific type of surface. When considering investments in the CAM department, remember that high performance machine tools are only as good as the tool path they are programmed to run. A sub-optimal part program has an adverse effect upon all downstream machining operations. It is a good idea to invest in CAM software and capable programmers before investing heavily in high performance machine tools.

Matching the Tool Path to the Machine

When a CAM system generates a tool path, it does not take into consideration the specific nature of the machine tool itself. To generate an optimal tool path, CAM users must recognize that for a given machine tool some cutting approaches are better than others.

For example, consider the electrode in Figure 6-16. Used to produce an aluminum die casting cavity, it consists of a large number of parallel ribs. Intuitively, most programmers would align the ribs with the X- or Y-axis of a VMC when developing the tool path. Which raises the question: If it makes sense to align the ribs with a machine axis, is one axis to be preferred over another? As far as the CAM system is concerned, the part can be oriented along any axis. If, for example, the ribs are aligned with the X-axis or Y-axis, or 45° to the X-axis, the cutting time, surface finish, and accuracy predicted by the CAM system will be the same. But, in reality, the orientation of the part with respect to the machine's axes affects the quality of the part.

When using parallel machining, the axis along which cutting is to occur should be that carrying the lightest load. On a c-frame VMC the X-axis is preferred over the Y-axis because it moves only the table, whereas the Y-axis must move the table as well as the saddle assembly. If the ribs of the part in Figure 6-16 were aligned with the Y-axis, the machine would have to work harder to cut the part, which reduces the life of the machine.

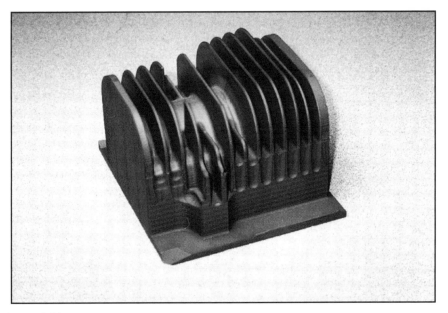

Figure 6-16:
The presence of many ribs on this electrode calls for the tool path, but not necessarily the ribs, to be aligned with the X- or Y-axis.

If the ribs of the part were aligned at 45° to the X-axis, both axes would need to move in a coordinated fashion to properly produce the part.[13] Any mismatch between the motion of the two axes would appear in the part as an error. Although the servo mismatch between axes of a high performance machine tool is generally small, it is a good idea to eliminate as many error sources as possible when undertaking high performance machining. In general purpose machine tools, servo mismatch can be more significant. The amount of servo mismatch in a machine tool can be determined using the ball bar test (Chapter 3).

Remaining Stock Modeling

When machining complex 3D surfaces, it is important to know how much stock is remaining on the part after each tool path has been run. Usually the amount of stock remaining differs across the surface of the part because a given tool is not able to access all of the geometry without gouging. This is particularly true when working with larger tool diameters, which are unable to enter areas with tight corner radii.

A limited number of CAM systems have well developed techniques for modeling the amount of stock remaining. Prospector™ from Softech Inc., designed for shop-floor programming of mold and die components, is one such CAM system. After each tool path is calculated and gouge detection is performed, the amount of stock remaining along the Z-axis is represented by applying a color spectrum to the part. Areas represented on the screen using the same color all have the same amount of remaining stock. The programmer selects areas with a specific range of remaining stock (as identified by color) and applies a tool path to them. This enables the largest possible tool to be used for each area, minimizing cutting time. The application of separate tool paths to areas with different amounts of remaining stock also enables feeds and speeds to better match the local cutting conditions on the part.

Without a means of representing the amount of remaining stock in this fashion, many CAM systems utilize bolt-on verification or solid modeling modules to illustrate the amount of stock that remains on top of the final part geometry. In many cases the visual representation of remaining stock these systems provide cannot be tied back to the generation of a specific tool path. The modeling function employed can only be used to verify that excess stock remains, rather than as a means of optimizing the application of tool path to a surface. When evaluating a CAM system, seek a highly integrated remaining stock modeling function. Proper use will lead to shorter machining times and better parts, particularly when working with difficult to machine materials such as hardened steel. The ability to locally define tool paths as a function of the amount of stock remaining can greatly reduce the risk of overloading, and breaking, a tool.

---

[13] An alternate approach to producing this part would move the tool path across the ribs at a 45° angle to improve surface finish. In this case, the X-axis should still be aligned parallel to the desired motion of the tool to minimize error and machine effort.

Establishing "Correct" Feeds and Speeds

Most CAM systems are extremely limited as to how feeds and speeds are established for each tool path. In most general purpose CAM systems, the axis feed rate and spindle speed are established for an entire tool path. To modify the feed rate for a specific area of part geometry, an independent tool path must be created. This simplification represents a significant detriment to the cause of high performance machining and neglects a number of important factors that affect the desired cutting parameters throughout the cut. Because the ability to alter feeds and speeds within a given tool path is often limited in CAM, the feed rates for the entire tool path must be lowered to accommodate the most difficult machining conditions experienced during the specific tool path. Alternately, the machinist overrides the CAM generated feed rates at the machine and introduces modifications that are not easily captured for integration into the program for future use.

A wide array of factors dictate changes in cutting parameters. The amount of stock remaining and the amount of tool engagement are two of the more important drivers. Variations in the surface speed on ball end mills based on cutter orientation and changes in chip thickness when cornering also impact the optimal feed and speed for milling processes.

Adjusting Feeds for Changes in Depth of Cut

When machining contoured surfaces, a tool will often encounter varying depths of stock over the part. As the depth of cut increases, the spindle experiences higher loads which may cause it to momentarily decelerate, particularly when using open-loop spindles. But, even when using closed-loop spindles, the sudden increase in cutting load can cause the spindle speed to momentarily decrease. This represents a dangerous condition for the tool as these circumstances can quickly cause it to be overloaded and break. When an area of increased stock is encountered, the feed rate should be momentarily reduced so that the spindle has time to recover to the full programmed RPM.

Unfortunately, most CAM systems do not provide a means of automatically adjusting the feed rate when the cutter becomes more heavily engaged in the workpiece.[14] To adjust for this phenomenon, the ability to gain more complete control over the tool path through a command line function, or other method, is required. The ability to "micro-manage" the tool path is essential to optimizing machining performance for high performance machining, particularly when working with less forgiving materials such as hardened steels and nickel-based alloys.

Adjusting for Tool Engagement

Another situation warranting micro-management of the tool path is variation in tool engagement. The extent to which the tool is radially engaged in the workpiece

---

[14] NUFORM® CAM from A.S. Thomas is one such exception.

impacts the chip load. Figure 6-17 illustrates variations in engagement angle as a function of the percentage of diameter engaged in the cut when side milling. Clearly, cutting conditions will vary based on the engagement of the tool. As the engagement angle decreases, so does the chip load. It then becomes necessary to increase the spindle speed and feed rate to optimize milling performance relative to when the tool is fully (180°) engaged. The engagement angle typically varies when pocketing complex shapes or performing Z-level cutting, because it is dependent on the relative dimensions of the tool radius and the local curvature of the part.

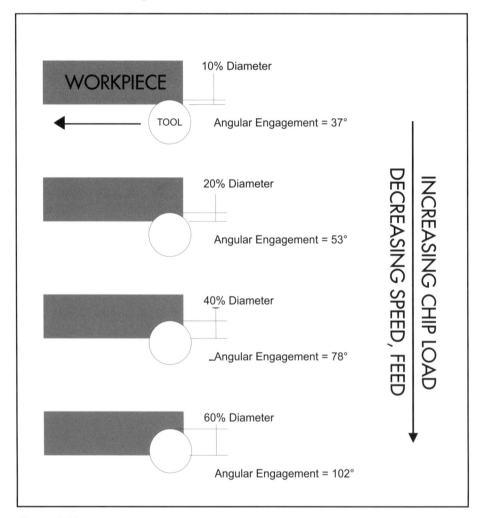

Figure 6-17:
The engagement angle increases non-linearly as radial depth of cut increases. As engagement angle increases, the chip load also increases.

As stated earlier, most CAM systems are not able to adjust cutting speeds and feeds to compensate for this effect. To do this, the CAM system would need to maintain a fully associative solid model of the workpiece, tool, and final geometry of the part. Only by continually analyzing the intersection of the tool with the workpiece can the actual stock removal conditions be derived. Most CAM systems use solid modeling as a layer on top of the tool path generation process. To detect collisions or gouging, a tool path must be generated before it can be intersected with a solid model of the workpiece. Localized models of the material removal process are rarely provided. To compensate for this weakness, the user must identify areas where tool engagement varies and adjust feed rates accordingly. Again, CAM systems that provide a mechanism for manipulating sections of the tool path, without editing G-code directly, are preferable to those which allow the tool path to be manipulated only as a complete entity through a graphical user interface.

Adjustments for Ball End Mills

Ball end mills are ubiquitous when 3D surfaces must be machined. Their spherical geometry allows them to maintain continuous contact with complex surfaces, as when moving up and down the walls, and across the floors of mold cavities or electrodes (Figure 6-18). Unlike standard end mills, ball mills present a number of unique challenges for high performance machining generally, and for CAM systems in particular. Adjustments to cutting parameters and machining strategy must be made to optimize their effectiveness.

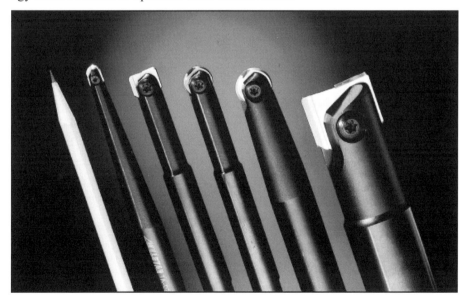

Figure 6-18:
Coated ball nose insert cutters, side cutting ball nose cutters, and flat bottom insert cutters are gaining wide spread acceptance in mold and die milling. (Courtesy of Millstar, LLC.)

Surface Speed

The effective surface speed on a ball end mill varies with position along the ball (Figure 6-19). When $\theta = 0°$, which corresponds to the bottom of the ball, the effective cutting speed is also zero. The effective diameter and surface speed increase until $\theta = 90°$, at which point a maximum is reached. The surface speed of a ball end mill, SFM, as a function of θ is governed by the following equation:

$$\text{SFM} = (\pi \cdot R \cdot S \cdot \sin\theta) / 6 \quad [\text{ft/min}]$$

where R is the radius of the ball end mill [in], and S is the spindle speed in RPM.

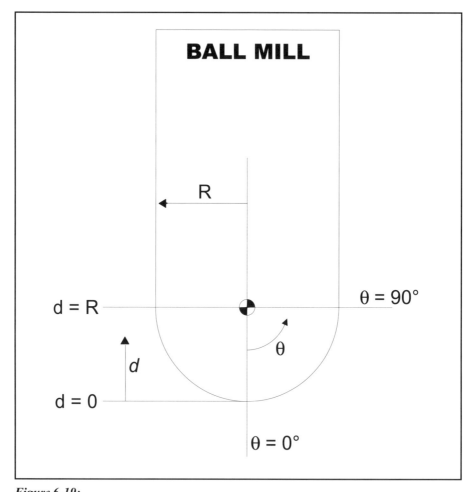

Figure 6-19:
Surface speed along a ball end mill increases as θ varies between 0° and 90°+. The surface speed can also be calculated as function of the distance, d, measured from the bottom of the tool.

Surface speed can also be represented in terms of the distance from the bottom of the tool, d, using the following relationship.[15]

$$\text{SFM} = (\pi \cdot S \cdot [R^2 - (R - d)^2]^{0.5}) / 6 \quad [\text{ft/min}]$$

---

[15] If the tool axis is not perpendicular to the workpiece surface, d represents the distance from the bottom of the tool to the point of interest, measured along the axis of the tool.

When a ball end mill moves along a contoured surface during finishing, the contact point between the ball and workpiece can change dramatically (Figure 6-20). As the contact point changes, so does the surface speed. Ideally, spindle speed would be set to reflect the contact point between the ball and workpiece for each pass across the part. In practice, CAM systems do not make this adjustment. CAM users must insert these adjustments manually to optimize cutting performance and to increase tool life. Table 6-1 indicates the decrease in surface speed as a ball end mill transitions from cutting at its "equator" ($d =$ radius of ball, $\theta = 90°$) — where the surface speed and effective cutting diameter are at maximum — to areas closer to the bottom of the ball where the effective diameter is much less. This table can be used to make rough adjustments to spindle speeds in programs using ball end mills.[16] When the ball end mill is more heavily engaged in the workpiece, an average angular value for the engagement range can be used to determine the appropriate spindle speed. As illustrated in Table 6-1, it is often impractical to boost spindle speed to maintain a constant surface speed on the tool as the contact point varies from 90° to 0°. To maintain the same effective surface speed at $\theta = 5°$ as at $\theta = 90°$, spindle speed would have to be 11× higher.

While spindle speed can be adjusted to partially compensate for variations in the ball-workpiece contact point, it is generally undesirable to machine near or at the bottom of ball end mills. Near the bottom of a ball end mill, the surface speed is very low. As a result, the tool tends to rub, rather than cut, the

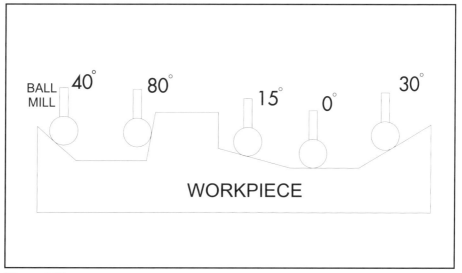

Figure 6-20:
When using a 3-axis machining center, the contact angle (θ) between a ball end mill and the workpiece is dependent upon the local part geometry. As θ varies from 0° to 90° surface speed increases from zero to the maximum value.

---

[16]Spindle speed adjustments must usually be made when the tool is not in contact with the workpiece. The inability to change speed on the fly creates the motivation for controlling tool orientation to achieve a constant SFM.

θ [degrees]	Relative Surface Speed
90°	100%
75°	97%
60°	87%
45°	71%
30°	50%
15°	26%
5°	9%
0°	0%

Table 6-1:
Relative surface speed at various locations along the surface of a ball end mill. θ is referenced to Figure 6-19.

material. The cutter will wear excessively, provide poor surface finishes, and often break in such conditions. One solution to this dilemma is to reorient the part with respect to the spindle so that the ball end mill spends less time cutting at $\theta = 0°$. This is most successful for parts that are dominated by a single shallow concave or convex surface (Figure 6-21). When the part is tilted, the cutter achieves higher surface speeds and cuts better. This approach does not work well for parts with highly variable geometry (Figure 6-9). In such cases, continuous control over the orientation of the cutter is required using 4- or 5-axis machine tools. This subject will be discussed below.

Figure 6-21:
Machining of this steel insert for a plastic lens mold benefits from orienting the part at an angle relative to the spindle. Otherwise, the undesirable condition of machining with the bottom of the ball mill occurs over most of the surface.

Chip Load

The above discussion of ball end mill surface speeds assumes that the cutter contacts the work at a single tangency point. When the tool is more fully engaged with the workpiece, feed rates must be modified to compensate for chip thinning.[17]

When the depth or width of cut equals the ball mill radius, the chip thickness equals the programmed feed per tooth. As the depth of cut decreases, the chip thickness diminishes as well, along with the volume of material cut. To maintain a constant chip load (chip thickness), the feed rate must be increased so that the average chip load equals the desired value. A simplified formula for adjusting the feed rate has been developed by Millstar LLC:

$$F_{modified} \approx F \cdot (D / a)^{0.5}$$

where F is the programmed feed rate based upon the required feed-per-tooth and other cutting parameters.[18] This formula is valid only when the tool is engaged $\leq 0.3 \times$ tool$\varnothing$, and with a similar step-over. Otherwise, only axial chip thinning is to be considered, which leads to feed modifications of about 50% of the value provided using the Millstar equation. If the standard feed rate values are used without making an adjustment for chip thinning, feed rate will be less than the optimal value, leading to increased machining cycle times.

For example, consider a 1" diameter ball end mill engaged in a 0.025" depth-of-cut.

$$F_{modified} \approx F \cdot (1 / 0.025)^{0.5}$$

$$F_{modified} \approx 6.3 \cdot F$$

When adjusting for the effects of chip thinning with a ball end mill, a feed rate up to six times the standard calculated value can be used.

Adjustments When Cornering

When machining cavities or other contoured components, the cutter is often brought into a filleted corner, which is the intersection of two surfaces. Inside corners are particularly challenging when using ball end mills. Figure 6-22 illustrates a ball end mill moving through a cross-section of a small hardened steel (55 Rc) mold cavity. Initially, the tool engagement is only 128°, but as the cutter approaches the corner the engagement increases substantially, to a maximum of 221°.

Extreme care must be taken when machining features such as these, particularly if working in hardened or difficult to machine materials. The increase in engagement places substantial loads on the cutter, which can lead to premature wear or failure and a degradation in surface finish. Unfortunately, the vast majority of CAM systems do not make adequate adjustments to feed rate when the tool enters a corner. Some adjust the feed rate to reflect the true tangential velocity of the cutter (rather than the cutter center-line), but this is inadequate. In the case of the part in Figure 6-22, the optimal tool path utilized a low feed rate (10 IPM) as the tool approached the corner, then increased the feed rate to 35

---

[17] This section courtesy of Wolfried Mielert. Millstar LLC Presentation, 1997.
[18] Chapter 4 identifies the factors which are part of the feed and speed calculations.

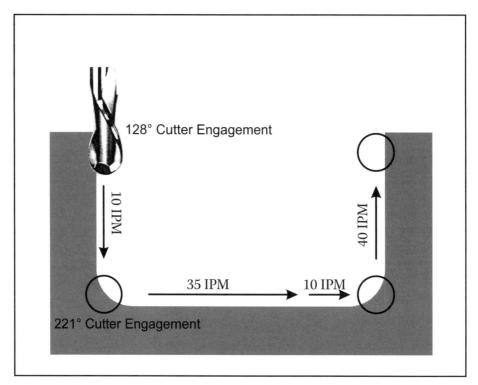

Figure 6-22:
Tool engagement varies significantly when a ball nose cutter is used to machine this mold cavity. Feed rates must be modified to reflect the change in engagement when entering and exiting corners, particularly in difficult to machine materials.

IPM when exiting the corner. The low entry feed rate ensured that the tool experienced a relatively slow increase in chip load, while the higher feed rate when machining the floor of the cavity reflects the constant chip load conditions. Interestingly, the ideal feed rate when exiting the second corner and moving up the cavity wall was found to be 40 IPM. The increased load on the tool caused by the higher feed rate on the up-cut helped to reduce chatter.

This example clarifies the need to modify feed rates continuously throughout the machining process. Unfortunately, the tool path created to machine this cross-section in most CAM systems would be assigned a single feed rate value. A limited number of CAM systems can adjust the feed rate dynamically within a tool path by scaling it in proportion to the Z-axis component of the tool's motion. The nominal feed rate applies to the case when no Z-axis motion is occurring. The feed rate is then scaled back as the move becomes increasingly Z-negative, and increases as the Z component of the move becomes increasingly positive. Shops without such a CAM system can write a program using Microsoft Visual Basic™ or another language to achieve the same result by post-processing CAM generated G-code files. Z-Feed is one such program.[19]

---

[19]Z-Feed software ©1997, G. Stilwell.

Z-Feed looks at each linear feed move (G01) in the part program and calculates a new feed rate based upon the slope of the move with respect to the Z-axis.

Another means of improving a cutter's performance in corners is to bring the tool through the corner with a circular move. When possible, this reduces the increase in chip load observed by the cutter as it moves through the corner. The larger the radius that can be used when applying this technique, the more constant the chip load will remain.

Establishing Cut Times with CAM

CAM systems typically determine the time required to perform a machining operation by dividing the total tool path length by the programmed feed rate. This always underestimates the time required to cut the part because it does not account for the accelerations and decelerations necessary each time the cutter changes direction. As discussed in Chapter 3, accel/decel is a major contributor to overall machining time, particularly when producing small detailed components with extensive details.

While this weakness is not particularly debilitating in and of itself, it does point out a major weakness of today's popular CAM systems. CAM systems typically do not contain well developed models of machine behavior. As a result, they cannot predict actual machine tool performance when producing a component. To improve CAM performance, and to enable parts to be produced faster with fewer errors, at least some information about the target machine's dynamic behavior should be integrated into the tool path development process. This will enable more accurate cut time estimates in addition to optimization feed rates, thereby preventing gouging due to servo lag and rough motion due to a lack of block processing capability. After an ideal feed rate profile has been established for a part, the spindle speed profile can be optimized to reflect variations in feed rate, and the overall result is a more finely tuned machining process.

One CAM system that does reflect machine performance limitations in its output is NUFORM™ from A.S. Thomas. NUFORM, while not fully comprehensive in its representation of machine dynamics, does account for the servo gain of the system by generating tool paths much less likely to demand unachievable accelerations or decelerations from the machine.

As higher machining speeds and tighter tolerances are sought, machining processes become increasingly sensitive to slight variations in the conditions surrounding the process. They become less robust as the envelope is pushed further and further. To help overcome this sensitivity, a better integration of machine and process knowledge characteristics is required. Taking into account machine characteristics when generating tool paths will lead to part programs that are more likely to produce the desired results the first time they are run on the machine. Currently, most part programs either require significant rework after preliminary test cuts, or they are produced with very conservative speeds and feeds, thereby generating much higher run times to ensure that the desired accuracy is achieved on the first piece.

Establishing Specific Surface Finishes with CAM

Most CAM systems allow the user to affect the part surface finish by specifying a step-over for the cutter. This works well for flat surfaces or parts with gently convex or concave curvature. But, because the step-over is set independent of the surface geometry, it can cause large scallops to appear in surfaces with highly variable curvature, steep walls, or many parallel ribs (Figure 6-16). To address this problem, some CAM systems allow the specification of the scallop height instead of the step-over. In such systems, the distance between successive tool passes across the part is set in the context of the local part geometry. This method is preferred when working with 3D complex surfaces. Unfortunately, part prints or CAD files do not specify surface finish using scallop height or step-over. Fortunately, surface finish, scallop height, and step-over are all interrelated, so that formulas can be used to convert a specific surface finish requirement into the data desired by the CAM system.

Listed below is a FORTRAN program for calculating step-over, average surface finish (R_A), and worst case surface finish for a given scallop height when using a ball end mill. Different values are obtained along the tool path and in the direction of the step-over for both R_A and the worst-case surface finish. When seeking finishes of 32 microinches or better, a good rule of thumb is to pick a scallop height value that will theoretically provide an R_A value at least 4 microinches better than required.

```
5                      PROGRAM BEM_CALC
6          C
7          C          _____
8          C          Calculate surface finish and step-over for a Ball
9          C          End Mill.
10         C          ========================================
11         C          ©A. S. Thomas, Inc. 1998
12         C          All rights reserved. Permission granted for publication
                      in High Performance Machining
13
14                    WRITE (6,100)
15         100        FORMAT('$Desired Scallop Height: ')
16                    READ(5,101)S
17         101        FORMAT(F10.5)
18                    WRITE (6,102)
19         102        FORMAT('$Ball Endmill Radius: ')
20                    READ(5,101)R
21                    WRITE(6,107)
22         107        FORMAT('$Feed per tooth: ')
23                    READ(5,101)FPT
24         C
25                    P=SQRI(8.*R*S)
26                    CALL CALC_AVG_FINISH(R,P,FB,FBM)
27                    CALL CALC_AVG_FINISH(R,FPT,FT,FTM)
28                    WRITE(6,105)P
29         106        FORMAT(' Stepsize =',F10.5)
30                    WRITE(6,108)FB*.5e6,FT*.5e6
```

```
31      108     FORMAT(´ Average Surface Finish, Across:´,F8.2,
32              1         ´, along:´,F8.2,´ tracks.´)
33              WRITE(6,109)FBM*.5E6,FTM*.5E6
34      109     FORMAT(´            Worst Surface Finish, Across:´,F8.2,
35              1         ´, along:´,F8.2,´ tracks.´)
36              CALL EXIT
37              END
38
39
40
41              SUBROUTINE CALC_AVG_FINISH(R,S,F,FM)
42      c
43      c       _____
44      c       Calculate Surface Finish (Average) given:
45      c
46      c           R       Effective Radius of tool
47      c           S       Stepsize
48      c           F       Average finish
49      c           FM      Maximum deviation
53      c
54              REAL*4 R
55              REAL*4 S
56              REAL*4 F
57              REAL*4 FM
58      c
59              REAL*8 R2,SO2,H,AR,AB,AT,SA,ALPHA,AW,A,FD
60      c
61              R2=R**2
62              SO2=S/2.
63              H=SQRT(R2-SO2**2)
64              FM=R-H                    ! Maximum Scallop
65              AR=R*S                    ! Area of rectangle
66              AB=H*S                    ! Area of rectangle
67      c                                       ! containing triangle
68              AT=AB/2.                          ! Area of triangle
69              SA=SO2/R
70              ALPHA=ASIN(SA)
71              AW=ALPHA*R2               ! Area of pie slice
72              A=AR-AB-AW+AT             ! Area below wedge
73              FD=A/S                    ! Average scallop
74              F=FD
75              RETURN
76              END
```

Although this program provides a general guide, the surface finish will also be affected by many other factors, including cutter flute geometry, sharpness of the tool, nature of the workpiece material, lubrication, etc. But by using the program, one gains insight into the best way to lay the tool path over the part. Whether the path should be run parallel to or perpendicular to a given flow line in the part depends upon the use of the part and if there is a preferred direction in which surface finish should be optimized.

Issues of CAD File Quality

One of the greatest frustrations when creating tool paths for high performance machining is the quality of the surface model geometry provided from CAD. To the amazement of most people (except CAM users), the geometry files are far from optimal. In Boston Digital's applications engineering department, for example, over 50% of the total part programming time is spent modifying or repairing the surfaces produced by CAD systems. Inadequacies in the IGES (or other) files provided for use in CAM systems are a major cause of the production bottlenecks that occur in the CAM departments of high performance machine shops. This does not mean that it is impossible to lay a tool path over these deficient IGES files. Rather, when seeking to optimize tool paths, it is necessary that the CAD generated data be of the highest quality.

To avoid these snafus, it is very important that the CAD model of the part be machining friendly. Very often, the engineers designing the part have relatively little knowledge about machining. It falls to the CAM users, and high performance machinists, to provide guidelines to engineers that enable them to create more easily machined parts and more easily handled CAD files of these parts. A number of suggestions for improving the quality of files provided for use in CAM are provided below. These are meant to initiate thought, not to serve as a comprehensive list of do's and don'ts.

CAM users should try to educate design engineers about the realities of tooling. Most engineers take a manufacturing class in school. One of the primary tenets of these classes is the importance of designing parts so that they can be manufactured using standard tooling. The premise that it is better to design a part with a 1" $\varnothing$ hole rather than a 1.07" $\varnothing$ hole is readily accepted by most engineers. Unfortunately, when broadly applied, this often leads to unnecessary difficulties for machining.

Consider the case of a radius between two walls in a mold cavity. If the radius is for cosmetic purposes (as is most often the case), it is best to design it slightly larger than a standard tool diameter. If the corner radius in Figure 6-22 was specified as 0.125", it would be undesirable to use a ¼"$\varnothing$ cutter, because a ¼"$\varnothing$ cutter could only enter the corner on a 90° move. This will adversely affect the surface finish and subject the tool to a sudden increase in chip load. And, if the machining process required a semi-finish pass leaving 0.005", for example, it would not be advisable to use the ¼"$\varnothing$ cutter for this cut because many CAM systems will gouge. Another smaller cutter would be required. If, in contrast, the radius was specified as 0.13", a ¼"$\varnothing$ cutter could be used, which would possibly eliminate an intermediate tool from the cutting process and reduce the length of the tool path significantly by enabling a larger step-over.

It is also very important to ensure that the CAD model is built of surfaces which are "machining friendly." Often a CAD model will look great on the screen, but is difficult to lay a tool path over. Typical problems include misuse of trimmed surfaces, improperly toleranced surface models, the presence of gaps between surfaces, and the inconsistent use of surface direction and normal vectors.

Often, a wire frame representation of the part rather than a true surface model, is imported into the CAM package. In this case, a surface needs to be built using CAM. A common misstep at this stage is to use the default surface tolerance within the CAM package. While this is not a problem in itself, it is important that the surface tolerance be established in the context of the chordal deviation used later when generating the tool path. Often programmers will set the chordal deviation very tight (e.g., 0.0002") but use the default surface tolerance, which might be 0.001". The result is a "very accurate" tool path (and a very large file) on top of an inaccurate surface.

Two additional problems when constructing tool paths are the presence of gaps between various surfaces and inconsistent alignment of the vectors defining surfaces in the model. Gaps, if too large, cause the tool path to "fall between the cracks" as it is laid over the model. These gaps must be eliminated, or at least minimized, through careful construction of the part geometry in CAD. The surface normals and directional vectors of each surface patch must also be aligned with care. If the normals are not applied consistently, the CAM system does not know which end is up, and highly suspect tool paths will be generated. Although the normals can be properly aligned within the CAM system, it is best if these issues are resolved prior to exporting the part geometry from CAD. In the case of directional vectors, if adjacent surface patches are defined with non-parallel vectors, it may not be possible to apply a continuous tool path across the patches (Figure 6-23).

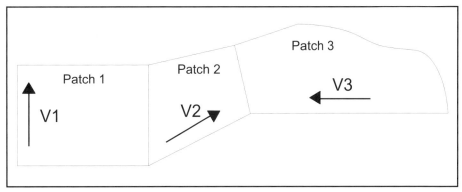

Figure 6-23:
Because the directional vectors (V1, V2, V3) for these adjacent surface patches are non-parallel, it may be difficult in some CAM systems to apply a tool path that will flow continuously across all three surfaces.

This sampling of problems encountered when importing CAD data into CAM is far from comprehensive, and is meant only to illustrate the need for close interaction between CAD designers and CAM users. With the advent of the Internet, intranets, and more sophisticated parametric CAD and CAM packages, the concept of electronic data exchange has been broadly adopted. Unfortunately, these developments have led many businesses to diminish the importance of "face time" between design engineers and CAM users. Too often, CAD designs are thrown over the wall to manufacturing with little consideration for the constraints under which manufacturing operates. Be sure when adopting new CAD/CAM technology or when establishing relationships with new suppliers or customers, that advanced technology is used to enhance the quality and frequency of communication between designers and manufacturing personnel. The opposite often occurs because the mentality is that the CAD systems are so good that the models explain themselves. This is rarely the case.

To facilitate improved communication and less rework of CAD designs, machining operations should create a "Design Guidelines for Machinability" (DGM) document. The DGM tells CAD users how to optimize part designs to reflect a shop's CAM and machining capabilities. The document should touch upon subjects such as the desired composition of surfaces, features to be avoided in the design because they add setups or process complexity, guidelines for creating radii between surfaces, realistic tolerancing guidelines, etc. Include an explanation, from the designer's viewpoint, of the time and/or money savings achieved by following each guideline. This motivation is necessary to foster adoption of the desired practices. Undoubtedly, the DGM will be a living document, changing as the design and manufacturing operations (even if they are in different businesses) spend more time considering these issues. The DGM can be a powerful forum for improved productivity while reducing frustration among CAM users, machinists, and design engineers by eliminating incompatibilities in their approach to creating machined components.

Eliminating "Muda"

Muda is Japanese for waste. The term initially entered the Western lexicon through the Toyota Production System, and has since become an integral part of the philosophy of Lean Production. In the context of tool path generation, a significant source of *muda* is embodied in the way CAM systems introduce wasted motion into part programs. Many machine shops go to great lengths to adopt high speed machining techniques, buying expensive machine tools and CAM packages, only to create highly inefficient part programs with much superfluous movement. These shops could increase throughput on their current machining centers by at least 10 to 15% simply by creating more efficient tool paths.

Most CAM systems allow multiple clearance heights to be set, usually one per tool. Be sure to set each clearance height independently, rather than accepting the height set for the first tool as the default for all successive tools. If the part to be machined involves significant numbers of small pocket routines, and therefore many tool entries and exits from the work, seek a CAM system which allows the tool retraction to be more efficiently shaped. Ideally, the clearance height should be a dynamic parameter, specified as an incremental distance above the local part surface. This minimizes non-cutting time and simplifies part programming as well. Unfortunately, adding such functionality to CAM systems is a lot of work.

Even if working with a less sophisticated CAM system, carefully review each part program for *muda* before releasing it to the shop floor. Often, by carefully managing the tool path generation process, the program can be made much more efficient. In particular, pay close attention to the order in which different features are machined, and the amount of time the tool spends moving off the part.

Another significant source of *muda* is the time spent setting up a machine to run once the part programs have been written. The machine typically sits idle while tools are loaded, fixturing is set up, and sometimes while part programs are drip fed to the CNC. In other instances the machine will sit idle waiting for raw material or tooling to arrive at the shop or work cell. It is a useful exercise to chart a machine's activities in detail over a one or two week period. Often this process turns up significant opportunities for increasing the utilization of the machine. This is not to say that one should run out and purchase process automation to boost machine utilization. Rather, one should seek to eliminate wasted time in programming, setup, and machining at every turn so that one piece part flow can be economically achieved. The benefits from a continuous process of *muda* elimination can provide throughput enhancements that match or surpass the benefits from adopting high speed machining, for less money. These benefits will be accrued in a manner that provides a more sustainable competitive advantage. Too often, new high speed technology allows firms to improve performance without addressing more fundamental weaknesses and inefficiencies in their production and business processes. As a result, these improvements and the competitive advantage they provide are often short lived. Before embarking on a significant investment in automation, or embracing JIT, TQM, or countless other improvement programs, reading Lean Thinking by James Womack and Daniel Jones is highly recommended. The techniques they describe have been successfully applied to a wide range of firms, improving their profitability significantly without substantial capital investment. The book provides a road map, with many examples, for eliminating *muda* and providing increased value to one's customers.[20]

Selecting the Best CAM System

Clearly it is impossible to identify the best CAM system for a given job within the confines of this text. But, in selecting a CAM system for a high performance machining operation, a number of guidelines should be kept in mind. These are discussed briefly below.

Many CAM suppliers are focusing their R&D on automating their software so that fewer choices are left to the part programmer. It is believed that this will aid shops that have a shortage of talented part programmers, and also speed the generation of part programs to feed the voracious appetites of high speed machine tools for part programs. Unfortunately, the result of much of this automation is to isolate the part programmer from the levers necessary to generate programs optimized for speed, accuracy, and/or surface finish. A good CAM

---

[20] Lean Thinking. James P. Womack, Daniel T. Jones. Simon & Schuster, New York, 1996.

system provides users with a great deal of access to the inner workings of the system. The ability to micro-manage the tool path and cutting parameters at each step of the process is absolutely critical for high performance machining. Avoid CAM systems that make choices which the programmer wants to control, and those that do not make it easy to override the CAM system's default methodologies.

High performance machine shops will tend to specialize in a specific class of work. A high performance machine shop might specialize in label dies, coining dies, engraving, plastic injection molds for automotive applications, can top tooling, titanium prosthetics, turbomachinery blades, etc. As such, high performance machine shops must adopt CAM systems that are highly focused on the type of parts they intend to machine. General purpose CAM systems are great at handling a wide range of different parts. Unfortunately, because of the breadth of applications they handle, general purpose systems tend to lack the depth necessary to optimize machining processes for a highly specific family of parts.

For example, consider turbomachinery blades or impellers. A number of higher end general purpose CAM systems report success in machining these components. But, because these systems must also support a very wide range of components, they lack the specialization and advanced features necessary to take machining of 5-axis turbomachinery components to the highest possible level. In contrast, NREC's MAX-5™ and MAX-AB™ CAM packages are designed expressly for the production of turbomachinery components, and in particular impellers and blisks. As a result, the features embedded in these products allow part programs for impellers to be developed quickly and efficiently, while taking into consideration the specific nature of the components.

Figure 6-24:
Tire pattern machining is a highly specialized application which is not likely to be handled well by a general purpose CAM system. (Courtesy of A.S. Thomas)

A.S. Thomas' NUFORM™ product is another example of a specialized CAM system which provides significant performance advantages over more generalized packages in its area of focus. One of NUFORM's areas of expertise is airfoil machining, and the system includes features which speed the process of program generation and create much more efficient programs for the production of blades and vanes. There are numerous other CAM systems which are well suited to specialized applications. SDRC's Camand® package, for example, provides broad 5-axis machining capabilities and has been applied with great success to a number of highly specific markets, including cylinder head porting. Type3 by Vision Numeric, on the other hand, is tailored to engraving and art-to-part applications. Each of these systems provides specific features and capabilities that allow more accurate components to be made with less programming and machining time. They usually pay for themselves quite quickly in a high performance machining environment (Figure 6-24).

Because high performance machining operations will tend to focus on a specific class or type of work, it is important to ascertain that CAM systems under consideration can efficiently produce the parts of interest. Obtain a reference list of shops using the system for similar applications before buying. Also, ensure that a demonstration is provided using one of your parts.[21] Be present for the demonstration, rather than letting the CAM company take the part away and return later. It is important to see the difficulties encountered when dealing with a specialized component for the first time not because this necessarily exposes weaknesses of the system, but because it will provide a good sense of how difficult it is to apply the system to a new application. Canned demonstrations are nice, but they don't prove anything other than that the system looks good, and that the demonstrator has taken the time to learn the demo script. Finally, do not be dazzled by fancy graphical interfaces and a space-age look and feel. Command line oriented systems are sometimes the best for a given type of application. Make a detailed list of required features and capabilities and ensure that the system provides the desired functionality in a manner that is straightforward to use. If a convoluted series of menu choices and dialog boxes are needed to access advanced functionality, it is best to assume that your CAM programmers will not use these features.

Many shops resist adopting a specialized CAM system because 1) general purpose CAM systems assert that they are fully capable of handling anything and everything, and 2) specialized CAM systems represent a significant investment. Resist the inclination to save a few dollars and make do with a more limited set of capabilities by buying a general purpose CAM product. To compete effectively in the high performance machining marketplace there is no substitute for the best available CAM system. In most shops it makes sense to have both a quality general purpose CAM system to handle a broad range of support tasks, and a more specialized CAM product to address the specific high performance work in which the shop intends to specialize.

---

[21] Be reasonable and ask for a demonstration on a typical part, not the most difficult part ever made. This is not a good test of how the CAM system will be used on a daily basis.

Shop Floor Programming — Pros and Cons

One of the more popular recent developments in CAM is the advent of shop floor programming. Essentially, the idea is to make programming the responsibility of the machinist, rather than having a dedicated CAM department generating programs off-line. There are a number of variants of shop floor programming, but the two basic types are programming at the CNC itself, and programming at a workstation on the floor which is independent of the machine's CNC. The pros and cons of both types of shop floor programming are discussed below.

Numerous benefits accrue when employing shop floor programming. First, it helps ensure that the person creating the tool path has in-depth knowledge of machining processes, and the specific machine on which the part will be run. Thus, shop floor programming can lead to more highly optimized tool paths with a better selection of tooling, speeds and feeds. Another benefit of shop floor programming is better utilization of the machinist's time. In the machining of mold cavities, for example, cycle times can be very long. If the machinist creates the next program while the machine is producing a cavity, significant labor savings are realized. Additional time savings are achieved by eliminating the inefficiencies which occur when trying to synchronize the activities of the CAM department and the machinist. Now all activities for a specific part are under the direct control of one individual, reducing the likelihood that the machinist will be waiting for a part program or that a miscommunication will occur.

These benefits, better tool paths and labor savings, are best realized when a shop produces a range of parts with similar characteristics, or when the components are relatively straightforward to program. Shop floor programming is most effective in a low volume/high mix machining environment (e.g., mold shop). In this environment the programming load is high relative to the machining load, and it is almost imperative that the machinists participate in program generation to maintain high levels of throughput.

Running a high performance machine tool requires relatively frequent interaction on the part of the operator, and the machine is often in a noisy environment with a lot of foot traffic. This is not an environment conducive to concentration for developing optimal machining strategies for new components or parts requiring extremely tight tolerances and top notch surface finishes. As a result, shop floor programming is not well suited to extremely complex tightly toleranced parts, particularly if the CAD data is not in pristine condition.

Of the two types of shop floor programming, CNC-based programming is not recommended for high performance machining. Installing CAM on the CNC detaches the machinist from the CNC interface during machining, and creates an uncomfortable working environment. The keyboards and mice used on PC-CNCs are rarely located so as to provide a good ergonomic environment over several hours of intensive use. They are intended for the more intermittent use typical of machining operations. Also, most CNCs are positioned so that the operator must stand in front of the control to access the keyboard and comfortably read the screen. Standing in front of the CNC leads to operator fatigue, and is impractical if a part is going to require several hours of programming time.

Placing the CAM system on the CNC adds further complexity to the system. The CNC, and its processing power, should be dedicated to optimizing the cutting performance of the machine tool. Likewise, CNC developers should focus on developing improved motion algorithms and machining related advances, rather than expending precious resources embedding CAM within the CNC. Some proponents of CNC-based CAM will note that the CAM system is running on Windows 95™ or Windows NT™, and therefore has no effect upon the CNC's performance. In this case, the CNC manufacturer has had to install additional hardware to operate the CAM system, and must necessarily mark up the cost of this hardware and software to cover the manufacturing and product support costs. There is no free lunch. Further, it is often difficult in these cases for the end user to upgrade the computer within the CNC to provide enhanced CAM performance in the future.

The best approach to shop floor programming is to utilize an independent programming station or stations, detached from the CNC. Products such as Tebis™ and Prospector™ run on PCs and are commonly housed in shop hardened workstations. By detaching the programming system from the CNC, a number of benefits are accrued. First, a number of machinists can utilize the same workstation, reducing the quantity of stations required. If the CAM is installed on the CNC, it is impossible for one machinist to do programming while another runs the machine. Second, it allows the shop to independently optimize the CNC and the CAM system. PCs are inexpensive enough, and their performance is improving so fast that it doesn't make sense to invest in a PC which is built into a CNC and may be hard to upgrade. When the PC is in the workstation, it can be easily upgraded. The use of a separate workstation also allows a more ergonomic work area to be setup. Chairs and tables (for laying out parts or raw material) can be arranged along with the workstation without restricting access to the machine tool's work area. And, if the shop philosophy ever changes to favor a centralized CAM department, the workstation's PC and software can easily be removed and placed in an office, with no additional expense. On a CNC with shop floor CAM, the PC often cannot be removed as it is integral to the CNC's operation.[22] The principal drawback of the workstation approach is that the machinist may not be in close proximity to the machine tool while programming. If the part is a first-piece or one-of, this can be risky. This concern also exists, although to a lessor extent, when programming at the CNC. If programming a CAM system, how much attention is the machinist able to pay to the machining operation?

To conclude, shop floor programming has widespread application, particularly when parts are of low to moderate complexity, lot sizes are very small, and programming time for each component is relatively short compared to ma-

---

[22] Again, if the PC can be removed from the CNC without affecting CNC performance, one is undoubtedly paying more for it than if the PC was bought through a superstore or direct from the PC manufacturer.

chining time. A workstation-based approach for shop floor programming is pre-ferred to a CNC-based programming system because of considerations of cost, ergonomics, programming efficiency, and CNC performance trade-offs. When producing very complex, accurate components or working in a low mix/high volume environment, it makes sense to have a specialized CAM department. In the final analysis, the best approach for a given high performance machining operation depends largely upon the skills of the workforce, and the type and quantity of parts being produced.

Hard Die Milling

The goal of hard die milling is to produce mold cavities or dies from hard mate-rials (50+ Rc) to final dimension and finish in order to eliminate most or all handwork and EDM processes. The concept is very appealing, and of late has become the "holy grail" of machining. In principle, hard die milling can signifi-cantly compress manufacturing lead times by reducing the number of opera-tions performed on the part, decreasing the amount of hand polishing, and elimi-nating the EDM process. Figure 6-25 illustrates the reduction in manufacturing

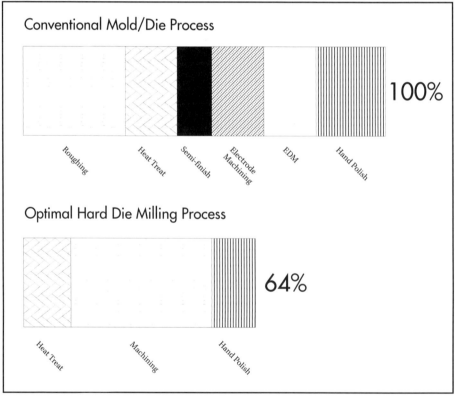

Figure 6-25:
Hard die milling can reduce overall processing time for a mold by eliminating other processes. Although it is possible to reduce total production time significantly on many components, some parts will not benefit from this approach.

time typically sought using hard die milling. While many shops are rushing to embrace hard die milling, others are intimidated by it. There is no magic here. Hard die milling is not the answer for every job. But, properly applied, it can enhance current practice.

While this book is not intended to provide a detailed guide to specific machining operations, hard die milling is closely linked to high performance machining. The potential to utilize hard die milling in lieu of EDM has generated significant interest in the subject. As such, this section outlines considerations for the adoption of hard die milling. Cutter requirements, process design, CNC and machine tool requirements, and the proper application of hard die milling are discussed in the context of "open surfaces" and "intricate surfaces." Open surfaces are loosely defined as those without tight corner radii (< 1/16") and steep walls. The surface to be machined is marked by gentle changes in curvature and easy tool access, allowing large diameter tools and cutter bodies to be employed. Airfoil forging dies (Figure 6-26) are examples of open surfaces.

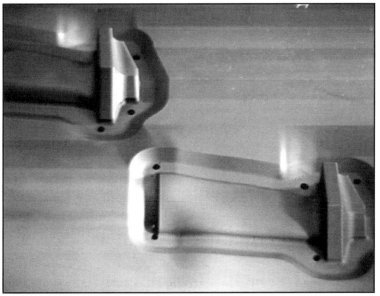

Figure 6-26:
Airfoil forging dies (electrode shown here) are well suited to hard die milling because the surfaces are generally free of rapid changes in curvature and tight corner radii.

Intricate surfaces are marked by steep walls with minimal taper, and rapid changes in curvature along the part floor. As a result, small tool radii with long cutter bodies are required to gain access to the surface. The bottle mold component illustrated in Figure 6-9 is an example of an intricate surface. The cutter path for this surface will require significantly higher accelerations and decelerations and a larger number of reversals than the path to produce the airfoil forging die. The corner radii are also significantly tighter. As a result, this is a more difficult part to produce in hardened steel. Table 6-2 provides a generalized comparison of the characteristics of open and intricate surfaces.

Characteristic	Open Surface	Intricate Surface
Corner Radii	Large, $>^1/_{16}$"	Small, $<^1/_{16}$"
Number of Z-axis reversals required on part	Few	Many
Likely curvature type	Convex	Concave
Rate of change of surface (1st derivative)	Slow	Fast
Depth of cavities relative to tool diameter	Shallow (2:1)	Deep (5:1)

Table 6-2:
Comparison of open and intricate surface characteristics (in the context of hard die milling).

Hard die milling in open surfaces is significantly easier, and more practical, than in intricate surfaces. Less capable machine tools and tooling will often prove adequate when producing open surfaces, while more advanced (and unfortunately expensive) capabilities need to be brought to bear upon intricate surfaces.

Cutter Requirements

To successfully machine hardened materials, milling cutters need to be stiff, tough, and highly heat resistant. TiAlN coated tools provide the best combination of wear resistance and aggressive material removal. TiN coated tools have provided good results, although tool life was less than the TiAlN tools. This is because TiN is only 70% as hard and 73% as heat resistant than TiAlN. Given that TiAlN coated inserts cost approximately 10% more than TiN, the extra cost is well worth the performance.

Standard carbide end mills have proven impractical for machining hardened steels, because they wear out quickly. Although they did remove material, and provide good surface finishes in tests on 55 HRc cavities, tool life was only 1 to 1.5 hours per tool, compared to 16 hours for TiAlN tools performing similar cuts.

As an example of the benefits of TiAlN tooling, consider a 2"×3"×0.5" mold cavity for a consumer product cut in S7 tool steel hardened to 55Rc. The part was an intricate surface, with a dozen or so bosses and ribs along the floor. After roughing out the part, a 1/16" ∅ TiAlN coated, 4-flute ball mill was used at 23,000 RPM and 40 IPM in a finish cut with a 0.005" depth-of-cut. The cutter lasted through the entire finish path length of 9,600 inches (6 hours) with no sign of wear other than the bottom of the ball.[23] A surface finish of 10 micro-

---

[23]Run time was 6 hours instead of 4 hours (9,600 ÷ 40) due to accel/decel and the effects of contour optimization which slowed down the machine to hold desired tolerances in tight corners.

inch R_A was achieved. After this cut, another 13 hours of similar machining time was put on the tool with no significant wear.

In roughing, the benefits of TiAlN coated tools are also readily apparent. A two inch square 50 HRc cavity 0.75" deep was roughed using a 0.5"∅ TiAlN end mill ($200) with high speed machining techniques. Average feed rates of over 200 IPM were achieved when machining in a spiral from a 0.75"∅ start hole at the center of the part. A 0.01" radial step-over and a 0.4" axial depth-of-cut were employed. Using pressurized air for cooling, the tool demonstrated minimal wear and completed the cut in less than three minutes. By comparison, a 0.375"∅ carbide end mill ($20) with a conventional coating machined the cavity using a feed rate of 4 IPM, a 0.2" radial step-over, and a 0.1" depth-of-cut. This conventional roughing process, supported by air-oil-mist lubrication, required over 20 minutes to complete. The conventional tool had a life of approximately two parts.

In addition to selecting the proper tool coatings, end mills for hard die milling should have large central cores and smaller flutes than conventional tools. This is particularly important to minimize deflection as the tools get longer, and to provide enough stiffness to resist vibration and premature tool wear.

Process Design

In addition to selecting appropriate tools, it is important to properly define the cutting process. This is particularly true when working on intricate hard die parts. Several important guidelines are provided below.

Coolant. Most users agree that flood coolant is not ideal for hard die milling. The use of air-oil mist or chilled compressed air is preferred. ITW produces a chilled air dispensing unit which runs on compressed air, and is ideally suited to such applications.

Tool path design. When working with hardened materials, it is very important to ensure that the tool sees a constant stock-on condition as it cuts. While the cutters can take heavy loads, rapid changes in the load can "shock" the tool and cause it to break. As a result, it is very important to smoothly exit and enter hardened workpieces. The roughing of hardened materials is best begun using a start-hole, which itself can be helical cut. The roughing tool path is then laid out as a spiral, beginning at the start-hole. Z-level cutting is also a useful approach for hard die milling, particularly when working with open or convex surfaces. By maintaining a constant radial and axial depth of cut, Z-level cutting ensures that the tool sees a constant chip load, increasing tool life.

Cornering. When working on intricate or concave parts such as small mold cavities, it is sometimes impractical to pursue a Z-level cutting strategy. In such cases, the tool path will consist of planar slices along the part. Figure 6-22 illustrates such a cross-section. In these cases, it is inadequate to use a single feed rate down the wall, across the bottom, and back up the opposite side. As the tool moves into a corner, it experiences more engagement and is likely to break, or at least breakdown, if the feed rate is not reduced.

Although many CAM systems generate a single feed rate for an entire cutter path, it is important to modify the feed rate as a function of the tool vector and the expected chip load. Otherwise, tool breakage will occur. This is particularly traumatic when finish operations can take 6+ hours as in hard die milling. Similar attention to the feed rate is required when cornering in side milling situations.

Importance of calculating true SFM. Hardened materials are much less forgiving than conventional steels when it comes to tool life. As such, it is important to calculate the true SFM when using ball end mills. If the depth of cut is less than the radius of the ball end mill, the true cutting diameter of the tool is reduced (as previously discussed).

Machine Tool and CNC Requirements

A wide array of machine tools and CNCs are capable of performing hard die milling, and it is not necessary to spend $300,000+ to acquire one. At EMO '97, a number of machines, some under $100,000, were observed machining hardened steels. But, while most of these machines were capable of removing the material, and some of them were capable of providing good surface finishes, they all seemed to have a hard time providing high quality cross-overs. One machine, producing a hardened connecting rod forging die, created a part with a beautiful finish, but left a ripple which appeared to be over 0.001" in size where the X-axis reversed!

To perform hard die machining, a machine should have the following characteristics. Most of these, readers will note, reiterate the general requirements for high performance machine tools discussed in Chapters 2 and 3.

- Stiffness: The machine should be highly rigid. C-frame VMCs and horizontals are good choices. Machines should employ linear roller ways. Avoid large axis stack-ups, and overhanging head stocks.
- Spindle: A high speed spindle is necessary for running smaller tools. Lower RPMs (often less than 6,000), are needed for roughing with tools approaching 1"$\emptyset$. But, a 30 HP 30,000 RPM motorized spindle is probably not the answer due to high cost and poor reliability. A more economical route, with better low-end torque, is to use a main+auxiliary spindle pair.
- Damping: A well damped machine structure is necessary to absorb the vibrations created during cutting. Seek heavy iron castings and/or polymer concrete bases. Avoid welded structures. The emergence of hydrostatic spindles and way systems promises help in this area.
- Accuracy: A machine with a high degree of dynamic accuracy is required. Don't be fooled by static positioning accuracy and repeatability numbers, unless they are to ISO specifications. Look closely at ball bar test results, and seek machines with better than 0.0003" TIR on a 12" ball bar at 20 IPM. Some builders can provide tighter values (0.00015" in some cases) as part of ultra-precision packages.
- Feed & Acceleration: Relatively high feed rates are important for hard die milling, particularly when roughing. But, because most time is spent

finishing the part (80%+ for intricate components), acceleration is more important than top end feed rate. A machine capable of feeding at 600 IPM with accelerations of 0.3g is of less use in hard die milling than one able to feed at 400 IPM and 0.7g. Open parts will tend to favor high feed rates over high accelerations. The opposite is true for intricate parts

- Motion Algorithms: Seek CNCs capable of high feed rates, but focus predominantly on available acceleration. Gain switching is very useful in hard die milling applications. The use of contour optimization and feed rate modification features to slow the machine, as it enters areas of increased material and tight corners, is also critical for hard die milling.

- Data Handling: Select a CNC armed with a large hard disk drive and ethernet to enable fast transfer and storage of large programs and the elimination of drip feeding. Programs for hard die milling are exceptionally large because the step-over used is very small, often 25% that of programs for milling graphite when working with small tools.

Practical Application of Hard Die Milling

Hard die milling can be used to economically produce open surfaces in lieu of milling plus EDM processes, so long as an EDM-type finish is not required. As parts become more intricate, the use of hard die milling becomes more technically challenging, and the options must be weighed more carefully. While hard die milling can reduce the manufacturing lead time for a mold or die, it is a less robust process compared to EDM because small tools in tight corners have a higher probability of breaking. Further, for shops machining small lot sizes, the time required to optimize a hard die milling process can be excessive. As a result of these factors, EDM will likely remain a more automated/unattended process than hard die milling. So, while the total process time required by hard die milling may be less, much of the time in a milling+EDM process elapses at night or on weekends, without operator intervention. Such unattended operation is much more difficult to achieve with hard die milling, particularly when producing small quantities of unique pieces.

This is not to say that hard die milling will not be a viable process for intricate parts. It is successfully being used by many machining operations today. Over the years ahead, it will continue to become more robust as machine tool builders, tooling manufacturers, and machine shops become more proficient in its application. For those shops adopting hard die milling, the selected machine should be well suited to the production of electrodes and other work because it is difficult to predict the hard die milling content of your work at the onset. Oddly enough, many of the requirements for producing good electrodes are shared with hard die milling: i.e., excellent machine geometry, a high degree of dynamic accuracy, a fast CNC, and a high speed, accurate spindle. Additional stiffness and a more powerful spindle are the supplementary requirements to enable hard die milling. Finally, set realistic expectations. The complete elimination of all EDM and hand finishing is not realistic in most cases. Build the justification for adopting hard die milling around a more likely scenario, where

EDM and hand finishing are reduced, but not eliminated. Creating a realistic assessment of the impact of hard die milling is a critical element of its successful adoption.

Graphite Machining

Relative to hard die machining, graphite milling is a much more robust process. The nature of graphite means that it is much more forgiving of "jerky" machine movements, tool runout, and other process inadequacies than hard die machining. These deficiencies will still adversely affect graphite part quality, but they will not be as likely to cause the process to be brought to a halt by broken tools. Nonetheless, graphite presents unique challenges for high performance machining, which are briefly outlined below.

Cutter Requirements

Graphite is a highly abrasive material, and tends to quickly wear out cutters. One of the greatest difficulties encountered when machining graphite is that cutter wear can reach unacceptable levels within the time required to machine a single part. The use of advanced tool coatings is, therefore, of significant benefit when producing graphite components. TiAlN, CBN, or diamond coating tooling is highly recommended for producing tight tolerance graphite components while minimizing wear and maintaining part accuracy. Uncoated carbide tools can be used, but are best restricted to roughing and semi-finishing, when tool wear is less of a concern.

When graphite is machined (unlike metals), a continuous chip is not sheared off the workpiece. Instead, a combination of crushing and flaking occurs. Flaking is undesirable, particularly when finishing, because it appears as chipping of the surface. Using cutter geometry with a negative rake angle can reduce the amount of flaking and provide a larger crushing zone, generating better overall surface finishes. Because a continuous chip is not created, no chip breaker is required on cutters used in graphite.[24]

Process Design

Unlike hard die milling, the process design when machining graphite is less critical in the sense that a poorly designed process is less likely to lead to broken tools. But, a well designed process is still imperative to competitively produce high quality electrodes. Although cutter breakage is less of a concern, the tool path must be designed to avoid flaking and chipping of the surface. Entry and exit from the part should use a ramping approach, rather than a direct step into the surface. Sudden changes in chip load should also be avoided to prevent chipping of the workpiece.

Very high spindle speeds and feed rates can be used when machining graphite due to the nature of the material. Inadequate consideration is usually given to

---

[24] Millstar, LLC.

the accelerations and decelerations required to support these high programmed feed rates, resulting in clipped surface geometry.[25] The use of contour optimization and gain switching features are of significant benefit in graphite machining because the feed rate can be managed by the CNC to eliminate gouging, and higher accelerations can be supported through gain switching.

Graphite is unforgiving of surface finish defects, reflecting even the smallest perturbations quite clearly. As such, it is important to use a fine step-over and small chordal deviation to optimize surface finish. This results in very large part programs that, given the high axis feed rates, often cause data starvation in the CNC. Careful consideration of the data processing capabilities of the CNC is necessary before releasing graphite machining programs into production.

Coolant is rarely used when machining graphite because of the difficulty in separating the graphite from the coolant for proper disposal. Compressed air is typically used to remove dust from the tool-work interface, and to make the dust airborne so that it can be entrained in the flow of air typically used to remove it from the work area. Some shops use a chilled compressed air source, described above, to maintain a lower temperature at the tool.

Machine Tool and CNC Requirements

Compared to hard die milling, a machine tool used for machining graphite experiences lower cutting loads. A high degree of stiffness is still required because the feed rates and accelerations used on graphite will be higher, creating the need for excellent dynamic performance and resistance to dynamic loads. Geometrically, the machine must be as accurate as a mill intended for hard die milling, and a high degree of damping is still required. Generally speaking, machines intended for graphite machining can provide less stiffness, but must provide superior CNC processing speeds and dynamic performance at high feed rates, as compared to hard die milling.

Spindles for graphite machining should provide very high speeds, but clearly require less power than for hard die milling applications. Maximum spindle speed should be at least 15,000 RPM, and preferably 25,000 RPM or more.[26] Because high spindle speeds and feed rates are used, the amount of thermal growth when machining graphite can be considerable, and the use of a thermal control system is necessary to produce graphite electrodes to a high degree of accuracy. Adequate sealing of the spindle nose to prevent contamination from graphite dust is a prerequisite for long spindle life. A taper air blast and an air seal to protect the front bearings of the spindle is preferred over a conventional labyrinth seal. The use of grease lubricated spindle bearings is recommended over air-oil because it is unacceptable for oil to drip onto the part. When cutting dry, dust removal from the machine work area is of paramount importance. A machine intended for graphite production should provide integrated dust removal and a well de-

---

[25] Chapter 3 describes how this happens in the context of servo lag.
[26]This does not mean that all tools should be run at 25,000 RPM. Spindle speed is highly dependent upon the tool – part interaction. Many tools will run at slower speeds.

signed system for protecting the machine subsystems (such as the drive trains) and shop environment from contamination. The BostoMatic 32GS, for example, pressurizes each axis with clean air to prevent dust from getting under the way covers. While machines without graphite protection can clearly produce graphite parts, their ball screws, linear ways, and spindles will experience accelerated wear and loss of accuracy.

The CNCs data processing speed is more important for graphite machining than hard die milling applications, because feed rates are typically higher. Therefore, the program must flow through the CNC at a faster rate when machining graphite. The ability of the CNC/machine system to provide a high degree of dynamic accuracy (as measured in part by the ball bar test) remains critical when producing electrodes.

When producing electrodes, many smaller shops find that they do not have enough work to expressly dedicate a machine to this purpose. When considering a machine tool for the production of electrodes, it is important to consider what other tasks can be assigned to the machine. Often, a high performance machine tool will produce electrodes so quickly that it could potentially sit idle for several hours each day. If the machine is also capable of supporting hard die milling or other metal cutting operations, a much higher return on investment can be achieved. Look for machines that can be easily switched between dry graphite machining and wet steel cutting. Not surprisingly, many machines designed for graphite production are not capable of cutting metal. Either they do not possess the appropriate spindle or flood coolant system, or they are not rigid enough to withstand the cutting loads experienced when machining steel. In fact, using some graphite machines to produce steel components will void the warranty.

4-Axis Considerations

A number of processing difficulties arise when programming and machining 4-axis cylindrical parts such as rotary cutting dies (Figure 1-1). A number of features, including direct part surface programming, Y-A interchange, and automatic land width control should be sought for high performance 4-axis applications.

Direct Part Surface Programming

Most rotary axes are programmed in degrees, minutes, and seconds of arc. For rotary dies, the ideal programming system directly programs part surface movement. The key to this system is user defined diameter for the A-axis, and a number of CNC-embedded features which simplify off-line CAM programming.

The BDC3200X CNC, for example, uses a programmable A-axis diameter to calculate the amount of rotation required to create the programmed movement at the part surface . A program with a three inch move can be run on a two inch diameter or six inch diameter roll, with no changes needed in the tool path, by simply adjusting the A-axis diameter to reflect the size of the stock being used. This adjustment is made in the CNC by the operator, or through a single line of G-code in a part program. Coupled with Y-A interchange, this feature allows programming a rotary part in simple X-Y moves, then "wrapping" the part around the appropriate diameter cylinder.

Y-A Interchange

When a machine can control the A-axis using distance rather than degrees, it is possible to program a rotary part as though it were in the X-Y plane. This simplifies many 4-axis programming tasks, such as programming a pattern for a roll die cutter. The program can be written, or digitized, directly from the original print or art work. After the part has been programmed, the Y-A interchange can be used to cut the pattern on a cylinder of the correct diameter. When Y-A interchange is turned on in the CNC, all Y-axis moves are output as A-axis moves and vice-versa.

Automatic Land Width Control

Automatic Land Width Control corrects a problem commonly experienced in roll die applications pertaining to cutter offset on cylindrical surfaces. This CNC software creates three axes moves to eliminate the deviation in the size of lands that run parallel and perpendicular to the axis of rotation.

When cutting a land or feature on a cylinder using a VMC's A-axis, the width of a land that ran parallel to the axis of rotation would not be the same as

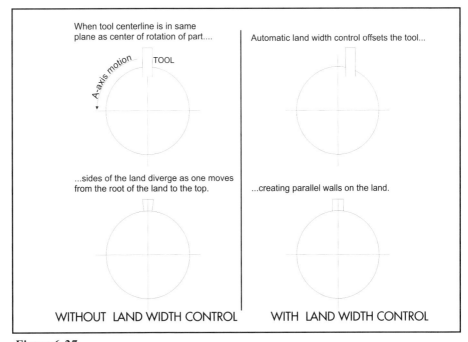

Figure 6-27:
Automatic land width control simplifies the programming of rotary dies and other 4-axis parts requiring consistently sized lands.

a land that ran perpendicular to the axis of rotation. This is due to the fact that under normal circumstances the tool centerline lies in the same plane as the center of rotation of the part. An exaggerated illustration (Figure 6-27) shows how the two sides of the land diverge as you go from the root of the land to the part surface. Because the width of the land is being determined by the programmed position of the tip of the tool, the land itself is too wide. A similar problem occurs when cutting cam follower paths or other recessed, rather than raised, features. The problem of land divergence does not occur in those sections of the land that lie in the plane perpendicular to the center of rotation.

To solve this problem, the tool centerline must be offset parallel to the centerline of the land, and the land centerline itself brought to the top of the roll. This can be accomplished by aligning the centerline of the land in the X-Z plane and offsetting the cutter in Y to create the appropriate width for the land. This calculation is time consuming for features that are straight and parallel to the A-axis of rotation and becomes much more complex if the features are curved or at an angle to the axis of rotation. Auto Land Width Cornering software solves this problem within the CNC. When used in conjunction with Y-A interchange, this feature greatly simplifies the programming of complex 4-axis geometries while enhancing accuracy.

5-Axis Considerations

5-axis machining processes are significantly more complex and difficult to program than those requiring three or four axes. This section examines a number of general 5-axis related processing issues, followed by a focus on the application of 5-axis technology to traditional 3-axis components.

Tooling Selection and Application

5-axis machining processes often require long, tapered tools to fully access the part geometry. Because the use of such long tools places high stresses on the interface between the spindle and the tool holder, it is highly recommended that HSK tooling be used in 5-axis applications. Otherwise, relative motion between the spindle taper and the tool holder will occur, damaging both surfaces through fretting.

In many 3- and 4-axis applications, the actual tool diameter is not very important because cutter diameter compensation (CDC) in the CNC compensates for variation between the nominal tool diameter and the actual diameter. In 5-axis applications it is important that the tool be as close to the programmed size as possible. Because the orientation of the tool changes with respect to the part, CDC cannot be applied simply in the X-Y plane to correct for errors in cutter geometry. Also, the use of tapered end mills and ball end mills in 5-axis applications requires that the tooling be manufactured as close to the nominal dimensions as possible. If the diameter of a cutter is significantly different than the value used when programming the part, the program typically must be reposted in the CAM system. Adjustments cannot be made in the CNC.

The same holds true for tool length in most 5-axis machining centers.[27] This causes further difficulties because tools must be set up to a specific overall length, rather than being measured on the machine and using the CNC's tool length compensation to adjust the part program to reflect the actual tool length. CNCs which have been designed for 5-axis applications get around this problem using a feature called 5-axis tool length compensation. For a tilting spindle machine, the CNC calculates X-axis and Z-axis offsets for each move in the part program as a function of the B-axis angular position. This prevents the program from being reposted each time a change in tool length occurs. This feature allows an automatic tool presetter to be used with 5-axis machining centers. Without 5-axis tool length compensation, all tools must be set off the machine so that a specific length can be established by adjusting the tool's position in the holder. This is a time consuming process that is best avoided.

CAM Systems and Tool Path Generation

Tool path generation for 5-axis applications is a fairly involved process that should not be attempted on the shop floor. Typically, 5-axis CAM packages allow the orientation of the tool to be controlled by establishing a series of relationships between the surface normal and the tool axis, or by simply fixing the two angular positions of the cutter followed by 3-axis translation to each point on the surface.

When collisions between the machine and workpiece are of concern, a methodology called "through point machining" is used. A control point is established outside the surface to be machined, and the tool orientation is constrained so that its axis always runs through the control point and the tool tip, which is on the surface of the part. Through point machining is particularly useful when the tool must access the inside of a cavity or recessed surface, as it helps prevent collisions between the machine and part. Alternately, a control boundary can be established along a surface, such as the mouth of a mold cavity or cylinder head port, rather than using a single point.

A range of more sophisticated methods for controlling the orientation of the tool in 5-axis machining have been developed to achieve a wide range of goals. Advanced strategies control the orientation of flat bottom or filleted end mills so as to maintain a fixed angle (typically 5° to 10°) relative to the plane, which is normal to both the surface tangent plane and the direction of motion plane (Figure 6-28). By angling the tool in this manner, the effective radius of the tool, as seen by the part, becomes much larger than a ball end mill of the same diameter. This reduces the scallop height significantly, improving surface finish and reducing the number of tool passes required.

Curvature matched machining, recently developed at Brigham Young University and Purdue University, represents another approach to using flat or filleted end mills in lieu of ball end mills to machine sculpted surfaces. Unlike the

---

[27] Machines using double-tilt rotaries can use standard cutter length compensation because the tool orientation remains fixed. Both rotary motions are in the part.

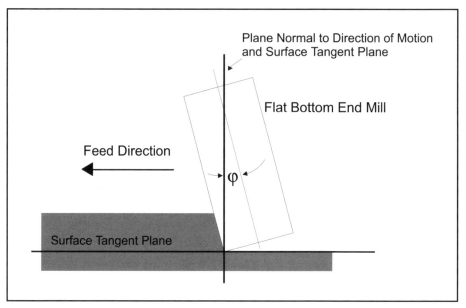

Figure 6-28:
Active control of tool orientation relative to the direction of motion and the surface provides better surface finishes in less time. φ is usually between 5° and 10°.

processes described above, curvature matched machining dynamically varies the angular orientation of the tool relative to the part surface as the tool moves across the part. This is achieved by locally matching the surface curvature to the curvature of the tool, and includes gouge detection processes as well. Initial results indicate substantial improvements in surface finish and reductions in cutting time using this process.[28] The process is currently being commercialized by a spin-off from the university project.

To optimize 5-axis machining processes, the feed rates and spindle speeds should be dynamically modified to reflect local machining conditions, just as in 3-axis machining. Unfortunately, few CAM systems provide the necessary feed and speed control capabilities. From a programming standpoint, keep in mind the adjustments for ball end mills discussed above. Similar effects are present when 5-axis machining, along with added complications that arise when flank milling with tapered end mills. Because the diameter of a tapered end mill varies along its length, the effective surface speed varies along the length of the flank cut as well.

Application of 5-Axis to Traditionally 3-Axis Components

Earlier in this chapter, the difficulties associated with using ball end mills were discussed. Specifically, the bottom of the end mill is non-cutting, and the surface speed varies significantly with the depth of cut and orientation of the ball

---

[28] *Synthesis of Cutting Tool Placement, Orientation, and Motion Based on Surface Analysis.* C.G. Jensen (Brigham Young University) and D.C. Anderson (Purdue University), March 11, 1995.

mill relative to the part surface. 5-axis machining technology provides a means of addressing this problem through active control of the orientation of the tool, leading to shorter machining times and improved surface finishes and tolerances. 5-axis machining provides a number of other benefits for the production of 3D sculpted surfaces as found in mold cavities, medical parts, and a range of other components. These benefits include the ability to access multiple sides of a part in a single setup, and the ability to gain improved access to deep cavities and convoluted surfaces.

Tool Orientation Control

5-axis machine tools provide the ability to dynamically orient a cutter with respect to a part's surface normal and the direction of motion of the tool along the part. Figure 6-29 illustrates how a 5-axis machine tool can be used to optimize the contact angle between a ball end mill and the surface of a concave cavity. The same benefits apply to convex shapes typically found, for example, on electrodes. By controlling the orientation of the ball end mill, the surface speed can be held relatively constant, resulting in improved cutting. This technique overcomes many of the problems associated with ball end mills, including the

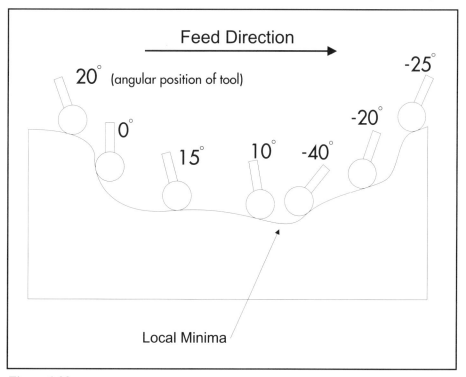

Figure 6-29:
Actively controlling the angle of the ball mill allows it to make contact with the workpiece at a larger effective radius, increasing the surface speed and creating better conditions for cutting. Only when the tool passes over a local minima or maxima in the curvature must the tool sweep across the zero speed area at the bottom of the tool.

difficulties associated with the zero speed condition present on the bottom of the ball. Figure 6-20 illustrates that when using a 3-axis machine, the point of tangency between the ball and part changes dramatically, as does the effectiveness of the cutting process. In contrast, the 5-axis approach provides a much more stable cutting process.

Some type of multi-axis tool orientation control is provided in many CAM systems intended for use with sculpted 3D surfaces. Usually the orientation of the tool is set to a fixed angle relative to the machine coordinate frame, making the orientation independent of the part surface (Figure 6-30). This approach effectively provides the same limited benefits as mounting the workpiece on an angle plate in the machine. Most systems that provide this fixed orientation facility do not provide crash detection. Therefore, the function can be dangerous to use, as the tool holder or spindle could easily collide with the workpiece, particularly when working within cavities. Extreme caution must be exercised

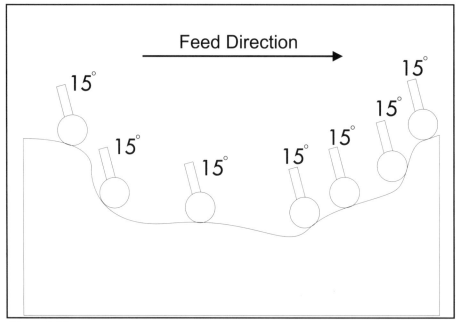

Figure 6-30:
Many CAM systems only provide the ability to orient the tool to a fixed angular position during a pass across the part. This provides significant benefits relative to 3-axis machining, but is an inferior approach relative to active tool orientation control.

by the programmer. Despite its simplicity, this process can provide significant benefits relative to 3-axis machining, while adding minimal complexity to the programming process. One benefit of the fixed angle approach is that, if the tool path is to be run parallel to the X- or Y-axis, only a one axis tilting spindle is required to orient the tool. In these cases a 4-axis machine with an indexable rotating spindle can be used. It is not necessary that the 4th axis be capable of continuous motion.

A more sophisticated approach allows an angle to be specified between the tool and workpiece, in the manner illustrated in Figure 6-28. As the tool moves across the workpiece, the angle of the tool relative to the workpiece surface is held constant. In the more simplistic method described above, the angle of the tool was held constant relative to the machine coordinate frame. The tool path illustrated in Figure 6-29 utilizes this approach. To continuously vary the angle of the tool with respect to the workpiece, a machine such as the one in Figure 2-27 is required. Again, if the direction of tool motion is maintained along the X-axis, for example, only four axes of motion may be necessary (X, Y, Z, B). A table mounted A- or C-axis not required.

The two methods described above essentially overlay single axis tool orientation on top of a conventional three axis parallel tool path. These methods represent a good incremental step from conventional 3-axis milling towards true 5-axis machining. When using machining approaches more sophisticated than parallel paths, true 5-axis machines become indispensable for achieving proper tool orientation. For example, if a Z-level cutting approach is used, true 5-axis machining is required. The orientation of the tool must continually change in two axes to maintain a fixed angle relative to the plane which is normal to both the surface tangent plane and the direction of motion plane (see above). The pencil milling of corners or ribs on a part also requires true 5-axis contouring capability, because the tool must follow the contour of the corner or rib. Rarely will this contour be parallel to the X- or Y-axis of the machine over its entire length. The ideal machine configuration for machining contoured surfaces in molds, dies, and other tooling using a VMC is often (X, Y, Z, B, C). The part is mounted on the C-axis, and the B-axis is embodied in the spindle. This allows the tool to either spiral down the part in a Z-level cutting approach, or to make passes down the side walls and across the floor. This machine geometry is particularly useful if the part contains ribs or other prominent features that run down the walls of the part. This method can also be used with flat bottom and filleted end mills, as described previously, to increase the step-over while maintaining or improving the surface finish.[29] A true 5-axis contouring machine tool and a CAM system of the highest order are required to effectively implement this powerful machining strategy.

Improved Part Access

5-axis machining greatly enhances the ability to access difficult-to-machine part geometries. Consider the cross-section of a mold cavity illustrated in Figure 6-31. Using a 3-axis machine, a 6" tool extension is required beyond the tool holder to reach the floor of the cavity. Total extension from gauge line is over 7". For a small diameter tool, as would be necessary to machine the corner radius at the bottom of the cavity, this is exceptionally long and feed rates must be dramatically reduced. Using a 5-axis approach, the overall tool extension is signifi-

---

[29] Sophisticated gouge detection within CAM is required when utilizing flat bottom or filleted end mills in this manner to determine the maximum tool size that will not violate the surface.

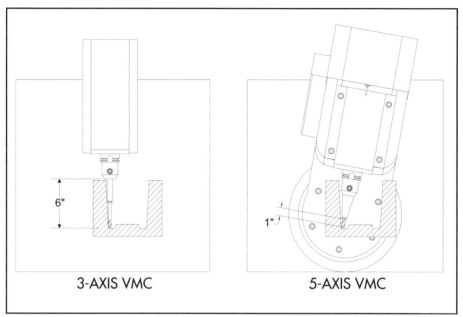

3-AXIS VMC   5-AXIS VMC

Figure 6-31:
The use of 5-axis machine tools improves access to concave shapes such as this mold cavity while employing shorter, stiffer tooling.

cantly less. Tool extension from the holder decreases from 6" to 1", while the overall length from gauge line drops by 2". Just as important, a larger diameter tapered holder can be used in the 5-axis process. This greatly increases the stiffness of the system, enabling more aggressive cutting and reducing the likelihood of chatter. As described previously, this approach also allows the cutter to be oriented with respect to the workpiece to improve the cutting action. The benefits of gaining access to cavities in this manner are very valuable to high performance machining. The ability to significantly shorten overall tool extensions dramatically increases stiffness. Remember, stiffness drops as the length of extension cubed.

5-axis machines can also access multiple sides of a part in one setup. When working with a (X, Y, Z, B, A or C) arrangement, it is possible to machine five sides of one part without refixturing it. For parts requiring multiple setups, most of the time spent in the shop is non-cutting time. Either the part is in the process of being set up or it is sitting in a queue between operations that are undertaken on different machines. 5-axis machines can dramatically reduce manufacturing lead times for parts that require machining on multiple faces. Tighter tolerances can be held between features on the part even though 5-axis machines are intrinsically less accurate than 3-axis models, because multiple refixturings are avoided.

In this regard, the applicability of 5-axis technology extends far beyond the 3D contoured surfaces which dominate this text. 5-axis machines are useful for drilling and tapping angled holes, and for milling features on arbitrary planes. Components such as optic and instrumentation mounting frames, gas turbine shafts, and oil well drilling components have all benefited from the application of 5-axis machining techniques, even though all of the features on these parts individually required only 3-axis machining. In each case, 3D contouring was not required, but the ability to orient the tool at a compound angle allowed holes and pockets to be quickly machined to a high degree of accuracy. In most cases, the features on these components were simple enough that programming was performed manually. All that was necessary was a knowledge of trigonometry to set the proper angles for the rotary axes.

Although 5-axis machine tools cost more than 3-axis machines, the value of 5-axis machines will outpace the additional expense by improving part quality and increasing throughput as components become more intricate and surfaces more complex. Although some components can only be manufactured using five axes, the use of 5-axis machines to produce what were conventionally considered 3-axis parts will continue to increase. And, as 5-axis machine tool builders and CAM suppliers work to make their offerings more cost-effective and easier to use, more widespread adoption is likely. This is not to say that 5-axis machine tools will challenge the dominance of 3-axis machines. Rather, an increasing proportion of high performance machine shops will seek 5-axis capabilities to augment their predominantly 3-axis arsenal of machine tools.

Chapter 7

Real-time Performance Monitoring

Overview

Following most machining operations, and after the manufacture of a part, there is normally an inspection process. Data acquired in the inspection process are then used to modify the machining process (to prevent it from drifting towards an out of specification condition), fix the process if it is producing scrap, or to improve process capability through compensation. This manufacture-inspect-correct loop resembles a closed loop servo system (see Chapter 3) and, like a servo loop, the presence of lag in the inspection loop must be avoided. In conventional mass production, the lag between manufacture and inspection can be as long as one hundred pieces. In screw machine production, the lag can be several thousand pieces. The greater the amount of lag, the larger the potential scrap costs. To optimize plant throughput and minimize operating costs, the lag between manufacture and inspection must be minimized to less than one piece. This is particularly critical when machining expensive tooling, such as injection mold cavities. If the part is inspected only after it has been finished and is found to be scrap, chances are that additional operations were performed on the part prior to this discovery. Effort has been wasted.

Before continuing further, it is important to recognize that there is a current trend to view inspection processes as non-value added, and to seek their elimination. The premise is that by significantly increasing process capability, the probability of creating bad parts can drop so low that the need for inspection is largely eliminated. There is some truth to this, and the idea is well suited to large volume production of identical components. Mass production enables highly specialized (and very expensive) equipment to be utilized for a singular task. Most high performance machining applications cannot afford this luxury. Further, the pursuit of defect rates in the range of a handful of defects per ten-thousand or more parts appears to be beyond the point of diminishing returns.[1] Taken to its logical extension, this philosophy calls for the use of jig borers to drill holes that would normally be made with a drill press. Never again will a hole be drilled out of tolerance!

The purpose of this chapter is to bring to the reader's attention ways in which the high performance machine shop can reduce the lag between machin-

---

[1] A number of process capability indexes, including C_{pk}, are used to define the capability of a process relative to the required part tolerance. If $C_{pk}=1.33$, then the $\pm 4\sigma$ bounds of the process are within the feature tolerance. This corresponds to less than two defects per 10,000 parts. If $C_{pk}=2$, then the $\pm 6\sigma$ bounds of the process are within the feature tolerance!

ing and measurement to the smallest possible elapsed time. The goal is to reduce the lag to less than one complete part. To achieve this aim, the machining
process must be continually monitored and adjusted. Final inspection of the piece
should only serve as a "gate keeper" to ensure that the customer receives only
high quality goods. The number of defects caught at the end of the line should
be very few if in-process performance monitoring is implemented effectively.

Real-time process monitoring requires that the state of the machine, and
not just the part, be measured on a regular basis. Only by constantly evaluating
and adjusting for the condition of the inputs to the machining process (e.g.,
tooling, machine structure, fixturing) can a high quality part be assured. When
seeking to optimize the capabilities of a high performance machining operation
while reducing scrap, continually assess potential refinements. How can the
process be made resistant to parameter variations? How can the inspection and
machining process occur closer together? How can process input modifications
compensate for machining errors?

Tool Management

One of the inputs that greatly affects the quality of a machined component is
tooling. The dimension and condition of the tooling dictates whether the part
will be made to size. As such, it is important to validate that the tooling in use is
correctly sized and in good running condition.

Traditionally, tool diameters and lengths have been measured off-line using an optical gauge, or in the machine using manual dial indicators. These
methods are effective for establishing a highly accurate base-line, but should be
augmented by on-machine probing for high performance machining.

Touch probes integrated into the machine tool are an improvement over
manual methods, particularly when measuring tool length in a VMC
(Figure 7-1). The CNC can automatically measure the tools for a process. Length
measurements can be made prior to the start of machining to establish initial
conditions, and throughout the process to check for excessive tool wear or
breakage. Using touch probes to measure tool diameter is a more difficult undertaking because the tool must be indexed through 360° and continually brought
in contact with the probe to identify high spots and thus determine the true
cutting diameter. Touch probes measure tools when they are not rotating. This
undermines their capabilities somewhat because they can not be used to measure axial or radial runout.

Touch probes, such as the Marposs Mida probe in Figure 7-1, provide
unidirectional repeatability of approximately 0.00004". But the accuracy of the
complete measuring process will be less accurate for a number of reasons. First,
the repeatability of the machine tool is typically worse than 0.00004". The measurement process can only be as capable as the machine tool itself. Second, the
machine's electronic systems, including the probe, have a non-zero response
time. In other words, it takes time for the system to recognize that the touch
probe, which is essentially an ON/OFF switch, has been triggered. Depending
upon how the probing cycle has been constructed by the machine tool builder,

Figure 7-1:
Table mounted touch probes
such as this are used by CNC
machine tools to automatically
gauge tool length.

significant inaccuracies can result. For example, consider a machine which polls
its axis encoders once every half millisecond (0.0005 s) to determine machine
position. If the tool approaches the probe at 10 IPM, between the time the probe
is triggered and when the CNC stops machine motion and determines the position, the tool could have traversed an additional distance of 0.00008".

To avoid this problem, some machine builders use a "forward and back"
approach. The tool is moved towards the probe at relatively high feed rate. Once
the probe circuit closes, the tool is slowly (< 5 IPM) retracted until the probe
switch re-opens. At this time the length of the tool is calculated by the CNC.

Laser probes represent a more sophisticated alternative to touch based tool
measurement probes. Laser probes also act as ON/OFF switches. The position
of the tool is identified by the CNC when the beam of the laser is broken (Figure
7-2). Laser probes provide a number of benefits over touch probes. First, the
laser is a non-contact probe. This reduces the chance of inadvertently damaging
the probe and enables much smaller tools (e.g., 0.01" end mills) to be
measured. Second, the laser probe can also be used to measure length and diameter, simply by entering the beam from above or the side. Third, the system can
measure tools while they are rotating. This enables runout to be accounted for in
the measurement, making it more accurate than a measurement of a non-rotat-
ing tool. This feature also reduces the time required to probe the tool, as the
spindle does not need to be brought to zero RPM prior to probing. The ability to
probe rotating tools makes it more practical to use this device during a machining operation. The tool can be brought to the probe after a pass across the part
and then re-enter the cut relatively quickly.

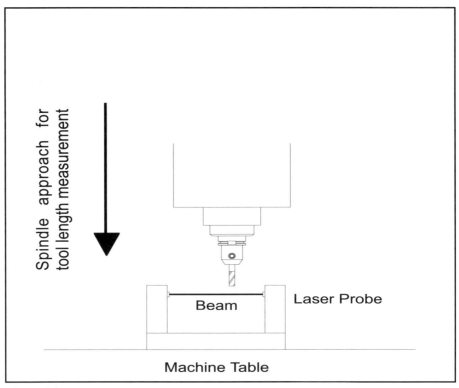

Figure 7-2:
The tool approaches the beam from above when measuring tool length, and from the front or back of the page when measuring diameter. The laser beam is not actually visible.

The one drawback of laser probes is that they can experience difficulty when trying to accurately measure the length of flat bottom or toroid bull nose end mills (Figure 7-3). Because the laser beam is so narrow, it is possible to underestimate the length of cutters with clearance on the bottom. Unless the laser contacts the tool at the optimal location, or a sophisticated probing routine is used to iteratively seek out the lowest point (a time consuming process), an error condition can be created. If the tool length is underestimated, the machine will tend to plunge too far into the workpiece, possibly damaging the part and tool. Before purchasing a laser probe carefully evaluate the accuracy of the probe and the capability of the accompanying software to measure a range of tools.

Both laser probes and touch probes can be integrated into sophisticated systems for tool management. Routines can be added to part programs to inspect tools periodically throughout the cutting process, and to make adjustments for wear and certain forms of thermal growth (see below) and machine inaccuracy. Redundant tools can also be called by the part program if wear exceeds a preset threshold. Many CNCs offer these features as part of a comprehensive package of tool management software. Resourceful shops can create their own tool management routines within their part programs by using variable based programs. Home-grown approaches are more likely to meet the shop's express requirements, and will save money as well. As the tool management

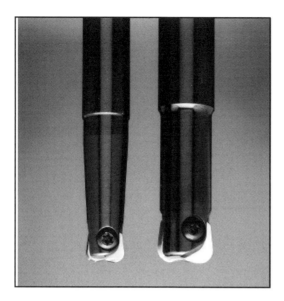

Figure 7-3:
Tools with backtaper or clearance on the bottom, such as flat bottom end mills or torrid bull nose cutters, present difficulties for some laser probes. The laser has trouble getting an accurate tool length measurement because of the backtaper. (Photo courtesy of Millstar, LLC).

approach is refined, it can be integrated into the tool change code output by the CAM system's post processor.

It is important to reiterate that tool measurement systems built into a machine tool are limited by the repeatability of the machine tool itself. Therefore, to achieve the ultimate accuracy when measuring tool diameter or length, off-line measurement methods are required. Unfortunately, this does not account for errors such as spindle runout, or runout in the tool-tool holder assembly. Therefore, in the most accurate applications, a machinist must inspect the tool using high magnification optical gauging while it is in the machine, or perform test cuts that are then optically measured by the machinist without removing the part from the machine. By measuring the width or depth of cut, an assessment of the cutting length and diameter of the tool can be established. Such a degree of manual intervention is rarely practical and, therefore, high performance machining operations must develop a realistic set of expectations for the accuracy of tooling.

Thermal Growth Control

In addition to the methods discussed in Chapter 5, laser probes and touch probes can be used to correct for thermal growth of the machine. This is best done by periodically measuring a master tool (a cylinder of known length and diameter) with the probe. Because the size of the master is known to remain essentially constant, differences in size identified by the probe are actually shifts in the position of the machine.[2] Most touch probes (and all laser probes) are essentially 2-axis devices, and it is important that they be aligned with the machine to provide measurement capability in the axes that will experience the greatest

---

[2] To minimize thermal growth, the master should be relatively short and made of a material with a low coefficient of thermal expansion.

amount of thermal growth. On a c-frame VMC, this would be the Z- and Y-axes. Once the shift in position of the machine is calculated by measuring the master, work offsets can be altered appropriately.

A number of important considerations should be kept in mind when using on-machine probes to estimate the thermal growth state of the machine. First, if a touch probe is used it is best not to turn the spindle off when making the measurement. Because the master does not have cutting edges, this can be done if the master is brought into the probe at a low feed rate. If the spindle is turned off, a significant amount of the spindle thermal growth will not be measured (see Chapter 5) because much of the growth or contraction of the spindle occurs when the speed of the spindle is first changed. With a laser probe, which can measure the tool while rotating, this is not an issue. Second, compensation for thermal errors must be made relatively often. Otherwise, discrete steps can be introduced into the surface of the part. Although the part will be "more accurate," these unsightly steps can be very detrimental to overall part quality, particularly when contoured surfaces must be blended together. The measurement period for thermal errors must be a fraction of the time constant of the thermal effect itself.

If it is not feasible to measure for thermal growth during the production process, on-machine probes can be used to qualify overall thermal growth of the machine spindle and axes off-line. This is discussed in greater depth in Chapter 8.

The use of table mounted touch or laser probes can help high performance machine shops to guard against some of the more important sources of inaccuracy — tool wear and thermal growth. To further optimize machining operations by reducing the lag between machining and measurement, spindle mounted inspection probes should be employed.

Fixture Offset Calibration

Spindle mounted inspection probes are available in two basic types, touch trigger probes and scanning probes. Touch trigger probes operate similarly to those described above, except that they reside in the spindle. They are ideal for taking a limited amount of point-to-point data and operate using an ON/OFF switch triggered by deflection of the probe stylus. Figure 7-4 illustrates a wireless touch probe in a 5-axis machine being used to probe a cylinder head. A high accuracy probe for machining centers, such as the Renishaw® MP700, provides 3D measuring performance of ±0.00004" with a 50mm stylus and ±0.00007" with a 100mm stylus. Repeatability on the MP700 is as low as 0.00001".

Scanning probes are analog in nature. They utilize an internal encoder or laser based system to identify the amount by which the probe stylus has been displaced. This information is referenced to the position of the machine or CMM axes in real time to identify the location of the surface in question. Typically, spindle mounted touch probes utilize a "forward and back" approach to take a reading. A typical probe might require 8 to 10 seconds to capture a data point. Scanning probes maintain continuous contact with the surface being

Figure 7-4:
Wireless touch probes can be used in machine tools to reverse engineer parts, or to perform limited inspection operations.

probed, enabling data to be collected at a significantly higher rate than when using touch probes. Both types of probes can be used to reverse engineer and inspect surfaces.

One way that touch probes can be used to eliminate processing errors is by determining the location and orientation of pallets and fixturing within the machine. By measuring two points along a reference edge of the pallet (Figure 7-5), the orientation of the pallet with respect to the machine's X-Y plane can be determined. Multiple probe hits should be made at each measurement point to average out random repeatability error. The CNC can then calculate the angle between the pallet and the X- and Y-axes by using the collected data within a parametrically written part program.[3] The error in pallet orientation is corrected by rotating the entire part program using the appropriate G-code at the head of the part program. Alternately, the probe can be used to measure two reference pins or reference holes a known distance apart to determine both the position and orientation of the fixture in the X-Y plane. The Z-axis component of the work offset can be adjusted by measuring a reference pad on top of the fixture or part.

The use of a touch probe in this manner is powerful, but again has its limitations. Any positioning errors inherent in the machine are reflected in the accuracy of the probing process. The process described above is intended only to help properly orient a palletized part in the work area. It does not validate the accuracy or geometric quality of the machine tool itself. That said, if the probe

---

[3] A parametric part program uses variables, rather than specific numerical values, as arguments to specific G-codes.

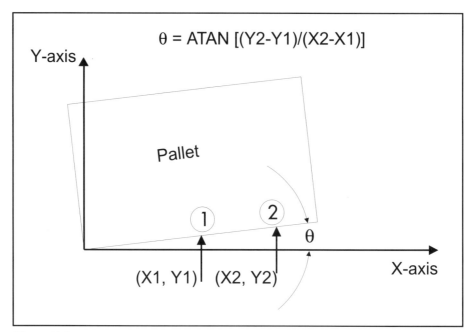

Figure 7-5:
By probing the edge of the pallet at two locations, the angle, θ, between the machine's X-axis and the pallet edge can be calculated. θ is used as an argument to a rotation command in the CNC to adjust for the error in pallet orientation.

data gathered during this process indicates that the adjustments to be made are of a magnitude that is less than the accuracy of the machine tool itself, it is not productive to make any adjustments. In this case, it is just as likely that the machine incorrectly measured the location of the pallet as it is that the pallet was in the wrong position to begin with.

Part Inspection and In-process Modification

The most logical use of spindle mounted probes would appear to be part inspection. Using a probe in this manner would reduce the lag between machining and inspection to seconds while eliminating the time and effort associated with moving the part from a machining center to a CMM.

Unfortunately, it is poor practice to inspect parts on the machine that produced them. Any geometric or positioning errors that affected the part during machining will be repeated during inspection. If, for example, the X- and Y-axes are out-of-square, the part will be machined out-of-square. When the part is inspected for squareness by the probe, it will find no error because both the machining and probing processes are affected in the same way by this error.

On-machine part inspection is useful only to identify error sources that are not a function of the machine geometry or positioning errors. Errors due to servo lag, spindle runout, thermal growth, and other dynamic effects may be successfully identified by using on-machine probing routines. Likewise, missing features due to tool breakage or gross programming errors (if the inspection program does not also include these errors), can be highlighted through the use of on-machine probing routines.

As a general rule, parts should not be inspected on the machine that produced them. Remember that the probing process is only as accurate as the machine tool itself, and that the goal for inspection equipment is that it be 10× more accurate than the tolerance of the feature being inspected. The capabilities of the machine tool would have to be greatly underutilized from a machining standpoint if it could provide 10× the accuracy of the machined tolerances when performing inspection processes.

Reference Comparison

On-machine probing should not, therefore, be used for general part inspection. But, through a process called reference comparison, it is possible to greatly enhance machine tool performance and to inspect and machine components beyond the general accuracy of the machine. Reference comparison utilizes a reference object similar to the workpiece as an objective measure of positioning error. By utilizing an objective standard, the capability of on-machine probing can improve from the accuracy of the machine (in the case of inspection) or machining process, to a level approaching that of the machine's repeatability.

The general concept of reference comparison works as follows.[4] Prior to a critical machining or inspection operation, the machine probes a reference of known dimension. Comparing its measurements to the known position of the reference (determined off-line), the CNC measures its own error. A temporary offset is generated and added to the critical machining or inspection move. In this way the CNC edits the measured error out of the process. This process has been used successfully by a number of firms to greatly enhance machining and inspection operations. Cincinnati Milacron, for example, uses its own patented version of reference comparison to hold 0.0005" tolerances on a part where the total process accuracy was previously found to be only 0.0028".[5] Similar processes are used by shops such as Faith Tool & Die to significantly improve the capabilities of their CMM equipment so that parts can be measured with an accuracy of tens of millionths of an inch.[6]

The key to the reference comparison process is the construction of a master gauge that closely resembles the component feature to be measured. If two holes twenty inches apart are to be measured, the gauge must be approximately 20" long, and its actual size must be established using a piece of equipment other than the target machine. The level of accuracy must be beyond the desired accuracy of the machining or inspection operation for which the reference is to be used. The importance of matching the reference gauge to the operation can-

[4] "Break the Accuracy Barrier" by Peter Zelinski, *Modern Machine Shop*, July, 1997.
[5] "Break the Accuracy Barrier" by Peter Zelinski, *Modern Machine Shop*, July, 1997.
[6] "Scanning for Process Improvements" by Mark Albert, *Modern Machine Shop,* March, 1998.

not be underestimated. The greater the extent to which the reference matches the features of interest in terms of material, size, and placement, the better it can account for a range of errors including thermal growth, machine positioning, and axis squareness.

An Example of Reference Comparison

A simple example, excerpted from "Break the Accuracy Barrier" by Peter Zelinski in the July, 1997 issue of *Modern Machine Shop*, helps clarify the concept. The article summarizes the insights of Andy Haggerty, the Cincinnati Milacron emeritus engineer who was instrumental in developing Milacron's reference comparison approach.

Reference comparison recognizes that errors accumulate over long machine moves. Consider the part (in Figure 7-6), which requires opposing machined surfaces to be located 30 inches apart in Y, to an accuracy of ±0.0005". By the time the CNC moves the slides 30 inches from one surface to the other, machine or process errors might cause the axes to stray from this position by more than ±0.0005". Therefore, instead of re-

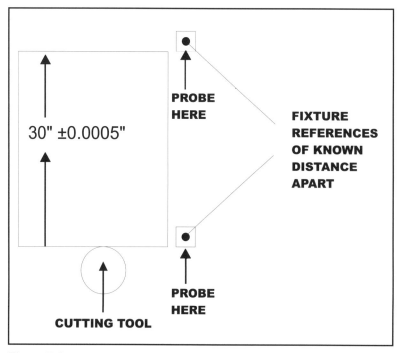

Figure 7-6:
Normal machine and process errors may make it impossible to hold the 30" dimension to the given tolerance, using just a straight-line move between the two surfaces. A more accurate method is reference comparison, where a reference of known position is probed by the CNC to update the machine position prior to a critical move. (Courtesy of *Modern Machine Shop*)

lying on a constant set of program coordinates, a reference comparison machining program checks positioning against two reference surfaces, one near each machined surface.

The distance between these surfaces need only be approximately 30 inches, but its true distance is precisely measured before machining begins - ideally on a CMM in a temperature controlled room. The reference comparison program treats this distance as a dimensional master, using it to update its own sense of positioning through the use of program offsets.

The procedure is simple. Assume that the machining center used for the operation (in Figure 7-6) is a horizontal, and that the references are indeed 30.0000" apart. The program would then be written to include offsets that assign coordinates to the two surfaces that are separated by the same distance – say, Y = 0.0000 and Y = 30.0000".

The program begins by probing the lower reference surface. Because of the influence of machine or process error, the program coordinates may show the surface to lie at Y = -0.0003", Y = 0.0001" or some other slightly inaccurate coordinate. However, the reference has already been positioned at Y = 0.0000, so the program is justified in adjusting the coordinates to match this value. It does this by subtracting the coordinate measured through probing from the known coordinate and storing the difference as an offset.

This offset is activated when the machine loads the milling cutter. With the offset in place, a machining pass programmed to bring the surface in line with the level Y = 0.0000 will meet the mark more accurately, because the machine already made its "mistakes" when it probed the reference surface.

Accomplishing that, the CNC probes the upper reference surface with the offset deactivated. Again, the difference between the known coordinate (30.0000") and the coordinate measured through probing is entered as an offset. The program activates this offset for the machining operation, allowing the second surface to be machined to the same coordinate.

The result will be a part with surfaces 30" apart, to approximately the same accuracy as the original off-line measurement of the distance separating the two reference surfaces - regardless of machine or process errors.[7]

---

[7] The result will be somewhat worse due to errors accumulated between the time when the probe is returned to the tool changer and the cutting tool is brought to bear upon the workpiece.

This example makes the value of reference comparison clear for operations that warrant the manufacture of a specialized reference gauge. In operations where production volumes are low, the concept can still be applied by designing more standardized reference gauges. Although the results will not be as good as when using a customized gauge, improved accuracy will still be achieved.

Process Mapping

The reference comparison method improves machining and inspection performance by anchoring machine motion to a reference gauge during the machining or inspection process. Another method of improving the capability of a machining process is through a highly iterative process of mapping a machine's errors, as evidenced in the parts it produces, and feeding that information back into the machine to alter its behavior. This closes the loop on the process and provides a methodology by which one can seek to achieve accuracies that approach the repeatability of the machine and process in question.

The following paper, written by Marinus B. (Ben) Bosma, explains how Bosma Machine and Tool Corporation significantly improved process capability for machining reflector panels for a radio telescope antenna. Although their method, termed parametric calibration, is not real-time per se, it demonstrates that significant improvements can be achieved by mapping the errors in a process and developing a means to integrate the error map back into the machining process for subsequent components.

A Short Course in Parametric Calibration

This paper describes a simplified method for removing environmental errors in a machining operation using axis calibration data, curve fitting software and parametric controllers. As part of a requirement to furnish very accurate aluminum reflector panels for a radio telescope antenna, we had to develop a technique for correcting the sum of the errors in our machining process. The basic concept exploits the machine's highly accurate repeatability and sound processing practices to achieve very close tolerance production machining at a reasonable cost. These techniques and the equipment are documented in U.S. Patent No. 5477602.

Concept

In very accurate machining processes, there is usually a correction applied to the position of the cutter to compensate for inherent errors in the machine tool geometry, its position feedback system and computer controls, and static loads on the machine. It is usually adequate to calibrate the machine tool by measuring the static errors in the machine tool and tabulating them in either a 2- or 3-dimensional array. This information is stored in the machine tool and used by the controller to correct the position of the machine.

This works well when you have an extremely stiff machine whose static position doesn't vary much from its dynamic position and if the tolerance of the workpiece falls inside the difference between static and dynamic position. When high speed cutting is required, machine tool builders often apply "ballistic" corrections to the cutter position to compensate for the computer's inability to provide closed loop computing that's fast enough. Various combinations of simple interpolation, parametric correction and physics "laws" can be applied to achieve amazing accuracy in a machine tool.

Another possibility is to measure the workpiece after machining and use the location of features on it to provide corrections to the machine tool. This involves simply, measuring the part and subtracting the errors from the cutter location program to eliminate the error. Again, this is not unusual nor is it difficult if the machine tool has good repeatability and your system for measuring the part is adequately precise to provide reliable correction data.

We faced a problem in machine tool correction that combined the worst of both environments. We were machining to a parametric surface and the requirement for precision was beyond the normal double digit (microns) normally associated with contoured surfaces.

The solution was to create parametric correction equations with the equations for surface profiles and continuously monitor the result until the part was "driven" into tolerance.

The Part

We had a contract to produce a quantity of reflector panels that would be mounted together to form a parabolic dish. As a consequence of the short wavelengths this dish would have to deal with, it was necessary for the surface to conform to a perfect parabola within 6 microns. Since we would have to assemble 72 independent panels measuring roughly 900mm square, we didn't have the luxury of creating any parabolic surface to 6 microns. They all had to be within 6 microns of the contract parabolic surface. To add to the difficulty, these panels had to be mounted to a rigid space frame and moved rapidly through a large loading envelope. There were limits on the number and location of supporting ribs, overall weight, environmental stability and surface finish.

The panels therefore had to be thin and lightweight at least for parts that have gauge-like accuracy. The panels would have to be made of aluminum.

The Machine Tool

Similar panels were fabricated using conventional five-axis machining techniques. Corrections were usually made to the cutter database. The existing state-of-the-art meant that we would have to cut, inspect, correct and re-cut continuously and that the corrections would have to be made to a huge database of five-axis cutter commands. This was unacceptable in the context of panel yields and budget.

We chose to build an entirely unique machine designed to machine any surface of revolution. The goal of the design was to provide a high degree of repeatability since we knew that much of the work would involve corrections to the cutter position based on inspection data. This machine was based on two very strong competencies at Bosma Machine and Tool Corporation, namely, planing and turning. The machine is a planer with a fixed pivot that provides an arcing motion rather than a straight line. If this machine were a lathe, it would have a chuck that made continuous 360 degree rotations. Instead we allow the chuck to oscillate through about 37 degrees of arc. Other features of the machine are designed only to produce a very repeatable part, including the use of granite, sand, mass, isolation, belt drives and linear scales.

The Curve

The requirement was for us to cut an aluminum surface to a parabolic surface of revolution. To a five-axis machining center this surface is expressed as:

$$z = (x^2 + y^2) \div 10080$$

To a lathe the two-dimensional curve that you turn is:

$$z = x^2 \div 10080$$

Since this curve is relatively easy to express in two-dimensions we elected to write a Visual Basic™ program to control the two axes of our lathe. We weren't home free, yet. The parts were to operate at 2.5° Celsius. That meant correcting the curve for temperature. Again, this is a lot simpler than it would seem. Since, aluminum is a fairly common material the coefficient of thermal expansion is well known and predictable. Our control algorithm thus becomes:

$$z = (x^2 \div 10080) \cdot k_{cte}$$

This works because the affect of thermal expansion is uniformly three dimensional for metals. Basically, we're cutting the part bigger in the warm 70°F machine shop. The total curve we were cutting was actually 3mm longer than it would be in service and, therefore is a significant correction. The actual surface, however, moves only a few microns over that temperature range. Nevertheless, we corrected for thermal expansion and "backsolved" all of our inspection reports to the actual temperature at which this telescope would operate.

Another influence was the problem of imperfection in the linear scales. We used Heidenhain 704 series glass scales. They have excellent resolution, but even asking for submicron resolution over 3 meters was asking a bit much of these excellent performing scales. So we did a very conventional calibration on the two-axis stage of our machine. This involved the use of our Hewlett-Packard laser interferometer, which has an accuracy of about a millionth of an inch over this length.

We took about a dozen passes at the x-Axis until our measurements started looking the same. We took the average of all the passes and declared that data to be legitimate calibration data. Heidenhain furnished us with calibration tables for their scales, but we still made our own to account for the environmental and installation factors of our application. The data was within a few tenths of microns and helped us confirm our process.

The effect on our algorithm is no longer static because the error is a function of the displacement of each axis. Therefore we had a choice of either applying the correction data using a lookup table or deriving an algorithm that could be plugged into our control algorithm. A lookup table is a common method of working the errors out of a positioning system. As the control traverses the part it monitors a table of errors and applies the appropriate correction. Unless the commanded point is exactly the same as a calibration point, the control needs to guess at a correction. This is usually done using some sort of interpolation.

This works well for most applications because most machine tools are straight enough between calibration points that a straight linear interpolation is adequate. In fact, our semi-lathe has less than 5 microns error over 3 meters, which most shops would have accepted without any correction. But, alas, our goal was to be able to control the cutter to within 1 micron anywhere on the working envelope and 5 micron "S" curve in our cross rail would have scrapped our parts.

Since it was always our intention to maintain parametric control over the cutter, we knew that we would be introducing some "stutter" in the smooth control if we didn't allow our system to have corrections that were parametric. Therefore, we had to take the error table which came out as a 2D array of displacement errors and generate a polynomial equation to solve the problem of scale error.

A polynomial is an equation with more than one term and can be expressed graphically as a curve. If we took all the points and connected them with straight lines, that "curve" could be expressed precisely with a polynomial equation with exactly the same number of terms as the number of data points times 2. We took 100 points along the 3 meter rail and, therefore, a perfect fit polynomial equation would have had 200 terms.

I guess this is the first time we compromised and chose to generate an equation with less terms than data points to "approximate" the error curve. As it turns out, you can get a pretty close curve with a polynomial equation out to only a few orders of magnitude. Not having a real solid background in this kind of math, I turned to an industry that's always trying to turn chaos into order — organic chemistry.

Chemists are always trying to correlate their experimental data with a neat equation. That's because they can only collect so much data, but really want to know what happens in those circumstances that fall just outside their data points and be able to predict what's going to happen even if they've never witnessed it. This sounded a lot like what we were trying to do. After all, we ran an experiment (laser calibration) and we wanted to predict something in an area we hadn't actually charted.

The tools these scientists use are mature and powerful. I did a little shopping and chose Jandel Scientific's TableCurve 2D to furnish polynomial equations from the error tables. TableCurve 2D uses the table and starts fitting various polynomial equations to the data. It tracks the accuracy and rates the various equations based on a lot of different factors, most of which we were clueless about. There was one factor which

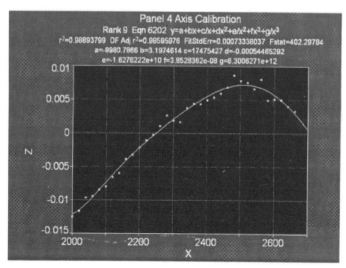

really interested us, however, and that was the fit of the parametric curve to the actual data points expressed as a maximum deviation.

The figure on the previous page shows the points in their native habitat with a curve running through that mess. This plot shows a curve that can be expressed as a 3rd order equation with only 7 terms. This is "child's play" for a computer to solve and therefore we would incorporate this equation into our control algorithm. We used the 9th best fit curve based on a compromise between computational economy and accuracy. The correction algorithm for errors based on our machine calibration is:

$-.99807866 \ 3.197461 \ x \ (17475427 \div x) - (.00054465292 \div x^2) - (1.627622e^{10} \div x^2) + (3.8528362e^{-8} \div x^3) + (6.32006271e^{12} \div x^3)$

We humans are probably more familiar with this form of the function which all you "control freaks" would recognize as a response curve to a mechanically damped system.

$(-.99807866 + 3.1974614 \ x) + (17475427 \div x) - (35850.760854527818551 \div x^2) + (1025457.2507619061 \div x^3)$

That means that we can incorporate this function into our control system with very little computer overhead. This equation has many placeholders and, at first glance, that may seem ridiculous with a machine tool that only positions to 4 decimal places, but every digit is necessary because we keep raising the X-position by powers and this causes the numbers to get really big. Incidentally, this function may look like a real "organic" response curve, but it's actually a parametric equation generated from random data. The guys who use this software in bio-chemistry derive real equations from the data. I'm using this software to approximate some very random error events.

Interestingly, the curve doesn't actually touch any of the points; however, the best curve for this particular error table doesn't stray more than 1 hundredth of a micron from the furthest actual data point. The noise in the correction tables was, of course, more than this so we were satisfied that we had a good correction curve. Not forgetting to change the sign, we included it in our positioning algorithm.

The result is a near perfect positioning of the cutter to the contract curve in air. One of the reasons I chose TableCurve 2D is that it has the option of outputting the algorithm in a choice of FORTRAN, Pascal, C or Basic language source code segments. This eliminates the need to hand code all those big numbers into your program. We wrote our control program in

Visual Basic™ so we just "cut" and "pasted" the code right into the main line of control code. Here's the output from Table Curve 2D:

```
'---------------------------------------------------------------
FUNCTION calib4# (X#)
'---------------------------------------------------------------
' TableCurve Function:D:\TCWIN3\panel4.BAS Mar 3, 1997 2:28:49 PM
' Panel 4 Axis Calibration
' X= X
' Y= Z
' Eqn# 6202  y=a+bx+c/x+dx^2+e/x^2+fx^3+g/x^3
' r2=0.9889379944194274
' r2adj=0.9859597621477348
' StdErr=0.0007333803661419148
' Fval=402.2978421474533
' a= -9980.786589748038
' b= 3.197461356214419
' c= 17475427.08462818
' d= -0.0005446529206531159
' e= -16276221756.30767
' f= 3.852836189870633E-08
' g= 6300627106327.623
'---------------------------------------------------------------
  DIM cf#(11)
  N#=1.0/X#
  cf#(1)=3.197461356214419
  cf#(2)=-0.0005446529206531159
  cf#(3)=3.852836189870633E-08
  y1#=X#*evalpn(2,X#,cf#())
  cf#(1)=-9980.786589748038
  cf#(2)=17475427.08462818
  cf#(3)=-16276221756.30767
  cf#(4)=6300627106327.623
  y2#=evalpn(3,N#,cf#())
  Y#=y1#+y2#
  calib4#=Y#
END FUNCTION

'---------------------------------------------------------------
FUNCTION evalpn# (order%, x#, cf#())
'---------------------------------------------------------------
'Polynomial Calculation Function
'Passed Array  must be dimensioned to 11
  ypn#=cf#(order%+1)
  FOR iter%=order% TO 1 STEP -1
  ypn#= ypn#*x#+cf#(iter%)
  NEXT iter%
  evalpn#=ypn#
END FUNCTION
```

But, like most machine shops, we know cutting air is not profitable and we would have to engage aluminum if we were to make parts. There is only one way to see how a part will cut and what the results are and that is to do it and measure the results. We were down to some very small dimensions and the errors were well under 10 microns (0.0004"). We had confidence that we were positioning just under 1/2 a micron and repeating to about 1/4 of a micron. This meant we could cut a part pretty close. We set out to introduce the last phase of the correction work by cutting parts and inspecting the results. Since our machine ran parametrically, that is, without a database (CNC program), we had to correct for the rest of the errors the same way we corrected for cutter positioning.

We used a CMM to do the data collection. We selected the SIP Opus 7 because of its incredible resolution. Since we are a very resourceful company without an unlimited budget, we had to buy one used. The machine was in great mechanical condition, but it had some very archaic software. We needed a retrofit in order to make the machine perform to its maximum. We selected a third-party retrofit from Electronic Measuring Devices, Inc. (EMD) of Flanders, NJ.

This retrofit involved removing all but the servo controllers and feedback cards from the original control cabinet. The entire computer system and servo controllers were scraped. The original system had no less than 1500 pounds of computer readouts and hardware replaced. EMD had the new controller operational 3 days after their arrival and calibrated by the fifth day back to original specification.

This retrofit also replaced the original SIP analog probe with a new analog probe. The difference being that the SIP probe utilizes optical scales while the EMD probe incorporates tiny internal lasers. The EMD software reads directly off the lasers and compensates for the non-linearities. The cost to write custom drivers for the SIP probe would have been more than the cost of a brand new laser probe.

Analog probes differ from touch triggers in two important aspects. First, they are constantly giving the computer information about the displacement of the stylus. It's a little bit like the original CMMs that didn't have any trigger mechanism for determining contact with a part. They had a rigid probe that gave position based purely on its location. The travel of these analog probes varies, but is usually enough to allow the CMM to stop before it reaches its limits even at the fastest rapids speeds.

The other nice feature of an analog probe is that you can control the amount of pressure you impart on the part as part of the probing process. This is very important to inspecting flimsy parts. An analog probe can measure the thickness of a .001" thick feeler gauge when held vertical and probed on both sides because it can bias out the spring of the gauge by subtracting the forces from opposing sides of the steel. Our reflector panels are only 5mm thick and start deflecting immediately upon contact with a probe. Digital touch-trigger probes require a certain amount of force to trip and that force varies too much depending on the direction you probe. An analog probe is giving position information the instant it comes into contact with an object and therefore we can program the system to actually "feel" for a part by making several touches and backing off in force until it collects the data at a preset force. We've found that 20 grams is just about right for us. If we go much more, we start getting too much deflection in the part, and less causes the probe to register a "hit" due to the inertia generated by the repositioning.

The analog probe furnished by EMD has very little mass and therefore a high frequency response which allows us to track other things in proximity to the probe such as turbulence the air, vibrations in the floor and changes in room pressure. The probe acts like a microphone and will pick up the least bit of noise and vibration. Again, there are software tricks to subtract these high frequency disturbances, which, when turned on, reduce the accuracy of the system.

We don't have an ideal environment for the SIP. It is in a manufacturing space with the usual conversation and activity. It is my fantasy some day to furnish this machine with a building all its own physically segregated from the factory with an air moat and isolated from thermal gradients, pressure changes, and noise.

We ran parts and inspected them. Since, our finish cut was very small we could take about 100 finish passes before we ran out of stock. Some pieces are real veterans at having a finished parabolic surface put on them. Every piece was inspected and each inspection revealed more and more about the affects of tool deflection, material springback, thermal deviation and how the operator was holding his tongue during the clamping operation. Volumes of data were collected on the surfaces of these early parts and averaged. It soon became apparent that we were seeing a noticeable trend in the semi-lathe's performance and it was repeating within a micron or so. Again, we went to either TableCurve 2D or one of our consultants to give us an algorithm we could attach to our control code to eliminate errors. By this time, the corrections were so small that it was difficult to tell if we put the correction in upside down or not. It took a few more parts just to confirm the corrections.

I've simplified the process somewhat in this paper. In the real application, we've refined our correction technique to segregate the travel of the machine into 4 zones. The reflector panels have a 1-mm air gap between them to allow the assembly to breathe. We're taking advantage of that air gap by introducing a new correction function across the gap. This allows us to contain the correction functions over a smaller domain, thus simplifying the function as well as increasing its accuracy.

This technology is not "rocket science." Actually, it is the kind of thing blacksmiths and machinists have been doing for centuries. It's called "eyeballing" the part into conformance. The only difference is the scale. Good machining practices, rigorous adherence to procedures, data recording and analysis and skilled workmanship have as much to do with the quality of each panel as does the math. The total amount of code written to control this machine, including its user interface, is less than one tenth the text of this paper. The amount of data collected averages several thousand points per part. It is the appropriate application of this data and the "borrowing" of another industry's tools that make it possible to control the surface of a 3-meter radius parabolic dish to within 6 microns. The technicians on this program haven't stopped. Everyday there is more analysis and further corrections. The average deviation our customer contracted for is 6 microns. The first lot was barely under the wire. The second lot was well within the performance criterion and as we begin the fifth lot, the average deviation is around 3.8 microns.[8]

The preceding paper identifies the steps that must be undertaken to achieve tight tolerances on a specific class of component, manufactured on an ongoing basis. Achieving an average deviation from the true form of the panel of less than 4 microns (0.00016") is no small achievement.

Similar steps can be taken to optimize the production of a wide range of components, particularly when there is an ongoing production requirement for the same part, or when a family of similar parts is to be produced over an extended period of time. Parts such as angioplasty balloon molds, knee implants, heart valves, impellers, blades, and tooling for high volume consumer products (e.g., styrofoam cups, soda bottles, cans, detergent bottles, printed labels) are all candidates for a process of parametric calibration. Fortunately, in the vast majority of cases it will not be necessary to develop a specialized machine tool! But it is important that the CNC be able to handle a wide range of input data to modify the machining process. At a minimum, the CNC must be able to run programs that make wide use of variables, and must be able to access data files during machining to adjust machine motions in real time.

Real-time Machine Monitoring

To fully optimize machining processes it is necessary to monitor and compensate for a wide range of conditions. From measuring the amount of spindle torque required to drive the cutting tool to observing the axial forces required to drive the machine axes, CNCs are increasingly capable of monitoring machine parameters. At present, many of the machine monitoring initiatives provided by

---

[8] Courtesy of Bosma Machine and Tool Corporation, Tipp City, OH.

CNC manufacturers have led to little more than snappy bar graphs on the screen. Although the real-time monitoring of machine tool performance may have a relatively bright future as a means of improving machining processes, its widest application will be as part of a comprehensive preventive maintenance program. For real-time machine monitoring to reach its market potential, better methods for separating information from the voluminous amount of data these systems generate is required.

For example, consider tool monitoring through spindle drives. It is well established that spindle drive torque commands reflect the condition of the cutting process. As the tool wears, the amount of torque required gradually increases. When a tool breaks, the amount of torque quickly spikes upward and then drops off to zero. When the tool enters an area of greater stock, torque increases as well. While the theory makes sense, the problem is that the signal to noise ratio when looking at spindle torque is fairly low. Variations in the workpiece material cause variations in the spindle torque, as do variations in the feed rate, spindle speed, exit of the chips from the cutting zone, etc. As a result, it is extremely difficult to develop general rules based upon measured drive torque for predicting tool breakage. It is even more difficult to use this data to build a model which can be used to modify the machining process in real time to optimize cutting.

The most successful implementations of tool monitoring are those where the machining process is identical for a large number of parts. Only then can enough data about the effects of tool wear, workpiece material, and other factors upon drive torque be collected. Such systems have proven useful in automotive and aerospace machining applications with large lot sizes. In applications where the lot sizes are small, the value of real-time monitoring systems is reduced.

In low volume/high mix high performance machining environments, real-time machine monitoring systems are best used as part of a preventive maintenance program. By tracking the temperature, vibration, torque or other relevant signature of a machine subsystem over time, failure of the system can often be predicted early enough to enable replacement or repair before the machine is down.

5-Axis Considerations

In many applications, 5-axis machines provide a number of advantages with respect to probing. The most important of these is improved access to convoluted surfaces. One application where 5-axis probing has helped to redefine an industry is the production of cylinder heads for racing. The following case study discusses the issues associated with the 5-axis probing and machining of CNC port cylinder heads for automotive, marine, and motorcycle racing circuits.

Cylinder Head Porting:
a 5-Axis Probing and Machining Application

Ports (the internal air and fuel passageways in a cylinder head) are designed and shaped differently to meet the demands of specific competition circuits. Engine builders are constantly striving to create more efficient port configurations. Efficient shapes bring more fuel and air into the cylinders at the ideal degree of turbulence for higher horsepower, and allow exhaust gases to escape unrestricted. Different port shapes, tailored to the competition class and/ or the individual race track, have evolved for each type of racing. For example, Busch and Winston Cup cars have different port configurations even though they race on the same tracks, and the shape of ports on Sprint car heads depends on the length of the track.

Until about 1988, ports were hand shaped by experts who spent years learning their craft. Each port required many hours of hand grinding. Heads were tested on a dynamometer or flow meter, then the ports were reworked and the heads retested, to optimize the port shape and engine performance for a particular race circuit. Once a desired port shape was achieved, the craftsmen who created it would measure the shape so that they could duplicate it as closely as possible on the rest of the cylinders in the head. A porter's skill is determined on the basis of how faithfully he can replicate the shape of a port. The greater the skill level, the more highly paid the porter. Hand porting a pair of heads can take 20 to 40 hours. The job can cost an engine builder up to $8,000, and differences still exist from engine to engine.

In 1989, Kenny Weld (a well-known sprint car racer and the first driver to hold the National Sprint Car Championship title four times) produced his first pair of CNC-ported cylinder heads (for a sprint car) on an old machining center he had bought at auction and modified. It took him a while to drum up business for his company, Weld-Tech, but customers soon became believers. They all wanted CNC-ported heads and they wanted them fast.

CNC-head porting begins with the creation of a port design that delivers desirable engine characteristics. Development of the ideal port is a craft. At Weld-Tech, five hand-porters, each with their own racing class specialty, develop new designs on a continuous basis. After a desirable design has been created, it moves into production. From this point forward, the goal is simple to articulate but difficult to achieve; produce hundreds of ports identical to the original.

Probing

The process of replicating a hand-ported design begins with probing. The port geometry must be probed to create a cloud of data points. These data points are then fed into a CAM system to generate surfaces for machining. Head ports are probed in several ways, including 3-axis CMMs, CMMs with articulating probe heads, and on 5-axis machines. To create accurate surfaces from probe data, a high density of data is required, and the part should be repositioned as few times as possible. An accurate probing system must also be used.

The most basic probing utilizes a manual CMM to probe the port. This process is inadequate because it is time consuming, and often relatively inaccurate. Automated 3-axis CMMs, or 3-axis probing on a VMC, is a better method because it reduces the time required to probe the port and chamber. But if the probe programs are not carefully written, erroneous probe data can easily be created. This occurs when the probe shank, rather than the probe tip, hits a surface in the port or chamber. Because of the torturous paths that the ports take (Figure 7-7), it is impossible to probe the entire port in one setup. Often 10 or more setups are required to probe the entire port and chamber geometry, depending upon machine geometry. Each setup leads to the collection of probe data which makes up a "patch." These patches will have to be joined together later in the CAM system. This is even true for many 5-axis machines and CMMs with articulating probe tips. Most of these machines do not make full use of all five axes during probing. Instead, only the linear axes are used to move through the probing routines. The rotary axes are used only to position the part in preparation for probing of a patch area.

5-axis probing significantly reduces the number of part setups required to characterize the port and chamber. By decreasing the number of setups, the number of resulting patches is reduced, and more accurate surface models of the hand-ported head can be created in CAM. 5-axis probing uses all five axes (three linear and two rotary) to position *and orient* the probe tip during the probing cycle. This allows significantly better access by the probe to the port, and reduces the number of patches of data points required to characterize the surface. 5-axis probe routines are used to reduce the number of patches to as few as two, depending upon the severity of the port geometry, and no more than three patches are typically created using this methodology. Figure 7-4 illustrates a BostoMatic 505 in the process of probing a head. All five axes are repositioned for each probe hit to optimize access to the port and chamber.

Figure 7-7:
A port cross-section illustrates the difficulty of accessing the geometry with a probe stylus or cutting tool.

When probing, seek as much data as possible. The more data collected, the better the surface model in CAM can be.

An alternative to probing data for use in a CAM system is the so-called "direct cut" method. With this method, a probe stylus the same size as the milling cutter is used. Once the probe data is collected, the CNC cuts the surface. No intermediate steps involving CAM are involved. Although this method is very fast and straightforward, the accuracy of the port suffers to some extent. Most areas of the port only require accuracies in the range of 0.005", but critical elements require tolerances of 0.001" to perform as desired. These tolerances are getting increasingly tighter as engine performance continues to be refined. An even higher degree of repeatability between the ports on a given head is desired. With the direct cut method, it is very difficult to maintain such tolerances. Equally important, very specific surface finishes are desired when porting heads to optimize the air flow. To develop the desired surface finish, a highly accurate and repeatable process is necessary. This is difficult to achieve unless a highly accurate machine tool, and a well developed CAM system, are employed.

Surface Generation (CAM)

After the port and chamber have been probed, the point data are transferred from the CNC to the CAM system where it is represented as poly-lines which must be built into surfaces. This process usually involves several steps. First, the data must be scrubbed for errant points, and then the poly-lines are built into surfaces. The difficulty in building the surfaces arises in trying to mate the edges of surfaces created from patches of probed data points.

If the probing routines are not very accurate, or if many patches of data were collected, it is difficult to get the surfaces to accurately line up with one another. The presence of gaps or overlap between the surfaces generates air turbulence in the final port which does not match the air flow present in the hand-ported original. For this reason, it is critical that 1) a highly accurate and repeatable machine tool (or CMM) is used for probing, 2) the number of probing setups is minimized, and 3) 5-axis probing routines are utilized if at all possible. Although it is possible to manually edit the surfaces in CAM so that they share the same edges without gaps or overlap, this is extremely time consuming. Also, the editing process creates a new port geometry which is not a faithful reproduction of the hand-ported original.

Figures 7-8 and 7-9 illustrate the resulting surfaces generated in CAM after collecting point data with a BostoMatic 505 compared to a less accurate 5-axis system. In Figure 7-8, two probing routines (one from each end of the port) were required, and the collected data was accurate enough to enable a single lofted surface to be built over the entire port and chamber. In Figure 7-9, the inaccuracy of the data collected required that a number of surfaces be used, reducing accuracy. Not all of the surfaces align in this model of the port.

After a surface, or series of surfaces, has been defined, tool paths are generated. It is important when working with the CAM model of the port that it

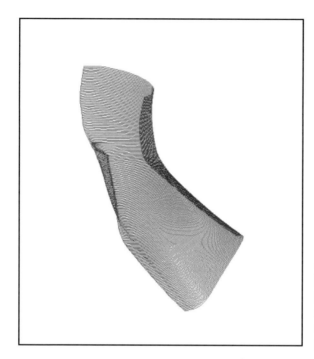

Figure 7-8:
Port geometry probed in two passes reduces CAM manipulations required to create an accurate geometry model, and improves air flow.

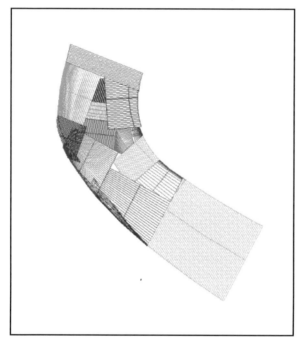

Figure 7-9:
Conventional probing routines require many patches to define the port surface. Errors are created when attempting to join the patches together.

be represented in its entirety so that adequate collision detection can be carried out by the CAM system.

Often, to refine the surface data prior to machining, several cycles of probing and surface generation in CAM are required. Often an initial probing cycle with sparse data is used to generate a rough model of the port in the CAM system. The CAM system uses this rough model to generate a new probing "tool path." The probe then collects further data and refines the model. Different probing tool paths (axial versus radial) are used depending upon whether a rough or final model is being developed. This iterative process of data collection and surface refinement continues until adequate definition of the port and chamber is achieved.

Machining

After the port and chamber have been modeled in CAM, it's time to machine additional ports. Two basic approaches exist. The most common is the use of modified 3-axis VMCs or HMCs. These machines are outfitted with stacked rotary axes to manipulate the cylinder head. Although inexpensive, several drawbacks of such machines adversely affect the quality of the heads produced (through both machining and probing). First, the head is mounted atop two rotary axes, often in a see-saw configuration, so that the center of B-axis rotation is 6" or more from the major axis of the cylinder head. Also, each port on the head moves through a different distance to create the necessary angles between it and the tool. This creates significant positioning errors when working on the ports at either end of the head because the effects of angular errors multiply with distance from the center of rotation.

Another weakness of HMCs or VMCs using stacked rotary axes is that the length of cutters needed to cut the ports increases. Because the cylinder head pivots towards the spindle, long tools are needed to provide enough clearance between the spindle and the cylinder head. Longer tools deflect more and induce chatter in the surface finish of the port. As a result, slower feed rates must be used on these machines, and it is more difficult to obtain the desired surface finish.

A better 5-axis geometry for head porting uses the tilting spindle with table mounted A-axis (Figure 7-4). It separates the rotary axes so that the spindle and the cylinder head rotate independently, and the cylinder head rotates about its length. With this geometry, each port is presented to the spindle in exactly the same manner. The spindle is designed so that it rotates about (or very close to) the tool tip which minimizes angular errors and allows shorter, stiffer tools to be used.

The tilting spindle design ensures that the tool – part interface is very close to the center of rotation of both axes (A and B). Therefore, when angular motion is required, the linear axes travel only small distances to maintain tool – part contact. In comparison, stacked rotary designs require large axis travels to maintain tool – part contact during part rotation. This requires higher axis feed rates, and contributes to inaccuracy. Visualized in terms of a "see-saw," when the tool is working near the center of rotation, only small Z-axis moves are required to keep the tool in contact. As the tool moves out towards the end of the head, a significantly larger Z-axis stroke is required for the same B-axis angular motion. This accuracy diminishing effect is not present in the tilting spindle design.

Spindle selection is also critically important to ensure long life and to enable aggressive machining. HSK 63A tapers should be used instead of CAT40 to minimize the risk of fretting and long-term spindle wear. The HSK taper provides a more accurate, stiffer tool – spindle interface, and is becoming increasingly cost-effective.

Another important consideration when 5-axis machining cylinder heads is CNC performance. Tool paths for porting can be quite large (1 to 5 MB is common) and data intensive. As a result, many machines will experience data starvation during head porting, because their block processing rates are inadequate, and/or they require that the program be drip fed during the machining process. A well designed 5-axis CNC will utilize a large hard disk, ethernet, and high 5-axis block processing rates to allow feed rates of over 100 IPM during head porting.

The design of the machine tool and the CNC will dramatically affect overall cycle times needed to produce high performance cylinder heads. Experienced shops, such as Weld-Tech, can machine a high quality head in about 2½ hours.

Off-line Inspection

In closing this chapter, a brief word about coordinate measuring machines (CMMs) is appropriate. To support high performance machining, a very capable CMM is a necessity. If tolerances of ±0.0005" to ±0.0002" are to be achieved in a low volume/high mix environment, a CMM which is accurate to ±0.0002" will not suffice. Unfortunately, many shops are extremely limited in their ability to measure the parts they produce, and this weakness is at the very heart of the problem of accuracy inflation.

While the process of reference comparison can help improve accuracies substantially, it ultimately depends upon a measuring machine to establish the accuracy of the reference gauge. Likewise, the work cited earlier by Bosma Machine and Tool depended upon the capabilities of their SIP Opus 7 CMM, which was retrofitted with a high performance scanning probe and special probing software. In short, one of the first (if not the very first) steps to becoming a high performance machining operation is to gain access to a very accurate measuring machine.[9] Without the ability to accurately measure parts being produced, it is impossible to trace the source of errors. Without an ability to trace the source of errors, it is not possible to improve the performance of a machining operation.

For those seeking an introduction to CMM technology, access the Brown & Sharpe web site (http://www.brownandsharpe.com). By perusing the firm's broad range of product offerings one can learn a great deal about CMM technology. The information includes accuracy specifications and site requirements necessary to hold specified accuracy and repeatability values. From the web site one quickly realizes the range of CMM capabilities in the marketplace, and the limited number of CMM products available that can adequately support a high performance machining environment.

---

[9] Often the cost of purchasing a highly capable CMM appears to be prohibitive for a small shop. If so, identify a subcontractor who can measure your parts. This is sub-optimal relative to having a CMM within your own facility, but it is better than nothing.

Chapter 8

Machine Evaluation Test Suite

This chapter describes a number of simple tests that can be performed to monitor and qualify a shop's machine tools, or to aid in the comparison of prospective machine purchases. It is not meant to be comprehensive. Instead, it is a survey which will help resourceful shops develop their own tests, attuned to specific high performance machining requirements.

The idea of the test suite is to present tests that can be performed with a minimum of specialized equipment. Where the use of specialized equipment is preferable, a "surrogate test" that gives a qualitative measure of the characteristic of interest is described.

Machine Structure and Geometry

Tests for Squareness, Straightness, Flatness, Spindle Tram, etc.

Measuring Tools

The best measuring device for testing machine geometry varies depending upon the characteristic. For impromptu tests, an indicator, a high quality granite square and straight edge, parallels, and a gauge block will suffice.

An electronic indicator is preferred, but if only a dial indicator is available, ensure that it is a 50-millionths indicator. A dial indicator with 0.0001" resolution is inadequate for testing errors that are only a few ten-thousandths of an inch in magnitude.

Ideally, the granite square and straight edge will enable the geometric measurements to be made over full machine travel. If not, the larger they are, the better.

Performance Requirements

The performance requirements for machine geometry are identified in Table 2-6.

Measurement Method

Methods for measuring critical elements of machine geometry are detailed in Appendix A. A number of 4- and 5-axis tests are also described.

Machine Stiffness (Static Tests)

Although measurement of a machine's dynamic or static loop stiffness is fairly involved, it is possible to evaluate the static stiffness of individual machine axes in a straightforward, albeit simplistic, manner.[1]

To test the X-axis stiffness of a VMC, for example, the following procedure can be followed.

1. Place a 50-millionths indicator (in a tool holder) in the machine spindle. Zero the indicator against a gauge block placed on the machine table. The indicator should be positioned to measure movement in the X-axis.
2. Person A watches the indicator.
3. Person B takes a bathroom scale and places the bottom of the scale against the end of the machine table.[2]
4. Person B pushes against the scale (where one's feet normally go), seeking to provide a constant load. Person B watches the bathroom scale readout to determine the force applied.
5. Person A writes down the amount of deflection measured by the indicator once the applied force is stable.
6. Stiffness of the X-axis is calculated as the force applied through the scale, divided by the displacement of the indicator. See Chapter 2.
7. To test the Y- or Z-axes, push against the slide to remove any backlash, reposition the indicator, and apply the force to the appropriate machine slide.

Similar tests can be undertaken to measure the stiffness of the machine column and other machine elements. In each case, apply a known force to the element for which the stiffness is sought, and set up an indicator so that it measures the relative displacement of the element in question. Positioning of the indicator is very important. In many cases it may be necessary to use an indicator stand which is mounted off of the machine itself. Otherwise, it is difficult to ensure that the surface to which the indicator stand is mounted is not also deflecting.

While this test is very simple, and fairly inaccurate, it can quickly provide a measure of the stiffness of one machine relative to another. Given the inaccuracy of the test, it should be repeated several times and the results averaged.

The overall accuracy of the test can be greatly improved by replacing the 50-millionths indicator with an electronic indicator or laser interferometer, and by replacing the bathroom scale with a better force measurement device, such as a load cell. Omega (1-800-USA-WHEN) offers a range of tension and compression load cells and output meters for less than $1000. Some are available in the form of bolts, which can facilitate test set-up. It is not necessary for the load cell to have a capacity of several thousand pounds. Usually the amount of force that a person can apply by pushing or pulling will be enough to register a noticeable deflection on the indicator.

---

[1] Thanks to Bruce Hammond for this idea.
[2] No joke!

To test the static loop stiffness of the machine, rather than a single axis' drive train, a setup like that of Figure 2-2 should be employed.

Static Accuracy

Laser Positioning Test

To accurately ascertain the positioning accuracy of a machine tool, a laser interferometer must be used. Although it may not be practical for smaller shops to own one, each machine intended for high performance work should be recalibrated for positioning accuracy once per year.

A number of firms, including many OEMs, provide accuracy recalibration services. By rerunning the laser interferometer tests used to ascertain machine accuracy in the factory, some of the adverse effects of ball screw wear upon accuracy can be eliminated. Further, the tests provide a good early warning sign that ball screws must be replaced because of excessive backlash or wear.

Backlash Test

Backlash is easily determined via the use of a laser interferometer. Fortunately, it can be measured more cost-effectively using a dial indicator and a gauge block.

To test X-axis backlash for example, follow these steps.

1. Place a 50-millionths indicator in the machine spindle. Zero the indicator against a gauge block placed on the machine table. When zeroing the indicator be sure to approach the gauge block in only one direction (e.g., +X), and to approach the block from at least 0.01" away. This will eliminate any of the backlash in the system.

2. Set the CNC's axis jog increment to the smallest allowable value. Prepare to jog the machine in the -X direction.

3. Jog the machine one increment. Check the indicator. Continue commanding the CNC to jog the machine one increment at a time until the indicator registers that the axis has moved.

4. The number of jog commands issued, multiplied by the increment value (e.g., 0.0001"), is the amount of backlash in the system.[3]

The above test is effective only if the machine has no linear scales. Otherwise, the CNC will know that the slide didn't move, and an accurate measure of the amount of backlash in the ball screw will not be obtained.

An alternate "push-pull" test can also be used to evaluate mechanical backlash in the system.

1. Place a 50-millionths indicator in the machine spindle. Zero the indicator against a gauge block placed on the machine table. When zeroing

---

[3]If the machine uses hydrodynamic ways (Chapter 2), the effects of stick-slip must be considered. To help minimize the impact of stick-slip on this test, exercise the machine prior to performing this test. This will warm up the oil and reduce its viscosity. Naturally, this test can be used to evaluate total system backlash, including not only mechanical effects but stick-slip as well.

the indicator be sure to approach the gauge block in only one direction (e.g., +X), and to approach the block from at least 0.01" away. Physically pull the table in the direction of the gauge block to ensure that all backlash in the +X direction has been removed from the system. Zero the indicator.

2. Manually push the table to drive the indicator off the gauge block. Stop pushing. Measure the position of the indicator.

3. Manually pull the table to drive the indicator onto the gauge block. Stop pulling. Measure the position of the indicator

4. The difference between the two indicator readings is the amount of mechanical backlash in the system.

CNC/Dynamic Performance

Data Processing Performance (BPS) Test

Measuring the block processing capability of a CNC is a relatively straightforward process.

1. Begin by creating a part program with nothing but linear incremental moves in 3D. Strip the part program of all superfluous characters, including line numbers. Do not include tool length or diameter compensation or any other features that might consume additional processing time. Make the length of each incremental move 0.001" long, and set the feed rate to 120 IPM. This combination of feed rate and move length corresponds to 2,000 blocks per second of throughput. Make the program long enough that it can run for at least ten minutes.

2. Load the program into the CNC.

3. Set the feed rate override to 10%. The control will now be required to process data at about 200 blocks per second.

4. Begin running the program. The machine should move without hesitation. Gradually increase the feed rate by adjusting the override. At some point, the machine will begin to hesitate and the motion will become jerky. The CNC is now experiencing data starvation.

5. Divide the feed rate by 0.06. The result is the "unencumbered" maximumblock processing rate.

6. Evaluate the other functions of the CNC while data starvation is occurring. Are other tasks (e.g., program editing) accessible? Has the machine stopped working altogether?

After the so-called unencumbered block processing rate has been calculated, rewrite the program, adding increased complexity of the sort typically present in the programs run in your shop. Add feed rate commands throughout the program. If your shop routinely uses line numbers, include them in the program. If your programs make extensive use of variables, cutter compensation, arc moves, contour optimization, or other features, write additional test programs that include them. As these complexities are added, ensure that the basic structure of 0.001" moves at 120 IPM is maintained in the program. This is necessary to provide a baseline for comparison. In the end, each shop will have a test suite of programs, beginning with the very simple program described above, and culminating in a complex program with every conceivable CNC feature included. In between will be a series of programs, each constructed by adding a single additional feature to the previous part program.

The feed rate at which each test program fails can be charted and compared to the feed rates obtained when running the test programs on other machines. In this way, a relative assessment of different machine and CNC brands can be made. Keep in mind that some CNCs will automatically decrease the feed rate (without changing the display) to prevent data starvation. It may be necessary to evaluate the true feed rate of the machine during this test using the methods described below under the heading "Acceleration Measurement."

A last important note on the subject of block processing. Many CNCs cannot store large programs within the CNC, and require that they be drip fed to the CNC via DNC. In such cases, it is important to evaluate the block processing capability of the CNC under this "drip feeding" condition, particularly if your shop routinely uses large part programs.

Ball Bar Test

As discussed in Chapter 3, the ball bar test is a valuable indicator of overall machine performance, both in terms of motion control and geometry. Every high performance machine shop should own a ball bar system. Renishaw Inc. (Schaumburg, IL) produces one of the most popular models, along with a very useful diagnostic package for evaluating the ball bar test results. Alternative systems are also available, including a grid encoder from Heidenhain (Figure 8-1).

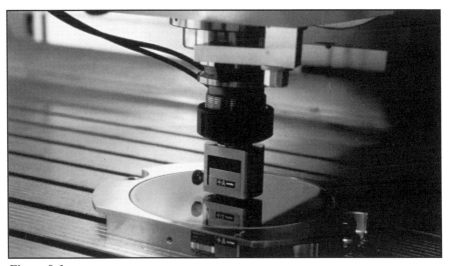

Figure 8-1:
A grid encoder can be used to evaluate a machine tool's performance when moving. Unlike the ball bar test, machine motion is not limited to a circle. (Courtesy of Heidenhain Corporation.)

Most shops adopting ball bar tests for VMCs carry out X-Y ball bar tests. This is the easiest, and in many applications the most important test to perform. But, ball bar tests should be carried out on all three planes of the VMC, particularly when a shop machines a lot of 3D surfaces. It is also a good idea for shops to perform ball bar tests at a variety of different feed rates for each machine. Although this is not necessary every time the ball bar test is performed, it is a good idea to establish the effects of higher (and lower) feed rates upon contouring accuracy. As indicated in Table 3-7, the impact of feed rate upon contouring accuracy is non-trivial. Again, the ability to compare ball bar test results between machines is critical when evaluating prospective purchases and when taking stock of the shop's current machine tool capabilities. Therefore, it is important that the ball bar test setup be highly repeatable, and that a well established test method be documented.

In addition to testing their machines on a regular basis using the ball bar, some high performance machine shops will quickly check a machine's performance before putting a critical job into production. This is a highly recommended practice, and can significantly reduce scrap costs.

An alternative to the ball bar test is to skim cut a complete 12"∅ circle in aluminum in the X-Y plane. The cut must be deep enough to create a vertical side wall which can be probed. The resulting part is inspected using a highly accurate CMM to evaluate many of the same errors that will be identified by the ball bar. Backlash, out-of-square conditions, servo mismatch, and other errors will all manifest themselves in the test cut.[4] To properly inspect this part, a highly accurate, and preferably scanning, CMM is required. The proper CMM will be capable of plotting the radius error all around the circle, rather than providing just a TIR value. In addition to identifying motion and geometry errors, errors due to the spindle will also be reflected in the part, principally in a change in the radius of the circle (due to runout). Aluminum is a desirable material for this test because it is easy to machine, and therefore does not introduce other errors, such as tool deflection. Surface finish defects are also readily visible to the eye.

To further refine this cutting test, an offset 12" square (misaligned 5° or 10° relative to the X-axis) can also be cut at a relatively low feed rate. This test cut provides insight into the squareness of the machine, and the extent to which the X- and Y-axes are working in concert. If the axes are not well matched, or one of the axes is experiencing excessive friction at low speed, the geometry of the square will be adversely affected.

Acceleration Measurement

As discussed in Chapter 3, the role of acceleration and deceleration in a high performance machine tool is critical, perhaps more so than maximum feed rate. It is desirable to test VMCs to determine their acceleration capabilities. The best way to do this is to hook an accelerometer up to a machine axis and record the acceleration profile, as the table transitions from being at rest to full speed

---

[4] Unlike the ball bar test, the CMM will not identify the root cause of the errors in the circle.

motion. In the absence of such equipment, a much simpler and relatively informative test can be performed with the aid of only a stop watch.

1. Write a part program which moves the X-axis back and forth along a 0.5" line segment 200 times at 100 IPM (alternate combinations of distance and feed rate can also be used if this proves too severe for the machine). Make each 0.5" move a single program block, rather than a series of very small moves. It is not the goal of this test to evaluate block processing capability.

2. Run the program. Measure with the stop watch the time required for the program to complete the program. Many CNCs include a very accurate internal clock which will log the start and finish time of each program. Use this function if it is available.

3. If the machine could accelerate and decelerate infinitely quickly, the program would be completed in 2 minutes (200 round trips of 1" each at 100 IPM). Undoubtedly, the program will require more than 2 minutes to run.

4. The average effective feed rate of the machine during this program can be calculated as the distance traveled (200"), divided by the program run time. If, for example, the program required 2 minutes and 20 seconds to complete, the effective feed rate would only have been 86 IPM, not 100 IPM.

Although this test does not explicitly define the acceleration of the machine, it provides a useful tool for comparing the relative accel/decel capabilities of one machine to another. The closer the effective feed rate is to the programmed feed rate, the higher the machine's rate of acceleration.

Variations of this test can also be performed to investigate a range of other machine characteristics. The test can be undertaken for each machine axis. If the results differ for the axes, then the axis with the lowest effective feed rate (lowest acceleration) will dictate the overall machine performance in 3D contouring. Another way to run the test is with look ahead or contour optimization features turned on. The results from this test will indicate how much the machine needs to slow down relative to the programmed feed rate, to achieve a specified tolerance.

Contour Machining Performance (Concentric Square Test)

When using a high performance machine tool to produce accurate parts, it is important to know the maximum feed rate that can realistically be used to achieve the desired tolerance. A test to gain an understanding of a machine's contouring capabilities (and, by association, the amount of servo lag) is to machine a series of inscribed squares, similar to Figure 3-14.

1. Place a small block (3"×3") of aluminum on the machine table. Face off the top.

2. Set up a small, single pointed engraving tool (scribe tool) in the spindle so that it will make a very shallow cut (< 0.005") in the top of the aluminum block.

3. Write a part program that machines a series of concentric squares. The innermost square should be programmed to run at 10 IPM. Each successive square should be programmed at a feed rate 20 IPM higher than the previous square. Space the squares at least 0.03" to 0.04" apart. Program squares until the maximum contouring feed rate is reached.

4. Run the program, ensuring that the scribe tool does not penetrate too far. Check that contour optimization or look ahead functions in the CNC are turned off.

5. Inspect the resulting piece with magnifying optics. Degradation of the corners of the squares should be present as the feed rates increase.

By evaluating this test part, upper limits on the feed rates that can be used to achieve a given tolerance band can be established. This can be done qualitatively, or if an optical measuring probe is available, the degradation when cornering at high feed rates can be quantified.

If the test cut does not indicate degradation in the corners at high feed rates, check that contour optimization and look ahead functions were turned off. If they were off, it is likely that the CNC is automatically decreasing the feed rate as the machine enters the corners to maintain an internally specified (and hidden from the user) tolerance. Return to the acceleration test described above and compare the machine to other machining centers. Most likely the acceleration test will show that the machine in question is slowing down dramatically, as evidenced by a low effective feed rate.

Another useful perturbation of this test is to run it with look ahead or contour optimization turned on. Compare the results to the test run with these features turned off. This is an excellent way to determine the improvements in contouring accuracy that can be expected in practice when using these features.

Thermal Performance

As discussed in Chapter 5, thermal growth is a significant detriment to high performance machining. It is a good idea for shops to try and quantify it. Tests for evaluating thermal growth in the machine as a whole, and in the spindle specifically, are described.

Thermal Monitoring

As discussed in Chapter 4, the effects of ambient temperature change upon process accuracy can be significant. It is important to determine how temperature changes as a function of location within the high performance machine shop and as a function of time. This is easily done using standard thermometers.

1. Set up a thermometer at each machining operation within the shop. Ideally, the temperature inside and outside the machine should be monitored. For this purpose, digital indoor/outdoor thermometers from Radio Shack (and widely available elsewhere) work well. Thermometers should also be set up in areas where raw stock is stored, where work-in-

process sits between machines, and in inspection areas.

2. Post a tracking sheet by each thermometer, and have the machinist or employee at each station input the temperature every 30 minutes, on a preset schedule (e.g., 7:00 a.m., 7:30 a.m.).[5]

3. Track the data for a week at a time, once per month. It is important to collect data across all four seasons.

4. Compile the data in a spreadsheet, like Lotus 1-2-3™ or Microsoft Excel™. Take particular note of the differences in temperature between adjacent work areas with respect to the work flow. If a part is moving from a "hot" area into a "cold" area, or vice versa, thermally induced errors may occur.

Use the above results, and the formulas in Chapter 4, to determine the maximum acceptable thermal variation between each of the workstations through which a part, beginning as raw material, will pass. If the temperature variation can't be significantly reduced or eliminated, determine how long the part should "soak" to reach the local ambient temperature before additional operations are performed.

Often, shops that collect this data find that over the course of a week the temperature varies so wildly that it is impossible to draw any conclusions. This is a sure sign that temperature control in the facility is inadequate. As temperature control is improved, the data will become more repeatable, and fine tuning of the thermal environment can be pursued.

Axes Drift Test

Excluding thermal growth in the spindle, the motion of the machine's axes and the operation of its various subsystems generates heat. This heat can cause inaccuracies when machining. To test the impact of these effects, perform this test.

1. Begin with a machine that has been powered off for several hours. If possible, leave the machine powered down over a weekend.

2. Set up a thermometer near the machine, and another within the machine work volume.

3. Take precautions that the shop will experience "typical" temperature variations. Do not take any steps to reduce the shop's normal temperature fluctuations.

4. Select a part program which is considered representative of the tight tolerance work the shop currently performs or seeks to perform. Remove all "spindle on" commands, or override the spindle through the control panel so that it will not rotate.

5. Set up a cylindrical gauge pin or tooling post at the center of what would be the work volume if the aforementioned program was actually going to produce a part.

---

[5] For the more ambitious, companies such as Omega® manufacture a wide range of temperature recorders and data acquisition systems capable of supporting over one hundred temperature probes. Running on a PC, these systems make it possible to collect temperatures automatically throughout the shop.

6. Mount a 50-millionths indicator in a tool holder and insert it into the spindle.

7. Tram the tool post in to the spindle. Record the indicator reading at 0°, 90°, 180° and 270° around the post. Log the current machine position as a set point to which the machine can be commanded to return through MDI.

8. Remove the tool holder with the indicator from the spindle.

9. Begin running the part program in an endless loop at the programmed feed rate. Make sure that the spindle is not running.

10. Every 30 minutes, stop the part program. Put the tool holder with the indicator into the spindle. Return to the set-point location and tram the tool post. Record the indicator readings at each quadrant.

11. Resume the program. Repeat steps 8 and 9 for eight hours or until the indicator readings stabilize.

12. Plot the drift in the tool post in the X- and Y-axes, relative to its start point. The change in position represents thermal growth due to machine axes motions, changes in the ambient temperature, and the operation of machine subsystems excluding the spindle.

This test is a good way to validate the thermal stability of a machine tool and a machine shop. If the above test is conducted with no axis motion (set up the test post, leave the machine idle, and measure it every half hour), the effects of ambient temperature change can be isolated. If the spindle operation is added to the test, its impact upon X- and Y-axis growth can also be evaluated. Variations of the test can be devised to include Z-axis growth as well.

If a shop runs this test and determines that there is an excessive amount of thermal drift, changes to ambient temperature controls can be made and the test re-run. This works well as a "before and after" test.

For shops with table or spindle mounted touch trigger probes, the above test can be modified to automatically collect data in 2- or 3-axes, depending upon the probe's capabilities. This eliminates the monotonous task of measuring the machine's position every 30 minutes.

Spindle Growth Tests

A similar set of tests can be performed to evaluate spindle growth. The above test can be run with the spindle operating at 100% of the programmed value. When evaluating spindle growth it is a good idea to measure more frequently than every 30 minutes. The thermal growth time constant of many spindles is approximately 40 minutes, and so it is useful to collect data every at least every 5 to 10 minutes.

A more generic test can also be performed to qualify the overall thermal behavior of the spindle.

1. The spindle should be off for at least four hours prior to commencing the test.

2. Insert a tool holder into the spindle with a gauge pin affixed in the holder.

3. Set up a touch trigger probe in the work area. If it is a 2-axis probe, align it to measure Z- and Y-axis position when working with a VMC.

4. Write a part program that runs the spindle at 25% for 3 hours, 0% for 3 hours, 50% for 3 hours, 0% for 3 hours, 75% for 3 hours, 0% for 3 hours, 100% for 3 hours, and finally 0% for 3 hours. Within the part program set up a routine that will bring the gauge pin in contact with the touch probe every 10 minutes. If possible, do this without shutting down the spindle. Make contact in both the Z- and Y-axes. Write the position data from the probing routine to a file.[6]

5. Graph the position data from the touch probe. The resulting curves will provide data similar to that in Chapter 5. Overall levels of thermal growth, and the time constant of that growth, can now be calculated.

6. If the growth of the spindle at any given speed range had not reached steady-state within three hours, re-run the test, increasing the time the spindle spends at a given speed from three to four hours.

The results from this test are useful because they provide information about the magnitude of thermal growth, and its time constant. The time constant is very important because it provides insight into how fast the thermal state of the spindle will change. This is important to know if the spindle must be regularly shut down during production to replace tooling, load and unload parts, or to inspect machine features.

---

[6]Use spindle orientation, if available, to repeatedly bring the gauge pin to the same rotary position relative to the probe. This will help to minimize measuring error due to runout of the tool holder and gauge pin.

Conclusion

Upon completing this book, many readers undoubtedly view high performance machining as a utopia hopelessly removed from the current state of their machining operations. Machining processes have been discussed in the context of tolerances of ±0.0005" to ±0.0002". These values represent an artificial threshold for high performance machining. But, because so many shops and machine tool builders claim that these tolerances are well within their reach, it was imperative to frame the discussion of high performance machining in these terms. Achieving these tolerances is a daunting task, and one that many shops will never achieve. Within each chapter of this book, readers can discover enough error sources to exceed this tolerance two or three times over.

This is not to say that achieving tolerances of ±0.0005" to ±0.0002" is not a worthy goal. But these tolerances are not an end in and of themselves. In order to compete effectively and move forward (and enjoy doing so), machine shops must sharpen their focus by developing a coherent body of knowledge about a specific type of part processing. Once a shop is focused — whether on can top tooling, impellers, rotary dies, or microwave components — a structured process of continuous improvement can be undertaken. This process will undoubtedly address many of the issues discussed within <u>High Performance Machining</u>, and, it is at this point that the usefulness of this book will be greatest. Whether ±0.0002" or ±0.008" is the relevant tolerance is not the issue. Rather, high performance machining is about systematically identifying and eliminating error sources in all phases of production so that better parts can be produced at a lower cost in less time, freeing up more time for the pursuit of new ideas.

Appendix A

Machine Geometry Tests

DRAWING NUMBER 14A370		1 OF 4	REV. –
TITLE: GEOMETRY TEST REPORT			F/N GEORPT1 3/98

NO.	TEST	ILLUSTRATION	RESULTS
1	Z–AXIS SQUARE TO THE TABLE IN THE X–Z PLANE TOOL P/N's INDICATOR P/N_____ GRANITE P/N_____		TOTAL DISTANCE TRAVELED — INDICATOR READING 0″ — ZERO INSP._____
2	Z–AXIS SQUARE TO THE TABLE IN THE Y–Z PLANE TOOL P/N's INDICATOR P/N_____ GRANITE P/N_____		TOTAL DISTANCE TRAVELED — INDICATOR READING 0″ — ZERO INSP._____
3	Y–AXIS SQUARE TO THE X–AXIS IN THE X–Y PLANE TOOL P/N's INDICATOR P/N_____ GRANITE P/N_____	TOP VIEW OF TABLE	TOTAL DISTANCE TRAVELED — INDICATOR READING 0″ — ZERO INSP._____

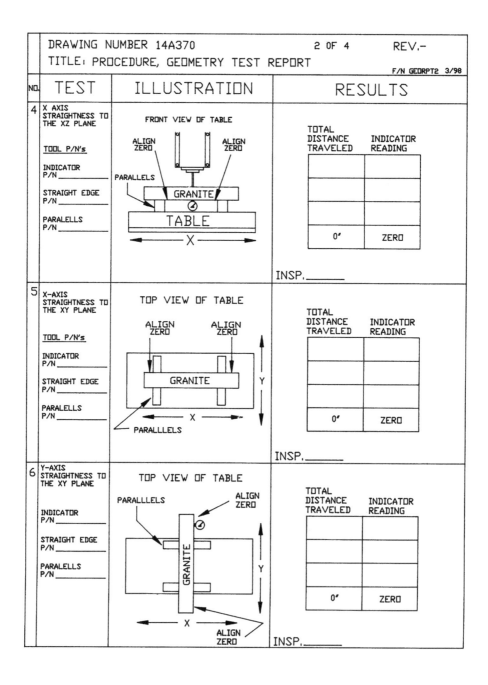

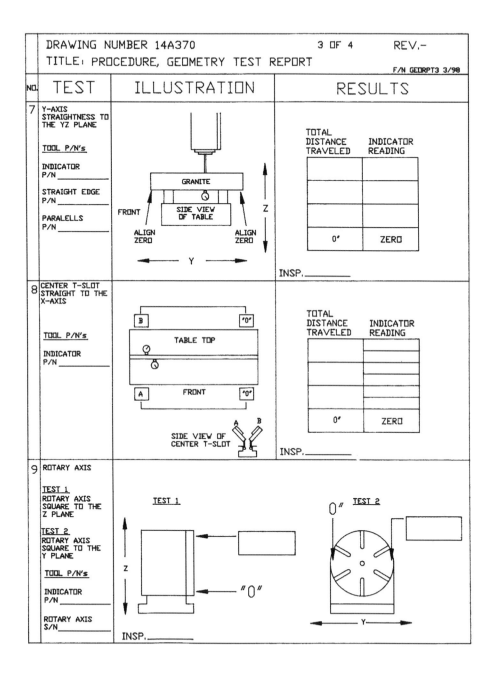

DRAWING NUMBER 14A370   3 OF 4   REV.-

TITLE: PROCEDURE, GEOMETRY TEST REPORT

F/N GEORPT3 3/98

NO.	TEST	ILLUSTRATION	RESULTS
7	Y-AXIS STRAIGHTNESS TO THE YZ PLANE TOOL P/N's INDICATOR P/N _____ STRAIGHT EDGE P/N _____ PARALELLS P/N _____	GRANITE SIDE VIEW OF TABLE FRONT ALIGN ZERO ALIGN ZERO Y Z	TOTAL DISTANCE TRAVELED / INDICATOR READING 0" / ZERO INSP._____
8	CENTER T-SLOT STRAIGHT TO THE X-AXIS TOOL P/N's INDICATOR P/N _____	B '0' TABLE TOP A FRONT '0' SIDE VIEW OF CENTER T-SLOT	TOTAL DISTANCE TRAVELED / INDICATOR READING 0" / ZERO INSP._____
9	ROTARY AXIS TEST 1 ROTARY AXIS SQUARE TO THE Z PLANE TEST 2 ROTARY AXIS SQUARE TO THE Y PLANE TOOL P/N's INDICATOR P/N _____ ROTARY AXIS S/N _____	TEST 1 TEST 2 Z "0" 0" Y INSP._____	

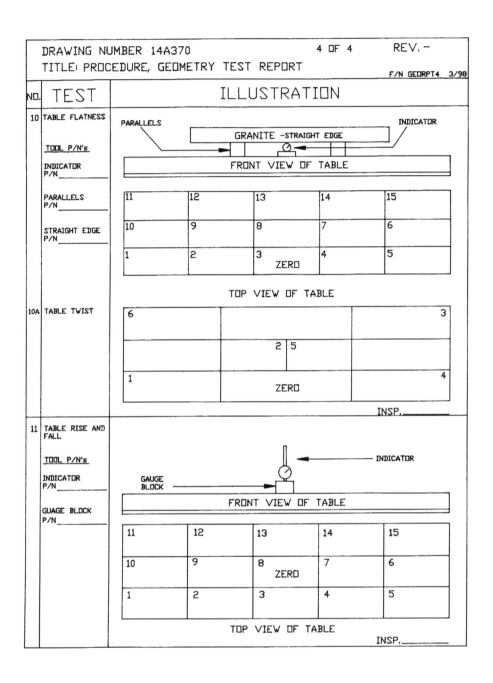

DRAWING NUMBER 14A370   4 OF 4   REV. -
TITLE: PROCEDURE, GEOMETRY TEST REPORT
                                                   F/N GEORPT4 3/98

NO.	TEST	ILLUSTRATION

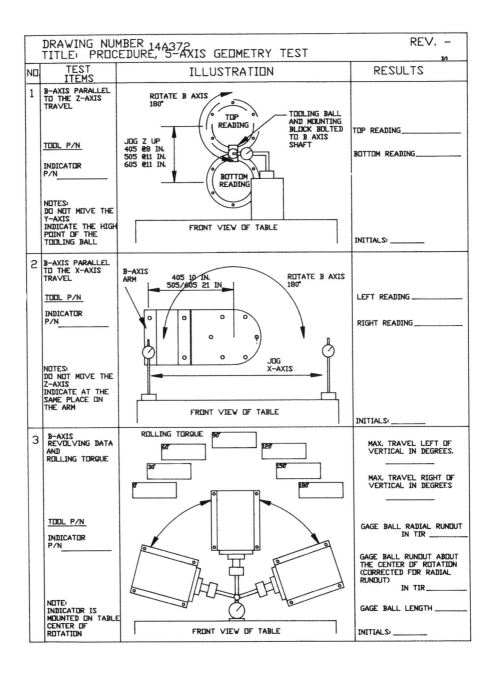

DRAWING NUMBER 14A372   REV. —
TITLE: PROCEDURE, 5-AXIS GEOMETRY TEST

NO	TEST ITEMS	ILLUSTRATION	RESULTS
1	B-AXIS PARALLEL TO THE Z-AXIS TRAVEL TOOL P/N ___ INDICATOR P/N ___ NOTES: DO NOT MOVE THE Y-AXIS INDICATE THE HIGH POINT OF THE TOOLING BALL	ROTATE B AXIS 180° TOP READING TOOLING BALL AND MOUNTING BLOCK BOLTED TO B AXIS SHAFT JOG Z UP 405 @8 IN. 505 @11 IN. 605 @11 IN. BOTTOM READING FRONT VIEW OF TABLE	TOP READING ___ BOTTOM READING ___ INITIALS: ___
2	B-AXIS PARALLEL TO THE X-AXIS TRAVEL TOOL P/N ___ INDICATOR P/N ___ NOTES: DO NOT MOVE THE Z-AXIS INDICATE AT THE SAME PLACE ON THE ARM	B-AXIS ARM 405 10 IN. 505/605 21 IN. ROTATE B AXIS 180° JOG X-AXIS FRONT VIEW OF TABLE	LEFT READING ___ RIGHT READING ___ INITIALS: ___
3	B-AXIS REVOLVING DATA AND ROLLING TORQUE TOOL P/N ___ INDICATOR P/N ___ NOTE: INDICATOR IS MOUNTED ON TABLE CENTER OF ROTATION	ROLLING TORQUE 90° 60° 120° 30° 150° 0° 180° FRONT VIEW OF TABLE	MAX. TRAVEL LEFT OF VERTICAL IN DEGREES. ___ MAX. TRAVEL RIGHT OF VERTICAL IN DEGREES ___ GAGE BALL RADIAL RUNOUT IN TIR ___ GAGE BALL RUNOUT ABOUT THE CENTER OF ROTATION (CORRECTED FOR RADIAL RUNOUT) IN TIR ___ GAGE BALL LENGTH ___ INITIALS: ___

DRAWING NUMBER   REV.
TITLE: SPINDLE DATA, SINGLE/AUXILARY   ECO   F/N SPINE

MAIN SPINDLE

MACHINE SERIAL # _____
SPINDLE SERIAL # _____
SPINDLE TYPE _____

TRAM 12″ SWEEP

SPINDLE PARALLEL TO Z-AXIS
USING A 6″ ARBOR.

SPINDLE RUNOUT
ON ARBOR

XZ PLANE _____
YZ PLANE _____   AT 2″_____

   AT 6″_____

TEST ARBOR ID# _____

INSPECTED BY _____   DATE _____

AUXILARY SPINDLE
(OPTIONAL)

SPINDLE SERIAL # _____

SPINDLE TYPE _____

TRAM 6″ SWEEP

SPINDLE PARALLEL TO Z-AXIS
USING A 4″ ARBOR

XZ PLANE _____   SPINDLE RUNOUT
YZ PLANE _____   ON ARBOR

   AT 2″_____
TEST ARBOR ID# _____   AT 4′ _____

Survey Discussion

A discussion of the questions presented in Chapter 1, as part of the High Performance Machining Survey, follows.

Question 1

This question addresses the impact of ambient temperature changes on high performance machining. If the reader answers C or D, the ability to hold tight machining tolerances must be questioned. The issues surrounding thermal growth and temperature control are discussed in Chapter 4.

Question 2

Many shops believe they are holding the tolerances indicated by answers C, D, or E. Unfortunately, many shops believe that "programming to tolerance X" is synonymous with "achieving tolerance X." Achieving tolerances of ±0.0005" when milling is extremely difficult, particularly when working in a low volume/high mix 3D contouring environment. The state of the art today enables shops to readily hold tolerances of ±0.005" and, with moderate attention to detail, ±0.001". On simpler shapes and point-to-point operations, it is possible to hold tighter tolerances than on contoured surfaces.

Question 3

The material (steel), and the complex nature of the part (3D contours with tight corner radii) conspire to make this a very difficult machining job.

Question 4

Most shops are poorly equipped with respect to inspection equipment. If the shop has a CMM, it is rarely capable of accuracies much tighter than the machine tool itself. It seems that many shops are investing in high performance machine tools before procuring the necessary inspection equipment to validate their work and to drive process improvements. This is a serious error. With respect to surface finish, most shops visually evaluate this important part characteristic. Every high performance shop should own a profilometer.

Question 5

Most shops assume that cutters are much more accurate than they, in fact, are. To achieve tight tolerances, special order cutters are required for finishing passes and, in some cases, semi-finishing (Chapter 6).

Questions 6 and 7

Surprisingly, most machining centers fall short of the programmed feedrate when machining complex contours. The importance of maximum feedrate, a popular marketing metric, is greatly exaggerated. Most machines are achieving less than 80% of the programmed value when machining complex 3D shapes. This figure improves as parts become larger and less intricate (Chapter 3).

Question 8

Similar to question 1, it is important that the inspection area be temperature controlled to a constant temperature (preferably 68°F). Many shops mistakenly believe that if the inspection is done at the machine, the actual temperature is unimportant. Unfortunately, this is not the case (Chapter 5).

Question 9

Most shops answer F. Most general purpose machines provide accelerations below 0.5g. For high performance machining, acceleration is equally, if not more important than maximum feed rate (Chapter 3).

Question 10

To hold tight tolerances, a chordal deviation value of less than 10% the desired tolerance should be used (refer to questions 2 and 3). Unfortunately, this creates large part programs that many CNCs cannot handle. NURBS is one possible answer to this dilemma.

Question 11

For most shops, the answer is A. If answering B or C, the shop should consider whether it is operating within an expanding or contracting marketplace. For the most part, the most profitable machining work requires 3D contouring (Chapter 1).

Question 12 and 13

Most shops are using spindles running at less than 10,000 RPM with CAT40 tooling. To improve throughput and part quality, higher speeds are required for many operations. But, this does not mean that very high horsepower is required (Chapter 4). A high performance machine shop should seek a mix of relatively low speed/high power spindles and low power/high speed spindles. These spindle types are relatively cost-effective, and provide the range of capabilities necessary to handle a wide range of machining tasks. Avoid spindles providing both very high speed and high power. They are expensive to own!

Question 14

Speed requirements increase with aluminum and graphite respectively, while power requirements drop. The requirements for hard die milling are discussed in Chapter 6. Chapter 4 discusses how to evaluate the spindle requirements for a range of different materials.

Question 15

Ideally, the accuracy of a CMM should be 10X the tolerance of the parts it is measuring. Unfortunately, as tolerances grow tighter this is increasingly difficult to achieve without spending an exorbitant amount of money. Nonetheless, for high performance machining, a CMM should provide accuracies of 0.0001" or better. Chapter 7 discusses a number of methods to enhance the accuracy of inspection processes.

Question 16

Most shops are not, but should be, using the ball bar test to evaluate machine tool performance. The test is an excellent diagnostic tool for a range of geometric and motion control errors. A good high performance machine tool will provide circularity of better than 0.0003" on a 12"$\varnothing$ ball bar test at 20 IPM.

Question 17

Shops should seek to recalibrate their machine tools at least once per year, particularly if the machine is being used for tight tolerance work. There are many companies that can provide this service on a contract basis, including a number of machine tool builders. A test for backlash is described in Chapter 8. The overall machine geometry must also be carefully monitored (Chapter 2).

Question 18

Guidelines for these measures are provided in Chapter 4.

Question 19

Most shops answer B or C. Today, even in an upbeat marketplace, the amount of competition to produce 2D parts is so intense that there is downward price pressure. Price pressure will intensify further during the next market downturn. It is critical for shops to develop capabilities which differentiate them from the competition to remain profitable over the long term. Low prices are usually a transient competitive advantage.

Question 20

Annual turnover of machinists is typically highest at shops competing on price in the production of 2D components. Shops that are focused on a highly specialized area of machining and have developed a unique skill set find it easier to retain employees. This in turn makes it easier to justify training expenditures, which again help to retain employees.

Question 21

Wage competition for machinists has intensified. It is increasingly critical to create a work environment which is challenging and enjoyable for machinists. Although this does not insulate a shop from increasing wages in the market at large, it helps hold wage growth to a reasonable level because the "intangibles" are valued by employees. Competitors with work environments of lessor quality will find it difficult to poach employees from well run high performance machine shops, even when offering higher wages.

Question 22

Accuracy standards are in and of themselves highly variable from one to the next. ISO standards and JIS standards provide very different results for the same machine. Understanding the role of accuracy standards and the measurement methods associated with each type of standard is important when selecting a machine tool (Chapter 3).

Question 23

Positioning accuracy specifications represent the best possible results that a machine tool can achieve. When the machine is in motion, accuracy can drop off dramatically. The ball bar test is a good measure of machine performance because it is dynamic in nature. When selecting a machine it is important to evaluate the dynamic as well as static performance (Chapter 3).

Questions 24 and 25

Block processing rate is a metric that is difficult to pin down. Every CNC builder has a unique definition, making it difficult to compare CNCs. Chapter 3 and Chapter 8 discuss methods for evaluating block processing claims.

Question 26

Most shops operate with a variation of A, B, or D. To optimize throughput the use of ethernet and large capacity hard disk drives is a prerequisite (Chapter 3).

Question 27

Chapter 7 addresses the pros and cons of different tool setting methods.

Index